Hodder Gibson

Scottish Examination Materi

HIGHER
MATHS

Through Practice and Example

Units 1, 2 and 3

Peter W. Westwood

A complete course of worked examples and exercises for Higher Mathematics

HODDER
EDUCATION
AN HACHETTE UK COMPANY

Orders: please contact Bookpoint Ltd, 130 Milton Park, Abingdon, Oxon OX14 4SB. Telephone: (44) 01235 827720.
Fax: (44) 01235 400454. Lines are open from 9.00–5.00, Monday to Saturday, with a 24 hour message answering service.
You can also order through our website www.hoddereducation.co.uk

British Library Cataloguing in Publication Data
A catalogue record for this title is available from the British Library

ISBN: 978-0-340-81308-9

Published by Hodder Gibson, 2a Christie Street, Paisley PA1 1NB.
Tel: 0141 848 1609; Fax: 0141 889 6315; Email: hoddergibson@hodder.co.uk
First published 2003
Impression number   10 9 8 7 6
Year   2009

Typeset by Pantek Arts Ltd, Maidstone, Kent.
Printed in Great Britain for Hodder Gibson, an imprint of Hodder Education, an Hachette UK company,
2a Christie Street, Paisley, PA1 1NB, Scotland, UK by Martins The Printers, Berwick upon Tweed.

PREFACE

This textbook is a complete course for the examination in Higher Mathematics (Units 1, 2 and 3), a National Qualification of the Scottish Qualifications Authority. While it has been written as a course book in its own right, it will also serve as a rich source of additional exercises for those using other Higher Mathematics textbooks.

Teachers using this text have complete freedom regarding the introduction of each topic. Proofs of introductory theory have been omitted and only reminders of relevant theory have been included. Naturally, teachers will want to introduce each lesson in their own way, and to provide notes or other revision guides containing the relevant theory.

The order of topics follows largely the syllabus listing provided by SQA. This order was never intended to define a teaching syllabus, and so there is no need for teachers to stick slavishly to it. Teaching more than one topic at a time has its merits.

This text includes an overview of Standard Grade Trigonometry within Unit 1, and so provides a sensible introduction to *Radians*. The SQA lists *Completing the square* as Unit 1 content, but here it is covered under *Quadratic Theory* in Unit 2, where it is better suited. (The process does not appear in the National Assessment Bank Unit 1 test, and so there is no harm done.) It is also recommended that *Quadratic Theory* precedes *The Remainder Theorem* so that pupils are able to justify when a cubic function has only one linear factor.

Each exercise is preceded with a brief reminder of theory, where necessary, and then appropriate worked examples. The worked examples include suggestions of good exam technique. (In addition to finding the correct answers to problems, candidates are expected to demonstrate adequate communication too.)

The exercises themselves are carefully constructed, well graded, and have been used extensively in the classroom. Later examples in some exercises are coded 'B' to indicate a greater level of difficulty. Competence in these examples might be expected from those aiming beyond a grade C pass in the examination.

Each topic concludes with a 45-minute test, so that progress may be monitored. Each Unit concludes with a practice Unit test (no time restriction), and two further 45-minute tests at Exam standard. Calculators may be used where indicated.

The author wishes success to all who use the book, and hopes that it is of much assistance.

Other volumes by the same author and relevant to Higher Mathematics Units 1, 2 and 3, are:

Practice Papers Higher Mathematics
(ISBN 978 07169 8019 3)
(6 typical exam papers with answers)

How to Pass Higher Maths Colour Edition
(ISBN 978 0340 973998)

Also available for Higher Maths:

Higher Maths Objective Tests: Revision and Practice Questions
(ISBN 978 0340 965184)
by David Smart and Graeme Smart

CONTENTS

CONTENTS

UNIT 2

CONTENTS

UNIT 3

Geometry Vectors

Calculus Further Differentiation and Integration

Algebra Logarithms

Trigonometry The Auxiliary Angle

Revision of Unit 3 (Practice Tests)

Answers

THE STRAIGHT LINE

1 The Distance Formula

> **Reminder**

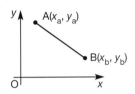

$$AB = \sqrt{(x_a - x_b)^2 + (y_a - y_b)^2}$$

Example   Calculate the length of the line AB where A is $(-5, 6)$ and B$(2, -18)$.

Solution $AB = \sqrt{(-5-2)^2 + (6+18)^2} = \sqrt{49 + 576} = \sqrt{625} = 25.$

Example   Find x if the distance between A$(3, 4)$ and B$(x, 11)$ is 25.

Solution
$$25 = \sqrt{(x-3)^2 + (11-4)^2}$$
$$\Rightarrow \quad 25^2 = (x-3)^2 + 7^2$$
$$\Rightarrow \quad (x-3)^2 = 25^2 - 7^2 = (25-7)(25+7) = 18 \times 32 = 9 \times 64 = (3 \times 8)^2$$
$$\Rightarrow \quad (x-3) = \pm 24 \qquad \text{hence } x = 27 \text{ or } -21.$$

Exercise 1

1 Calculate the distance between each of the following pairs of points:
   a) $(3, 5)$ and $(7, 8)$ b) $(3, -9)$ and $(-2, 3)$ c) $(-1, -2)$ and $(-2, -1)$
   d) $(0, 0)$ and $(-6, 8)$ e) $(0, 0)$ and $(1, -2)$.

2 Use the distance formula and the converse of the Theorem of Pythagoras to show that the triangle with vertices P$(3, -1)$ Q$(9, 5)$ and R$(6, 8)$ is right-angled.

3 Show that the triangle with vertices K$(2, 5)$, L$(2, 7)$ and M$(2+\sqrt{3}, 6)$ is equilateral.

4 Show that the triangle with vertices F$(-4, 6)$, G$(8, 2)$ and H$(3, 7)$ is isosceles.

5 Calculate the distance between these pairs of points:
   a) $(a + b, a - b)$ and $(b, -b)$ b) $(2a, -a)$ and $(-2a, 2a)$.

6 Find y if A is $(8, y)$, B $(-7, 1)$ and AB $= 17$.

7 Find k if X is $(15, k)$, Y $(-5, -4)$ and XY $= 29$.

8 Find x if P is $(x, 3)$, Q $(3, 5)$ and PQ $= \sqrt{8}$.

2 Midpoint of a Line

> **Reminder**

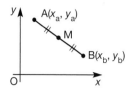

$$M \text{ is } \left(\frac{x_a + x_b}{2}, \frac{y_a + y_b}{2}\right)$$

Example Find the coordinates of the midpoint of AB where A is (11, 4) and B(–3, 6).

Solution M is $\left(\dfrac{11 + (-3)}{2}, \dfrac{4 + 6}{2}\right)$ i.e. (4, 5).

Exercise 2

1 Write down the coordinates of the midpoint of the line joining:
  a) (2, 3) and (4, 5)   b) (7, –1) and (9, 3)
  c) (2, –4) and (8, 6)   d) (–1, 7) and (7, –11).

2 ABCD is a quadrilateral, with midpoints
   P Q R and S, as shown.
   Find the coordinates of the midpoint of
   a) PR b) QS.

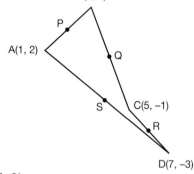

3 In triangle ABC, A is (3, 7) B (–1, 1) and C(5, 3).
   P and Q are the midpoints of AB and AC respectively.
   a) Find the coordinates of M, the midpoint of PQ.
   b) If R is the midpoint of BC, show that M is also the midpoint of AR.

4 Find the coordinates of the midpoints of the lines joining:
   a) (a, b) and $(3a, 5b)$
   b) $(m + n, m - n)$ and $(m - n, n - m)$
   c) $(a^2 + b^2, a - b)$ and $(b^2 - a^2, b - a)$
   d) $(a + b + c, a + b - c)$ and $(a - b + c, -a - b - c)$.

3 The Gradient Formula

> **Reminder**

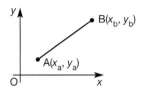

$$m_{AB} = \frac{y_b - y_a}{x_b - x_a}$$

Example   Find the gradient of AB where A is $(2, -3)$ and B$(7, 4)$.

Solution $m_{AB} = \dfrac{4 - (-3)}{7 - 2} = \dfrac{7}{5}$.   Remember (i) y coordinates on top
(ii) same order top and bottom.

Example   Find the size of the angle between the positive x-axis and a line
with gradient

a) $\dfrac{2}{3}$ b) $\dfrac{-2}{3}$.

Solution   a) $\tan^{-1} \dfrac{2}{3} = 33.7°$.   b) $180 - \tan^{-1} \dfrac{2}{3} = 146.3°$.

Example   Find a) The gradient of the line $x = 2$.
b) The equation of the line through the origin at $65°$.

Solution   a) undefined (or infinite).   b) $m = \tan 65° \approx 2.14$
hence $y = 2.14\, x$.

Exercise 3

1 Find the gradient of the line joining:
a) $(6, 7)$ and $(8, 9)$ b) $(0, 0)$ and $(7, 3)$ c) $(4, 5)$ and $(7, 8)$
d) $(0, 3)$ and $(4, 0)$ e) $(2, -1)$ and $(-1, 3)$ f) $(6, -2)$ and $(-3, 7)$
g) $(4, 2·5)$ and $(-1, 0·5)$ h) $(0, 0)$ and $(-k, \ell)$ i) $(3am, an^2)$ and $(3an, am^2)$.

2 Find the gradient of the line joining:
a) $(2, 6)$ and $(5, 6)$ b) $(6, 2)$ and $(6, 5)$
c) $(0, 3)$ and $(0, 7)$ d) $(8, 9)$ and $(11, 9)$.

3 Find the size of the angle between the positive x-axis and a line with gradient:
a) 1 b) $\dfrac{1}{\sqrt{3}}$ c) $-\sqrt{3}$
d) $\dfrac{1}{2}$ e) -2 f) 4.

4 Find the gradient of a line inclined to the positive x-axis at an angle of:
a) $45°$ b) $120°$ c) $30°$
d) $145°$ e) $71·6°$ f) $116°$.

5 Show that AB is parallel to CD where
  a) A is (2, 1), B (5, 2), C (−2, −6) and D (4, −4)
  b) A is (7, −1), B (6, 4), C (1, 3) and D (2, −2).

6 The straight line joining P (2, 4) to Q (3, 2) is parallel to the line joining R (5, 6) to S (a, 2). Find the value of a.

7 Triangle ABC has vertices A (−3, 2), B (−4, 6) and C (5, −2). P and Q are the respective midpoints of AB and AC. Show that PQ is parallel to BC.

8 Use gradients to prove that WXYZ is a parallelogram, where:
  a) W is (−2, −4), X (5, −1), Y (6, 4) and Z (−1, 1)
  b) W is (6, 5), X (8, 8), Y (5, 6) and Z (3, 3).

9 PQRS is a parallelogram with P (1, 1), Q (−1, 0) and R (−2, 3). Find the gradient of:
  a) RS   b) PS.

10 AD is the median of triangle ABC drawn from A (to D, the midpoint of BC). Find the gradient of AD given that:
  a) A is (0, 0) B (4, 12) and C (6, 8)
  b) A is (−2, 1) B (7, −1) and C (−5, 5)
  c) A is (6, −3) B (−2, 7) and C (10, −1).

11 The points A and B have coordinates (a^2, a) and ($4b^2$, $2b$) respectively. Determine the gradient of AB in its simplest form.

12 The points P and Q have coordinates (p^2, $2p$) and (q^2, $2q$) respectively. Determine the gradient of PQ in its simplest form.

4 Collinearity

> **Reminder**

Collinear points are points which lie on the same straight line.

Example   Show that the points A (−3, −1), B (2, 2) and C (12, 8) are collinear.

Solution $m_{AB} = \dfrac{2 + 1}{2 + 3} = \dfrac{3}{5}$ $m_{BC} = \dfrac{8 - 2}{12 - 2} = \dfrac{6}{10} = \dfrac{3}{5} = m_{AB}$

$\Rightarrow$ AB ∥ BC with B a point in common *
$\Rightarrow$ A, B and C are collinear.

* Note: AB and CD have equal gradients $\Rightarrow$ AB ∥ CD,
    so AB and BC have equal gradients $\Rightarrow$ AB ∥ BC.

In examinations you may lose a mark for failing to mention both 'parallel' and 'common point'. Or, if you find it easier to remember, write 'common direction and common point'.

Exercise 4

1 Prove that the following sets of points are collinear:

a)   X $(-6, 2)$, Y $(2, -6)$, Z $(-2, -2)$ b) P $(-12, -8)$, Q $(0, 1)$, R $(-4, -2)$

c)   K $(4, 7)$, L $(1, 1)$, M $(-2, -5)$ d) T $(-1, -7)$, S $(8, 5)$, V $(5, 1)$.

2 A is the point $(8, -3)$, B $(6, 5)$ and R is the midpoint of AB.
P is the point $(-1, -5)$ and Q is $(11, 4)$. Show that P Q and R are collinear.

5 Lines Parallel to the Axes and through the Origin

> **Reminder**

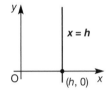 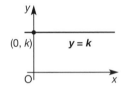 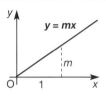

Example   A is the point $(4, 3)$.
Write down the equation of the line through A
(i)   and the origin,
(ii)   parallel to the x-axis,
(iii) parallel to the y-axis.

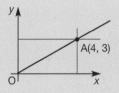

Solution   (i) $m = \dfrac{3-0}{4-0} = \dfrac{3}{4} \Rightarrow y = \dfrac{3}{4}x$

(ii) $y = 3$
(iii) $x = 4$.

Exercise 5

1 Plot each of the following pairs of points on a separate coordinate diagram (on plain paper) and hence find the equation of the line through each pair of points:

a) $(2, 0)$ and $(2, 5)$ b) $(2, 5)$ and $(7, 5)$ c) $(1, 1)$ and $(1, -1)$

d) $(6, 1)$ and $(7, 1)$ e) $(4, 2)$ and $(4, 4)$ f) $(2, 1)$ and $(-2, -1)$

g) $(0, 0)$ and $(5, 3)$ h) $(-1, -2)$ and $(0, 0)$ i) $(-1, 3)$ and $(2, -6)$.

2 On separate coordinate diagrams, sketch the lines whose equations are :

a) $x = 2$ b) $y = 3$ c) $x + 1 = 0$

d) $2y + 3 = 0$ e) $y = \dfrac{3}{4}x$ f) $3x + 2y = 0$.

3 Write down the equation of the line through the point P
(i) and the origin   (ii) parallel to the x-axis   (iii) parallel to the y-axis
where P is   a) $(3, 2)$ b) $(4, 5)$ c) $(-1, 3)$ d) $(-2, -6)$ e) $(5, -2)$.

4 Write down the equation of the line through the origin with gradient

a) 2   b) $\frac{1}{3}$ c) $\frac{-3}{5}$ d) -1 e) 0.

5 Write down the equation of OA where O is the origin, A is the midpoint of BC, and B and C are the points:

a) $(2, 1)$ and $(1, 2)$ b) $(3, 5)$ and $(5, -1)$

c) $(-5, 1)$ and $(-1, -3)$ d) $(6, -2)$ and $(-2, 5)$.

6 The Line through (0, *c*) with Gradient *m*

> **Reminder**

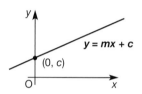

Example

Find the equation of the line through $(0, -2)$ with gradient 7.

Solution

Using $y = mx + c$ with 'm' = 7 and 'c' = -2 gives $y = 7x - 2$.

Example

Find the value of k if the lines $kx + 4y + 17 = 0$ and $3x - 2y + 5 = 0$ are parallel.

Solution

$kx + 4y + 17 = 0 \Rightarrow 4y = -kx - 17 \Rightarrow y = -\frac{k}{4}x - \frac{17}{4} \Rightarrow m_1 = -\frac{k}{4}$

$3x - 2y + 5 = 0 \Rightarrow 2y = 3x + 5 \Rightarrow y = \frac{3}{2}x + \frac{5}{2} \Rightarrow m_2 = \frac{3}{2}$

for parallel lines, the gradients are equal, so $-\frac{k}{4} = \frac{3}{2} \Rightarrow k = -6$.

Exercise 6

1 Write down the equation of the straight line passing through the point $(0, 3)$ with gradient

a) 1   b) -2 c) $\frac{2}{3}$ d) $-\frac{3}{4}$ e) 0.

2 Write down the equation of the straight line with gradient 2 passing through the point

a) $(0, 1)$ b) $(0, -2)$ c) $(0, 0)$ d) $(0, 5)$ e) $(0, -6)$.

3 For each of the following lines find:

(i) the gradient

(ii) the coordinates of the point of intersection with the y-axis

a) $y = 2x - 3$ b) $y = 5 - 3x$ c) $2y = x + 6$

d) $2y = 4x - 3$ e) $2y = x + 5$ f) $x + y - 1 = 0$

g) $3x + 4y = 7$ h) $x + y = 5$ i) $2x - 3y + 4 = 0$.

4 Find the equation of the straight line making the given angle with the positive direction of the x-axis and with the given intercept on the y-axis:

a) $45°, -1$ b) $135°, 2$ c) $68·2°, -\frac{1}{2}$

d) $145°, 0·1$.

5 Show that the following pairs of lines are parallel:

a) $\begin{cases} 3x + y - 5 = 0 \\ 6x + 2y - 5 = 0 \end{cases}$ b) $\begin{cases} 7x + 14y = 11 \\ 8x + 16y + 9 = 0 \end{cases}$ c) $\begin{cases} 5x - 2y + 3 = 0 \\ 20x - 8y + 7 = 0 \end{cases}$.

6 Find the value of t if the straight lines $5x + 4y + 3 = 0$ and $15x + ty + 7 = 0$ are parallel.

7 Write down the equation of the straight line through the origin parallel to:

a) $5x + 7y - 3 = 0$ b) $2x + 3y + 4 = 0$

c) $5x - 2y = 7$ d) $3x + 4y = 8$.

8 Write down the equation of the straight line passing through the point $(0, 5)$ parallel to:

a) $y = 5x$ b) $x + 3y = 0$

c) $2x - 3y = 10$ d) $5x + 4y = 7$.

7 The General Equation of the Straight Line

▶ Reminder

Every line is *EITHER* of the form $y = mx + c$ OR $x = h$, hence every line is of the form $ax + by + c = 0$.

Example   Does   a) $2x + 3y = 0$

                          b) $x^2 + y^3 = 5$ represent a straight line ?

Solution   a) Yes ($a = 2, b = 3, c = 0$)

                  b) No (x^2 or y^3 indicate a non–linear curve).

Example   Does $(1, -2)$ lie on the line $3x - 4y = 10$?

Solution $x = 1, y = -2 \Rightarrow$ l.h.s. $= 3x - 4y = 3 + 8 = 11 \neq 10 =$ r.h.s.

                  $\Rightarrow (1, -2)$ does not lie on the line $3x - 4y = 10$.

Exercise 7

1 Which of the following equations represent straight lines ?

a) $3x + 2y + 5 = 0$ b) $x = 5$ c) $y = 17$

d) $x^2 + 3x + 4 = 0$ e) $xy = 12$ f) $x + y = 12$

g) $\frac{x}{3} + \frac{y}{4} = 1$ h) $x^2 + y^2 = 25$ i) $y = 4x^2$.

2 Express the equation of each of the following lines in the form $ax + by + c = 0$:

a) the line with equation $y = \frac{4}{3}x + \frac{2}{3}$

b) the line through the origin with gradient $\frac{-2}{3}$

c) the line through $(0, 5)$ with gradient 3

d) the line through $B(0, -1)$ and $D(4, 3)$.

3 Which of these points lie on the line $3x - 4y + 5 = 0$?

a) A $(1, 2)$ b) B $\left(-1, \frac{1}{2}\right)$ c) C $(0, 5)$

d) D $(7, 6)$ e) E $(-7, -4)$.

4 Find p and q if $(p, 2)$ and $(-5, q)$ lie on the line $7x - 6y + 5 = 0$.

8 Intersection of Lines

▸ Reminder

Example   Find the coordinates of the point of intersection of the lines
$2x + 3y = 13$ and $3x - y = 14$.

Solution   Method 1

$$2x + 3y = 13)$$
$$3x - y = 14 \ ) \quad \Rightarrow$$

$$2x + 3y = 13$$
$$9x - 3y = 42$$
$$\overline{11x \qquad = 55}$$
$$\Rightarrow \qquad x = 5$$
$$\Rightarrow \quad 15 - y = 14 \quad \Rightarrow \quad y = 1 \quad \Rightarrow \quad (5, 1).$$

Method 2

$$y = 3x - 14 \quad \Rightarrow \quad 2x + 3(3x - 14) = 13 \quad \Rightarrow \quad 11x = 55$$
$$\Rightarrow x = 5 \quad \Rightarrow \quad y = 3(5) - 14 = 1 \qquad \text{as above.}$$

Exercise 8

1 Find the coordinates of the point of intersection of the lines with equations:

a) $x + y = 2$ and $x - y = -1$ b) $2x + 5y = 1$ and $x - 3y = -5$

c) $x = 3$ and $2x + y = 4$ d) $2x + 3 = 0$ and $3x - y = 4$

e) $y + 3 = 0$ and $2x + 3y + 1 = 0$.

2 Find the coordinates of the vertices of the triangle whose sides have equations:

a) $x = 3$ $x - y = 2$ $2x + y + 5 = 0$

b) $x + 3 = 0$ $y = 4$ $4x - 3y = 0$.

3 Find the equation of the straight line joining the origin to the point of intersection of

a) $x + y = 4$ and $2x - 3y + 1 = 0$

b) $3x + y + 2 = 0$ and $x - 3y = 4$.

9 Concurrence

A set of concurrent lines all pass through a common point.

Example   Show that the lines $3x + 2y = 3$, $2x - 3y + 11 = 0$ and $x + 2y = 5$
are concurrent.

Solution   Solving the first and the third: $3(5 - 2y) + 2y = 3$
$\Rightarrow \quad 15 - 4y = 3 \Rightarrow 4y = 12$
$\Rightarrow \quad y = 3 \Rightarrow x = -1$

substituting $x = -1$ and $y = 3$ in the 2nd equation
l.h.s. $= -2 - 9 + 11 = 0 =$ r.h.s. $\Rightarrow$ these lines are concurrent.

Exercise 9

1   Show that the following sets of lines are concurrent:

a) $\begin{cases} x + 2y = 6 \\ 3x - y = 4 \\ 2x + y = 6 \end{cases}$
   b) $\begin{cases} x + y + 3 = 0 \\ 2x - y = 0 \\ 3x - 2y = 1 \end{cases}$
   c) $\begin{cases} 3x + y = 0 \\ 2x - y + 5 = 0 \\ x + 4y = 11. \end{cases}$

2   Find the value of k if the lines $x + 4y = 7$, $3x + y = 10$ and $x - 5y + k = 0$ are concurrent.

10 Perpendicular Lines

The lines $y = m_1x + c_1$ and $y = m_2x + c_2$ are perpendicular $\Leftrightarrow m_1 \times m_2 = -1$

Example   A is the point $(3, 5)$ and B $(2, -1)$.
Find the equation of the altitude
from O in triangle OAB.

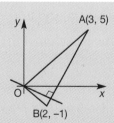

Solution $m_{AB} = \dfrac{5 - (-1)}{3 - 2} = 6$

$\Rightarrow m_{alt} = -\dfrac{1}{6}$

$\Rightarrow$ equation is $y = -\dfrac{1}{6}x$

i.e. $x + 6y = 0$.

Exercise 10

1 Write down the gradient of a line which is perpendicular to a line with gradient:

a) 2 b) -1 c) $\frac{2}{3}$ d) $-\frac{3}{4}$ e) $\frac{5}{4}$ f) $-\frac{7}{3}$.

2 Write down the gradient of a line which is perpendicular to the line with equation :

a) $y = 2x$ b) $y = -\frac{1}{4}x$ c) $y = 3x - 5$

d) $y = 1 - 2x$ e) $x + y = 1$ f) $2x + 3y = 0$.

3 Write down the equation of the straight line through the origin perpendicular to a line with gradient:

a) -1 b) $\frac{1}{2}$ c) -3 d) $\frac{2}{3}$ e) $\frac{5}{4}$ f) $-\frac{1}{5}$.

4 Find the equation of the line through the origin perpendicular to the line with equation:

a) $y = x$ b) $y = -5x$ c) $2y = x$ d) $y = 2x - 1$

e) $3x + 2y = 0$ f) $3y = 4x + 5$ g) $2x + 7y = 9$ h) $x - 3y = 4$.

5 Find the equation of the straight line through $(0, 2)$ perpendicular to the line with equation:

a) $x + y = 3$ b) $2x - y = 5$ c) $5x + 4y = 7$.

6 Prove that the given pairs of lines are perpendicular to each other

a) $\begin{cases} x + y + 1 = 0 \\ x - y - 1 = 0 \end{cases}$ b) $\begin{cases} y = 2x + 5 \\ y = 7 - \frac{1}{2}x \end{cases}$ c) $\begin{cases} 2x + 3y = 5 \\ 3x - 2y = 4. \end{cases}$

7 Find the gradient of a line perpendicular to the line joining the points:

a) $(1, 2)$ and $(3, -4)$ b) $(3, 2)$ and $(-7, 2)$ c) $(2, -1)$ and $(-3, -2)$

d) $(4, 4)$ and $(-1, -3)$ e) $(-1, 2)$ and $(2, 5)$ f) $(6, 1)$ and $(1, 6)$.

8 Find the equation of the straight line perpendicular to $2y = 3x + 4$ and passing through the point:

a) $(0, 5)$ b) $(0, -2)$ c) $(0, -7)$.

9 Find the equation of the straight line perpendicular to $6x + 7y = 11$ with an intercept on the y-axis of :

a) -1 b) $\frac{1}{6}$ c) $\frac{1}{2}$.

10 Find the equation of the straight line passing through

a) A $(3, 4)$ perpendicular to   (i) $x = 5$ (ii) $y = 2$

b) B $(4, 7)$ perpendicular to   (i) $x = 6$ (ii) $y = 5$.

11 Show that AB is perpendicular to CD where

a) A is $(5, -7)$ B $(-1, -3)$ C $(4, 7)$ D $(6, 10)$

b) A is $(1, 4)$ B $(0, 6)$ C $(-2, -3)$ D $\left(7, \frac{3}{2}\right)$

c) A is $(-5, 8)$ B $(1, 6)$ C $(-4, -4)$ D $(-3, -1)$.

12 Find y if AB is perpendicular to CD, where A is $(3, 4)$, B $(4, 2)$, C $(5, -4)$ and D $(4, y)$.

13 Find z if PQ is perpendicular to RS, where P is $(3, 1)$, Q $(5, -5)$, R $(1, -2)$ and S $(3, z)$.

14 Find t if KL is perpendicular to MN, where K is $(4, 2)$, L $(5, 0)$, M $(6, -6)$ and N $(5, t)$.

15 Find k if UV is perpendicular to XY, where U is $(1, 4)$, V $(3, -2)$, X $(-1, 1)$ and Y $(1, k)$.

16 PQRS is a kite with P $(5, -3)$ and R $(2, -6)$. Find the gradient of QS.

17 Find the equation of the altitude OD of triangle OAB where A is $(4, 7)$ and B $(8, 2)$.

18 ABCD is a rhombus with A $(-2, 3)$ B $(3, 4)$ and C $(4, -1)$. Without calculating the coordinates of D, find the gradient of:
a) DC   b) DA   c) DB.

19 Find the value of k if the given pairs of lines are perpendicular:
a) $\begin{cases} x + ky = 3 \\ x - y = 1 \end{cases}$ b) $\begin{cases} kx + 3y = 4 \\ y = 4x - 5 \end{cases}$ c) $\begin{cases} 2x + 5y = 7 \\ kx - 3y = 8. \end{cases}$

20 Find the equation of the altitude ON of triangle OKL, where K and L have coordinates:
a) $(3, 4)$ and $(-1, 6)$ b) $(2, -3)$ and $(-2, 5)$ c) $(5, -7)$ and $(-2, 3)$.

21 Use gradients to show that each of the following sets of points are the vertices of a rectangle:
a) $(4, 5)$, $(-1, 10)$, $(-9, 2)$, $(-4, -3)$ b) $(-2, 2)$, $(-1, 1)$, $(6, 8)$, $(5, 9)$
c) $(1, -2)$, $(5, 2)$, $(3, 4)$, $(-1, 0)$.

11 The Line through (x_1, y_1) with Gradient m

> **Reminder**

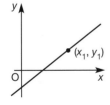

$$y - y_1 = m(x - x_1)$$

When (a, b) is used in place of (x_1, y_1)
we have $y - b = m(x - a)$

Example   Find the equation of the straight line through the points $(2, 7)$ and $(-1, 5)$.

Solution $m = \dfrac{7 - 5}{2 + 1} = \dfrac{2}{3}$

$\Rightarrow$ equation is $y - 5 = \dfrac{2}{3}(x + 1)$

$\Rightarrow$ $3y - 15 = 2x + 2$ (always clear the fractions first)

$\Rightarrow$ $3y = 2x + 17.$

Exercise 11

1 Find the equation of the straight line through the given point and with the given gradient:

   a) $(3, 4)$; 1 b) $(-2, -5)$; -1 c) $(3, -2)$; 3

   d) $(4, 2)$; -2 e) $(5, -1)$; $\frac{2}{3}$ f) $(-6, 3)$; $-\frac{1}{3}$

   g) $\left(5\frac{1}{2}, -3\frac{1}{2}\right)$; 4 h) $\left(-\frac{8}{3}, \frac{7}{3}\right)$; $-\frac{2}{3}$ i) $(p^2, 2p)$; $\frac{1}{p}$.

2 Find the equation of the straight line through the given pair of points:

   a) $(4, 3)$ and $(6, 7)$ b) $(1, 2)$ and $(3, 3)$ c) $(-1, 5)$ and $(1, -1)$

   d) $(2, -7)$ and $(8, -9)$ e) $\left(2\frac{1}{2}, 3\right)$ and $(-2, 0)$ f) $\left(\frac{7}{2}, \frac{5}{2}\right)$ and $\left(-\frac{3}{2}, \frac{1}{2}\right)$.

3 a) Find the equation of the straight line through $(1, 2)$ parallel to $y = 3x + 4$.
   b) Find the equation of the straight line through $(-1, 3)$ parallel to $x + y = 0$.
   c) Find the equation of the straight line through $(4, -5)$ parallel to $2x - 3y = 5$.
   d) Find the equation of the straight line through $(1, 2)$ parallel to $3x + 4y = 7$.

4 a) Find the equation of the straight line through $(1, -1)$ perpendicular to $x - y + 5 = 0$.
   b) Find the equation of the straight line through $(-2, 3)$ perpendicular to $2x + y = 8$.
   c) Find the equation of the straight line through $(4, -2)$ perpendicular to $2x + 3y = 5$.
   d) Find the equation of the straight line through $(-7, 2)$ perpendicular to $3x - 4y = 1$.

5 Find the equation of the straight line passing through:
   a) $(4, -4)$ parallel to the line joining A $(3, 2)$ and B $(1, 3)$
   b) $(1, -2)$ parallel to the line joining P $(5, 6)$ and Q $(-1, 7)$
   c) $\left(\frac{1}{4}, \frac{1}{2}\right)$ perpendicular to the line joining C $(1, 1)$ and D $(-1, 2)$
   d) $\left(\frac{5}{2}, -\frac{7}{2}\right)$ perpendicular to the line joining E $\left(\frac{1}{2}, \frac{1}{4}\right)$ and F $\left(-\frac{3}{2}, \frac{5}{4}\right)$.

6 A is the point $(-2, 3)$, B $(-4, -3)$ and C $(4, -1)$. Find the equation of the line through:
   a) A parallel to BC   b) A perpendicular to BC   c) B parallel to AC
   d) B perpendicular to AC   e) C parallel to AB   f) C perpendicular to AB.

7 KLMN is a parallelogram with K $(-3, 2)$, L $(3, 4)$ and M $(1, -2)$.
   Find the equation of: a) KN   b) NM.

8 Find the equation of the straight line passing through the point A $(4, -5)$ and the point B, which is the intersection of the lines $3x + 4y = 19$ and $2x - 3y + 27 = 0$.

9 A is the point $(2, 3)$, B $(5, 6)$, C $(4, 8)$ and D $(-1, 3)$. P and Q are the midpoints of AB and CD. Find the equation of PQ.

10 Find the equation of the perpendicular bisector of the line joining:
    a) $(4, 5)$ and $(5, 4)$ b) $(2, 2)$ and $(8, 6)$
    c) $(-4, 5)$ and $(17, 17)$ d) $\left(\frac{3}{2}, -\frac{7}{2}\right)$ and $\left(\frac{5}{2}, \frac{9}{2}\right)$.

11 P is the point (1, 5), Q (8, 12) and R (7, 13).
a) Find the equations of the perpendicular bisectors of PQ and QR.
b) Show that their point of intersection lies on PR.

12 K is the point (−3, 1), L (9, −7), M (8, −2) and N (2, 2). A and B are the midpoints of KL and MN respectively. Find the equations of KN and LM and show that they meet on the line which passes through A and B.

13 K is the point (3, 3), L (1, −7) and M (9, −3). Find
a) the equation of the altitude from K of triangle KLM
b) the equation of the perpendicular bisector of KM
c) the coordinates of the point of intersection of these two lines.

14 The vertices of a triangle are F (2, 7), G (−11, −3) and H (9, −7).
The median FK and the altitude GL intersect at Q. Find the coordinates of Q.

15 The vertices of triangle STV are S (−4, 10), T (10, 3) and V (0, −10). Find the coordinates of the point of intersection of the median TM and the altitude VP.

16 Triangle ABC has vertices A (0, −2), B (−2, 2) and C (7, 1). Find:
a) the equation of the line through C parallel to AB
b) the equation of the line through A perpendicular to BC
c) the coordinates of the point of intersection of these two lines.

17B PQRS is a square with vertices P (1, 1), Q (3, −3), R (7, −1) and S (5, 3).
The diagonal QS meets the line from P to the midpoint of QR at T.
Find the coordinates of T.

18B P is the point (1, 9), Q (−2, 3) and R (4, 7). Show that the midpoint of PR lies on the line through the midpoint of QR parallel to PQ.

19B ABCD is a square with A (2, 3) and C (6, 5). Find the coordinates of the point of intersection of the diagonals and the coordinates of B and D.

12 Centroid, Orthocentre and Circumcentre

> **Reminder**

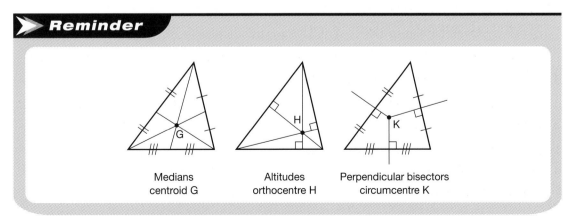

| Medians | Altitudes | Perpendicular bisectors |
| centroid G | orthocentre H | circumcentre K |

Exercise 12

1B Find the equations of the medians of triangle ABC, prove they are concurrent, and state the coordinates of the centroid, where
- a) A is (4, 5)   B (3, −6)   and C (11, −2)
- b) A is (−1, 2)   B (3, −1)   and C (4, 5)
- c) A is (−6, 1)   B (4, 5)   and C (8, −3).

2B Find the equations of the altitudes of triangle PQR, prove they are concurrent and state the coordinates of the orthocentre, where
- a) P is (3, −2)   Q (5, −3)   R (2, 1)
- b) P is (−1, 2)   Q (3, −1)   R (4, 5)
- c) P is (2, −1)   Q (0, 1)   R (3, 5)
- d) P is (6, 6)   Q (−3, 0)   R (0, −3).

3B Find the equations of the perpendicular bisectors of the sides of triangle XYZ, prove that they are concurrent, state the coordinates of the circumcentre, and find the radius of the circumcircle, where
- a) X is (−2, −8)   Y (2, −6)   Z (1, 1)
- b) X is (−4, 2)   Y (3, 4)   Z (0, 2)
- c) X is (−3, 1)   Y (5, 5)   Z (6, −2)
- d) X is (0, 2)   Y (2, −4)   Z (4, −6).

13 Miscellaneous Revision

Exercise 13

Most of these exercises should be done at home as revision.

1 Show that PQ is perpendicular to RS where
- a)   P is (2, 8)   Q (0, 12)   R (−4, −6) and S (14, 3)
- b)   P is (−3, 6)   Q (3, 4)   R (−2, −6) and S (−1, −3).

2 A is the point (8, −3), B (7, 2), C (2, 1) and D (3, −4). Prove the following:
- a) AB is parallel to CD   b) CB is parallel to AD
- c) AB is perpendicular to BC   d) CD is perpendicular to AD
- e) AC is perpendicular to BD .

3 Use gradients to show that K (5, −3), L (0, −8), M (−8, 0) and N (−3, 5) are vertices of a rectangle.

4 P, Q, R are the points $(1, 1−t)$, $(1+t, 1)$, $(1−t, 1+t)$ respectively. Show that PQ is perpendicular to the line joining R to the midpoint of PQ.

5 K, L, M are the points (1, 7), (−3, −3), (6, 5) respectively, and F, G, H are the midpoints of KL, LM, MK respectively. Show that FGHK is a rectangle.

6 B is the point $(-1, 8)$ and C is $(6, 4)$. A is the point where the line $x + y + 5 = 0$ cuts the x-axis.

a) Write down the coordinates of D if ABCD is a parallelogram.

b) If M is the midpoint of BC, show that AM is perpendicular to the line with equation $5x + 4y = 16$.

7 The lines $x - y - 1 = 0$ and $x + 2y - 7 = 0$ intersect at A, and cut the x-axis at B and C respectively. Find the coordinates of A, B and C and the area of triangle ABC.

8 P, Q, R are the points $(-5, 6)$, $(9, 0)$, $(3, 14)$.

A and B are the midpoints of PQ and QR respectively.

a) Find the equation of AB

b) Find the equation of the perpendicular bisector of AB

c) Show that Q lies on this perpendicular bisector.

9 The line ℓ with equation $4x + 3y = 24$ cuts the y-axis at A and the x-axis at B.

a) Find the coordinates of A and B

b) D is the point $\left(0, -\frac{1}{3}\right)$. Find the equation of the line CD which is parallel to ℓ.

c) Find the equation of AC, which is perpendicular to ℓ.

d) Find the coordinates of C.

10 Find the gradient of

a) AB

b) AC

c) BC

(correct to one decimal place where necessary).

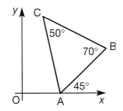

11 P is the point $(-5, -3)$, Q $(-1, -5)$, R $(-5, -2)$ and S $(k, 1)$.

Find the value of k for which RS is perpendicular to PQ.

12 A is the point (a^2, a) and B is (b^2, b).

Find an expression for the gradient of AB in its simplest form.

13 The diagram shows a rhombus OABC with OB = 8 units and AC = 6 units.

Calculate the gradient of OB.

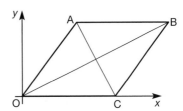

14 The diagram represents two cog-wheels linked by a chain.

The centres of the circles are A $(5, 7)$ and B $(15, 7)$.

CD and EF are common tangents. C is $(4, 10)$.

Find the equations of

a) the radii AC and BD

b) the tangent CD

c) the axis of symmetry AB

d) the tangent EF.

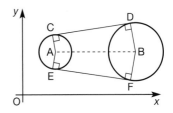

15 Triangle ABC has vertices A (−2, 3), B (8, 5) and C (2, −4).

Find a) the equation of the median CD

   b) the equation of the altitude AE

   c) the coordinates of F, the point
   of intersection of CD and AE.

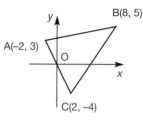

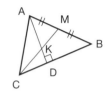

16 Triangle ABC has vertices A(−2, 5), B(8, 1) and C(−3, −3).
The median CM and the altitude AD
are drawn and meet at K.

Find a) the equation of CM

   b) the equation of AD

   c) the coordinates of K.

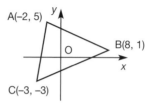

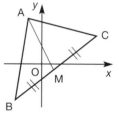

17 Triangle ABC has vertices A(−1, 5), B(−2, −5) and C(6, 3).
Find the equation of the median AM of triangle ABC,
expressing your answer in the form $ax + by + c = 0$.

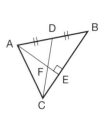

18B The quadrilateral PQRS has vertices P(−2, 3), Q(4, 7), R(16, 2) and S(1, −8).

   a) Show that PQRS is a trapezium.

   b) If PQRT is a parallelogram, find the coordinates of T.

   c) Find (i)   the equation of ℓ, the perpendicular bisector
        of PQ.

      (ii) the equation of QS

      (iii) the coordinates of U, the point of intersection
         of ℓ and QS.

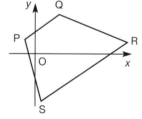

19B Triangle PQR is isosceles with PQ = PR.
P is the point (2, 10) and Q is (−3, −5).
QR has equation $y = 2x + 1$.

Find a) the equation of the altitude PT of triangle PQR

   b) the coordinates of R.

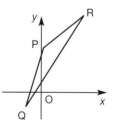

20B Triangle OAB has vertices $O(0, 0)$, $A(6, 24)$ and $B(30, 0)$.

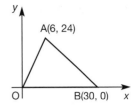

a) Write down the equation of the altitude of this triangle which passes through A.

b) Find the equation of the altitude of triangle OAB which passes through O, and hence show that the altitudes meet at $H(6, 6)$.

c) Show that the point $C(15, 9)$ is the centre of the circle through O, A and B.

d) Find the equation of the line CH, which is called the Euler Line for this triangle.

e) Find the equations of the medians OM and AN of triangle OAB, and hence the coordinates of the point G where they intersect.

f) Show that G lies on the Euler Line, and find the ratio in which G divides HC.

14 TOPIC TEST on The Straight Line

🕐 **Allow 45 minutes for this test**

1 A is the point $(-3, -1)$ B is $(5, 5)$, and M is the midpoint of AB.

Find a) the length of AB

b) the coordinates of M

c) the gradient of OM

d) the equation of OM

e) the equations of the lines through A parallel to the coordinate axes

f) the gradient of AB (in its simplest form)

g) the equation of AB (in the form $ax + by + c = 0$).

2 The lines p and q intersect at right angles at C as shown. p has equation $4x + 5y = 2$.

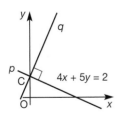

Find a) the gradient of p

b) the coordinates of C

c) the gradient of q

d) the equation of q (in the form $ax + by + c = 0$).

3 Show that the points P $(-5, 7)$ Q $(-2, 5)$ and R $(7, -1)$ are collinear.

4 At what angle to the x-axis is the line with equation $5y = 3x + 1$ inclined?

Calculator required 🖩

5 Triangle STV has vertices S $(2, 6)$ T $(-4, -4)$ and V $(8, -1)$.

Find the coordinates of the point of intersection of the median VM and the altitude SL.

FUNCTIONS

15 Practice in using set notation

Set notation can allow greater clarity of expression, which makes it ideal for describing mathematics. The Higher Mathematics Examination does not test the theory of sets as such, but questions may be expressed in set notation and answers also can often be expressed more precisely by this means. This simple piece of mathematics used to be taught in first year, so you should not find it very taxing.

> **Reminder**

A set can be defined in three different ways

listing	*describing*	*by a characteristic property*
$\{1, 2, 3, 4, 5\}$	$\{$the first five natural numbers$\}$	$\{x \mid 1 \leqslant x \leqslant 5, x \in N\}$

Venn diagrams are a useful way to depict sets.

the intersection of A and B   the union of A and B   the complement of A

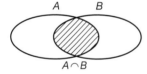

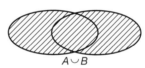

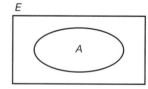

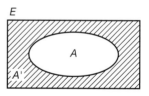

Example E = the universal set = $\{1, 2, 3, 4, 5, 6, 7, 8, 9, 10\}$
$A = \{$even numbers$\}$ $B = \{x \mid x$ is odd$\}$
$C = \{$multiples of 3$\}$ $D = \{1, 4, 7, 9\}$

a) List the sets $A \cap B, A \cup B, A', B', A \cap D, B \cap C \cap D, (C \cup D)'$.
b) Draw a Venn diagram to illustrate the sets A, C and D.

Solution   a) $A = \{2, 4, 6, 8, 10\}$ $B = \{1, 3, 5, 7, 9\}$
$C = \{3, 6, 9\}$ $D = \{1, 4, 7, 9\}$

> **Reminder** continued

$$A \cap B = \emptyset \qquad (A \text{ and } B \text{ have no elements in common,}$$
$$\emptyset = \{\} = \text{the empty set})$$
$$A \cup B = E \qquad (\text{all the elements of } A \text{ and } B \text{ together make up } E),$$
$$A' = B \qquad (A' \text{ contains all the elements which are not in } A,$$
$$\text{and none in } A),$$
$$B' = A \qquad (\text{the opposite of the above or } (A')' = A),$$
$$A \cap D = \{4\} \qquad (4 \text{ is the only element in both } A \text{ and } D),$$
$$B \cap C \cap D = \{9\} \quad (9 \text{ is the only element in } B \text{ and } C \text{ and } D),$$
$$(C \cup D)' = \{1, 3, 4, 6, 7, 9\}' = \{2, 5, 8, 10\}.$$

b)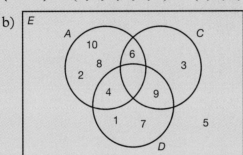

Exercise 15

1 a) $A = \{1, 2, 3, 4, 5\}$ $B = \{3, 6, 9\}$ $C = \{2, 4, 6, 8\}$

    List the sets $A \cap B,$ $B \cap C,$ $A \cap C,$ $A \cap B \cap C$
                     $A \cup B,$ $B \cup C,$ $A \cup C,$ $A \cup B \cup C.$

  b) For A, B, C above, the universal set is $E = \{1, 2, 3, 4, 5, 6, 7, 8, 9\}$.

    List the sets $A',$ $(A \cup B)',$ $(A \cup B \cup C)'.$

  c) Draw a Venn diagram to illustrate these sets.

2 $E = $ the universal set $= \{a, b, c, d, e, f, g, h\}$ $P = \{a, b, c, d\}$ $Q = \{c, d, e, f\}.$

  a) List the sets $P \cap Q,$ $P \cup Q,$ $P',$ $Q',$
                      $P' \cup Q',$ $P' \cap Q',$ $(P \cap Q)',$ $(P \cup Q)'.$

  b) Draw a Venn diagram for E, P and Q.

  c) By inspecting your previous answers, suggest what the right hand sides might be for
    these set statements (known as De Morgan's Laws):

     $(P \cap Q)' = \dots\dots\dots\dots$ $(P \cup Q)' = \dots\dots\dots\dots\dots$

3 A and B are subsets of the universal set E, which can be illustrated as shown

   $E = \{x \mid -2 \leqslant x \leqslant 4\}$
   $A = \{x \mid -2 \leqslant x \leqslant 1\}$
   $B = \{x \mid 0 < x < 3\}$
  Taking great care with the inclusion or
  exclusion of all end points, list the sets
   $A \cap B, \ A \cup B, \ A', \ B', \ (A \cup B)', \ (A \cap B)'.$

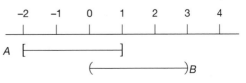

16 Types of Relation

► **Reminder**

SUMMARY OF DEFINITIONS

RELATION

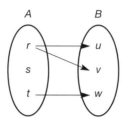

not a mapping because (either)
a) x has two images
b) y has no images

MAPPING (OR FUNCTION)

Each element in A has exactly
one image
(i.e. not none, not two).

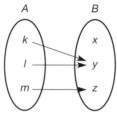

Domain $= A = \{a, b, c\}$
Codomain $= B = \{p, q, r\}$
Range $= \{q, r\}$

1–1 FUNCTION

separate elements in A map
to separate elements in B.

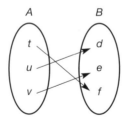

domain $= \{h, k\}$
codomain $= \{r, s, t\}$
range $= \{s, t\}$

1–1 CORRESPONDENCE

a 1–1 mapping where each
element of B is the image of
an element in A.

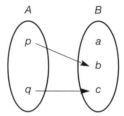

domain $= \{a, b, c\}$
codomain $= \{x, y, z\}$
range $= \{x, y, z\}$

When the arrows of a 1–1 correspondence are reversed, another 1–1
correspondence is obtained.

▶ Reminder continued

Example

Explain which type of relation each of these arrow diagrams represents.

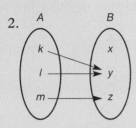

1.

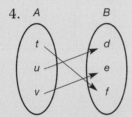

3.

Solution

1. *RELATION*
   Not a mapping because has two images

2. *MAPPING (OR FUNCTION)*
   Each element in *A* has exactly one image

3. *1–1 FUNCTION*
   Separate elements in *A* map to separate elements in *B*

4. *1–1 CORRESPONDENCE*
   A 1–1 mapping where each element of *B* is the image of an element in *A*

Example   Explain which type of relation each of these graphs represents.

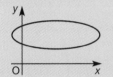 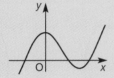 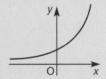 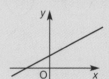

▶ Reminder continued

Solution   The *x*-axis is the domain and the *y*-axis is the codomain.

RELATION
Some *x*-values have no corresponding *y*-values, and others have two. [The graph does not go all the way across the page and can be at the same height twice.]

FUNCTION
Each number on the *x*-axis maps to exactly one number on the *y*-axis. [The graph goes all the way across the page. This makes it the graph of a function.]

1–1 FUNCTION
This is a function with no *y*-value being the image of more than one *x*-value. [The graph goes all the way across the page and is never at the same height twice.]

1–1 CORRESPONDENCE
This is a 1–1 function with the range equal to the entire codomain. [The graph goes all the way across the page and all the way up and down the page as well, without ever being at the same height twice.]

Exercise 16

(Do not spend too long on this basic exercise.)

1 Decide whether each arrow diagram shows
    (i) a relation but not a function, or (ii) a function but not a 1–1 function, or
    (iii) a 1–1 function but not a 1–1 correspondence, or (iv) a 1–1 correspondence.

a) 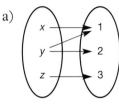 b) 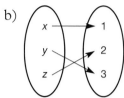 c)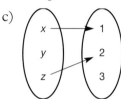

d) 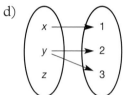 e) 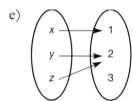 f)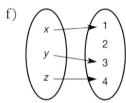

g) 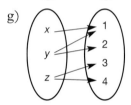 h) 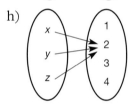 i)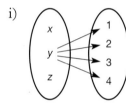

j) 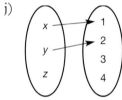 k) 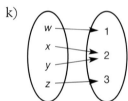 l)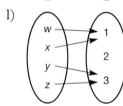

m) 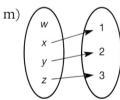 n) 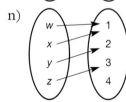 o)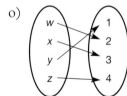

p) 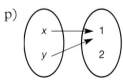 q) 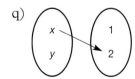 r)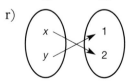

s) 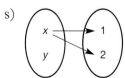 t) 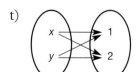 u)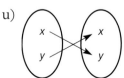

(steps continued indefinitely, each step includes left end point, excludes right end point.)

2 The graphs of several relations defined on $\Re$, the set of all real numbers, are shown below. Classify each relation as in question 1.

a)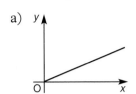

b)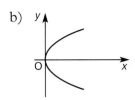

c)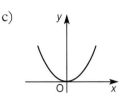

d)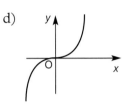

e)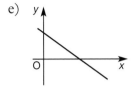

f)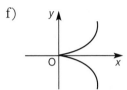

g)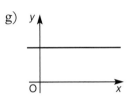

h)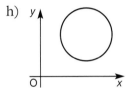

i)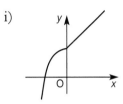

j)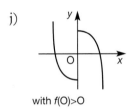

with $f(0) > 0$

k)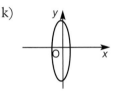

l)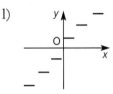

3 (i) Sketch the graphs of these functions which are defined by different algebraic formulae in different subsets of their domains:

a) $f(x) = \begin{cases} 2 + x : x < 0 \\ 2 - x : x \geq 0 \end{cases}$

b) $g(x) = \begin{cases} -x : x < 0 \\ 2x : x \geq 0 \end{cases}$

c) $h(x) = \begin{cases} x + 1 : x \leq 0 \\ x^2 + 1 : x > 0 \end{cases}$

d) $s(x) = \begin{cases} 0 : 0 \leq x < 1 \\ 1 : 1 \leq x < 2 \\ 2 : 2 \leq x \leq 3 \end{cases}$

e) $u(x) = \begin{cases} 3^x : x < 0 \\ 3 + x : 0 \leq x \leq 3 \\ 2x : x > 3 \end{cases}$

f) $v(x) = \begin{cases} x - 1 : x < -1 \\ x^3 : -1 \leq x \leq 1 \\ 4 - x : x > 1 \end{cases}$

(ii) List those of the above that are 1–1 functions but not 1–1 correspondences.

(iii) List those of the above that are 1–1 correspondences.

4 Find the largest possible domain on which each of the following functions could be defined:

a) $f(x) = 2\sqrt{x}$

b) $g(x) = \sqrt{(x + 1)}$

c) $h(x) = \sqrt{(2 - x)}$

d) $k(x) = \sqrt{(x^2 - 1)}$

e) $p(x) = \dfrac{3}{x}$

f) $q(x) = \dfrac{5}{x^3 - 8}$.

5 For each of the following functions defined on the set of all real numbers,
(i) sketch the graph   (ii) state the range
    a) $f(x) = 2x$ b) $g(x) = x^2$ c) $h(x) = x^3$ d) $k(x) = 1 - x^2$.

6B Find the range of each of these functions by sketching their graphs:

a) $f(x) = \begin{cases} x + 1 : x \leqslant 0 \\ x^2 + 1 : x > 0 \end{cases}$ b) $g(x) = \begin{cases} -x : x \leqslant 0 \\ x^2 + 1 : x > 0 \end{cases}$ c) $h(x) = \begin{cases} x + 2 : x < 1 \\ 1 - x^2 : x \geqslant 1 \end{cases}$

17 Composition of Functions

> **Reminder**

Example

Two functions $f : A \rightarrow B$ and $g : B \rightarrow C$ are defined by this arrow diagram.

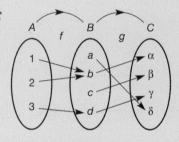

Evaluate $g(f(1))$ and $g(f(3))$.

Solution

Note that $f : A \rightarrow B$ signifies that the function f has domain A and codomain B

$g(f(1)) = g(b)$ [The arrow maps 1 to b.]
$\qquad = \alpha$ [The arrow maps b to α.]
$g(f(3)) = g(d)$ [The arrow maps 3 to d.]
$\qquad = \gamma$ [The arrow maps d to γ.]

Exercise 17

1 Functions $f : A \rightarrow B$, and $g : B \rightarrow C$ are defined by
   the following arrow diagram:

   a) Copy and complete the following:

   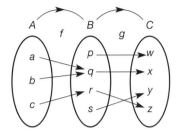

$$
\begin{array}{lll}
\quad f & \quad g \\
a \rightarrow q & \rightarrow x \\
b \rightarrow & \rightarrow \\
c \rightarrow & \rightarrow
\end{array}
$$

   b) Hence evaluate $g(f(a))$, $g(f(b))$, and $g(f(c))$.

   c) State the domain and the range of the function $g^0 f$.

2 Functions f and g are defined by $\quad f : \mathfrak{R} \rightarrow \mathfrak{R} : x \rightarrow x + 1 \quad g : \mathfrak{R} \rightarrow \mathfrak{R} : x \rightarrow 2x - 1$.
   Calculate $\quad f(2), \qquad f(1), \qquad f(0), \qquad$ and $\qquad f(-1), \qquad$ and hence calculate
   $\qquad g(f(2)), \quad g(f(1)), \quad g(f(0)), \quad$ and $\qquad g(f(-1))$.

3 Functions f and g are defined by $\quad f : \mathfrak{R} \rightarrow \mathfrak{R} : x \rightarrow x + 2 \quad g : \mathfrak{R} \rightarrow \mathfrak{R} : x \rightarrow x^2$.
   Find $\qquad g(f(1)), \quad g(f(-3)), \quad g(f(4)), \quad f(g(1)), \quad f(g(-3)), \quad$ and $\quad f(g(4))$.

4 Functions f and g are defined by $\quad f : \mathfrak{R} \rightarrow \mathfrak{R} : x \rightarrow x + 1 \quad g : \mathfrak{R} \rightarrow \mathfrak{R} : x \rightarrow x^3$.
   Find $\qquad g(f(1)), \quad g(f(-3)), \quad g(f(4)), \quad f(g(1)), \quad f(g(-3)), \quad$ and $\quad f(g(4))$.

18 The Formula for the Composition of Functions

> ### Reminder

Example

For the functions $f : \mathfrak{R} \rightarrow \mathfrak{R} : x \rightarrow x + 1$ and $g : \mathfrak{R} \rightarrow \mathfrak{R} : x \rightarrow 2x - 1$,
obtain formulae for $g(f(x))$ and $f(g(x))$.

Solution

To obtain a formula for $g(f(x))$, first replace $f(x)$ by the expression
for $f(x)$ i.e. $g(f(x)) = g(x + 1)$.

Now think $g(?) = 2(?) - 1$
? = 'something' and replace the 'something' by $(x + 1)$.

So $g(x + 1) = 2(x + 1) - 1 = 2x + 2 - 1 = 2x + 1$
i.e. $g(f(x)) = g(x + 1) = 2x + 1$.

Similarly,
$f(g(x)) = f(2x - 1)$ [replacing $g(x)$ by the expression for $g(x)$]
$\qquad\qquad = (2x - 1) + 1$ [using f(something) = something + 1]
$\qquad\qquad = 2x$.

Exercise 18

1 a) Functions f and g are defined by $f : \Re \to \Re : x \to x + 2$ $g : \Re \to \Re : x \to x^2$.
Find formulae for $f(g(x))$ and $g(f(x))$.
b) Functions f and g are defined by $f : \Re \to \Re : x \to x + 1$ $g : \Re \to \Re : x \to x^3$.
Find formulae for $f(g(x))$ and $g(f(x))$.

2 Functions g and h are defined by $g : \Re \to \Re : x \to 2x$ $h : \Re \to \Re : x \to x^2 + 4$.
Find, in their simplest forms, formulae for:
a) $h(g(x))$ b) $g(h(x))$ c) $g(g(x))$ d) $h(h(x))$.

3 Each of the following mappings has domain and codomain $\Re$.
In each case, find and simplify the formula for $g(f(x))$.
a) $f(x) = x + 1$ $g(x) = x^2$ b) $f(x) = x + 3$ $g(x) = 2x + 1$
c) $f(x) = x - 1$ $g(x) = x^2 + x + 1$ d) $f(x) = x^2$ $g(x) = 2x^2 + 1$
e) $f(x) = 2x - 1$ $g(x) = x^2 - 1$ f) $f(x) = x^2 + 1$ $g(x) = \dfrac{1}{x^2 + 1}$
g) $f(x) = -3x$ $g(x) = x^3 - 2x$ h) $f(x) = x^2$ $g(x) = \sin x^\circ$

4 For each of the pairs of functions in question 3, find and simplify the formula for $f(g(x))$.

19 Inverse Functions

Finding the formula for the inverse of a given function is not examined in the Higher Mathematics Exam. Nevertheless, given the graph of a function, you must be able to draw the graph of the inverse function and the concept of inverse must be understood for you to see the connection between exponential and logarithmic functions. If you have to miss out part of the next exercise, make sure that you try questions 5 and 6, checking your answer to part (c) of each. This is the important result which you will use again.

> **Reminder**

Example Show that the functions $f(x) = 2x + 5$ and $g(x) = \dfrac{x - 5}{2}$ are inverses of each other.

Solution $f(g(x)) = f\left(\dfrac{x - 5}{2}\right) = 2\left(\dfrac{x - 5}{2}\right) + 5 = x - 5 + 5 = x = i\,(x)$

$i\,(x)$ is the identity function, which maps x to x for all x
hence f and g are inverses of each other.

alternatively:

$g(f(x)) = g(2x + 5) = \dfrac{(2x + 5) - 5}{2} = \dfrac{2x}{2} = x.$

Example Find the formula for the inverse of the function $h(x) = 2x^3 - 5$.

Solution   Let $y = h(x) = 2x^3 - 5$ [and change the subject of the formula to x]

$$\therefore y + 5 = 2x^3$$

$$\therefore x^3 = \frac{y + 5}{2} \quad \Rightarrow \quad x = \sqrt[3]{\frac{y + 5}{2}} \quad \Rightarrow \quad h^{-1}(x) = \sqrt[3]{\frac{x + 5}{2}}.$$

Alternatively (more intuitively):

the function h does three things (in order) to x:

  cubes x doubles x^3 subtracts 5 from $2x^3$

to undo this process, invert each step in the reverse order
[c.f. the opposite of putting on your socks and shoes is taking off
your shoes and socks]

  add 5 to x halve $(x + 5)$ take the cube root of $\frac{x + 5}{2}$

hence $h^{-1}(x) = \sqrt[3]{\dfrac{x + 5}{2}}.$

Exercise 19

1 Show that in each case the function g is the inverse of the function f.

  a) $f(x) = 2x + 1$ $g(x) = \dfrac{x - 1}{2}$

  b) $f(x) = x^3 - 1$ $g(x) = \sqrt[3]{x + 1}$

  c) $f(x) = 5 - 2x$ $g(x) = \dfrac{5 - x}{2}$

  d) $f(x) = 11 - x$ $g(x) = 11 - x$

2 $A = \{2,3,4,5\}, B = \{5,6,7,8\}$. Draw an arrow diagram to illustrate the function f given
  by $f: A \to B : x \to x + 3$.
  Draw a separate arrow diagram to illustrate $f^{-1} : B \to A$, and state the formula for $f^{-1}(x)$.

3 Each of the following functions is defined on $\Re$. Find the formula for $f^{-1}(x)$ in each case.

  a) $f(x) = 2x$ b) $f(x) = x + 4$ c) $f(x) = x^3$

  d) $f(x) = x + 2$ e) $f(x) = 5x$ f) $f: x \to -3x$

  g) $f: x \to x^5$ h) $f: x \to \dfrac{1}{x}$ i) $f: x \to 7 - x$

  j) $f: x \to 2x + 5$ k) $f(x) = 3x - 1$ l) $f(x) = 1 - 3x$

  m) $f(x) = 1 - x$ n) $f(x) = x - \dfrac{1}{2}$ o) $f(x) = x$

4 The functions f, g, h are defined on the set $A = \{x \in \Re \mid x > 0\}$ by
  $f(x) = x + 1$ $g(x) = 2x$ and $h(x) = x^2$.
  a) Find formulae for the inverse functions f^{-1}, g^{-1}, h^{-1}.
  b) Evaluate   (i) $f^{-1}(5)$ (ii) $g^{-1}(8)$ (iii) $h^{-1}(4)$.

5 a) Sketch the graph of the function $f : \Re \to \Re : x \to 2x + 1$.

   b) Obtain the formula for $f^{-1}(x)$ and sketch its graph on the same coordinate diagram.

   c) What transformation of the plane maps one graph to the other?

6 Repeat question 5 for $g : \Re \to \Re : x \to 4 - 2x$.

7 For each of these functions, sketch the graph of the function and on the same diagram sketch the graph of the inverse function without finding its formula.

   a) $f(x) = 3x$ b) $h(x) = \frac{1}{2}x + 1$ c) $k(x) = 8 - 4x$ d) $g(x) = -x^3$.

20 Graphs of Related Functions

> **Reminder**

Given the graph of $y = f(x)$, several related graphs can also be sketched. Thus:

$y = -f(x)$: reflect the graph of $y = f(x)$ in the x-axis

$y = f(-x)$: reflect the graph of $y = f(x)$ in the y-axis

$y = -f(-x)$: give the graph of $y = f(x)$ a half-turn about the origin

$y = f(x) + k$: give the graph of $y = f(x)$ a translation of k units up the y-axis

$y = f(x - k)$: give the graph of $y = f(x)$ a translation of k units along the (+ve) x-axis

$y = kf(x)$: stretch the graph parallel to the y-axis with a scale factor of k

$y = f\left(\frac{x}{k}\right)$: stretch the graph parallel to the x-axis with a scale factor of k

$y = f'(x)$: stationary points on the graph of $y = f(x)$ give the zeros of $f'(x)$

Example   The graph of $y = f(x)$ is shown.
Sketch the graphs of :

a) $y = -f(x)$

b) $y = f(-x)$

c) $y = -f(-x)$

d) $y = f(x) + 1$

e) $y = f(x + 1)$

f) $y = 2f(x)$

g) $y = f\left(\frac{x}{2}\right)$

h) $y = 1 - f(x)$

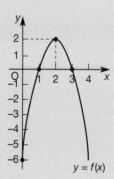

$y = f(x)$

Reminder continued

Solution

a) reflect in the *x*-axis

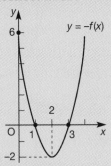

b) reflect in the *y*-axis

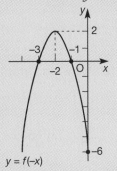

c) half-turn about O (0, 0)

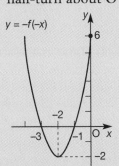

d) translate 1 unit up

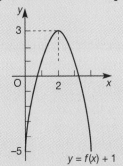

e) translate 1 unit left

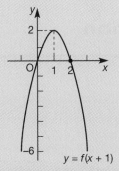

f) stretch × 2 in *y* direction

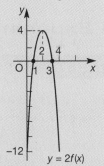

g) stretch × 2 in *x* direction

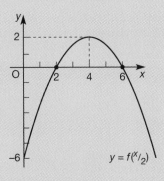

h) reflect in O*x* then translate 1 unit up

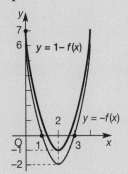

Exercise 20

1 The graph of $y = f(x)$ is shown. Sketch the graphs of:

a) $y = -f(x)$

b) $y = f(-x)$

c) $y = -f(-x)$

d) $y = f(x) + 1$

e) $y = f(x - 1)$ ★

f) $y = 14 - f(x)$

★Do not try to find where graph (e) crosses the y-axis.

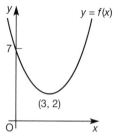

2 The graph of $y = g(x)$ is shown. Sketch the graphs of:

a) $y = -g(x)$

b) $y = g(-x)$

c) $y = -g(-x)$

d) $y = g(x) + 2$

e) $y = 2 - g(x)$

f) $y = g(x + 2)$

g) $y = 2\, g(x)$.

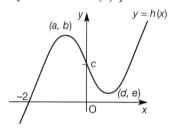

3 The graph of $y = h(x)$ is shown. Sketch the graph of the image after $y = h(x)$ undergoes each of these transformations, and write down its equation [in terms of $h(x)$].

a) the translation $\begin{pmatrix} 0 \\ 1 \end{pmatrix}$ [i.e. 1 unit up the y-axis]

b) reflection in the x-axis

c) reflection in the y-axis

d) a half-turn about the origin

e) the translation $\begin{pmatrix} 2 \\ 1 \end{pmatrix}$.

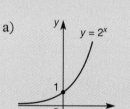

21 The Exponential Function

▸ **Reminder**

Example

The graphs of

a) $y = 2^x$ b) $y = e^x$

are shown.

a)

b)

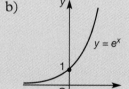

Sketch the graphs of

(i) $y = 2^x - 1$

(ii) $y = 2^{2x}$

(iii) $y = 2e^{-x}$.

> **Reminder** continued

Solution　(i)　Move 1 unit down the y-axis, remembering to show the asymptote.
(ii)　$y = 2^{2x} = (2^2)^x = 4^x$ which passes through $(0, 1)$ & $(1, 4)$.
(iii) Reflect in the y-axis and stretch by a factor of 2 in the y direction.

(i) 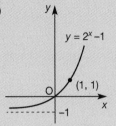　(ii) 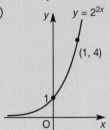　(iii)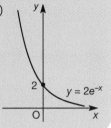

Exercise 21

1 Use your calculator to evaluate
a) e^5　　b) e^{-2}　　c) e^3　　d) e^{-1}
e) $2e^{1.6}$　f) $3e^{-3}$　g) $10e^{1.5}$　h) $20e^{-2.5}$.

2 Sketch the graphs of
a) $y = 1 + 2^x$　b) $y = 3^x - 1$　c) $y = 2e^x$　d) $y = -e^x$
e) $y = 1 - e^x$　f) $y = 2^{x-1}$　g) $y = 3^{x+1}$　h) $y = 3^{2x}$
i) $y = e^{-x}$　j) $y = 500e^{-x}$　k) $y = \frac{1}{3}3^x$　l) $y = 2 - e^{-x}$.

3 Find the value of the constants a (and where used) b for each graph:

a) 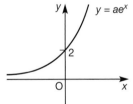　b) 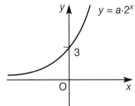　c)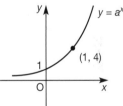

d) 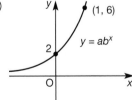　e) 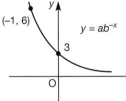　f)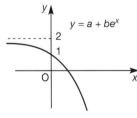

g) 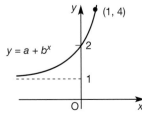　h) 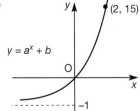　i)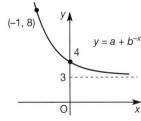

22 The Logarithmic Function

> **Reminder**

Example

The graph of $y = \log_3 x$ is shown. It was obtained by reflecting the graph of $y = 3^x$ in the line $y = x$. Sketch the graphs of

a) $y = \log_3 (x - 1)$
b) $y = 1 + \log_3 x$.

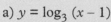

Solution

a) Translate 1 unit to the right remembering the asymptote.

b) Translate 1 unit up the y-axis (you can't find where this graph crosses the x-axis, yet).

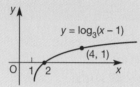

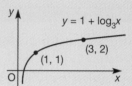

Exercise 22

1 Use your calculator to evaluate

a) $\log_{10} 4$
b) $\log_e 3$
c) $\log_{10} 17$
d) $\log_e 6\cdot6$
e) $\log_{10} 89$
f) $\log_e 18\cdot2$
g) $\log_{10} 31\cdot7$
h) $\log_e 36\cdot6$.

2 Evaluate without using a calculator

a) $\log_{10} 10$
b) $\log_5 1$
c) e^0
d) $\log_e 1$
e) $\log_e e$
f) $\log_{10} 100$.

3 The graph of $y = \log_2 x$ is shown. Sketch the graph of:

a) $\log_2 (-x)$
b) $-\log_2 x$
c) $\log_2 (x-1)$
d) $\log_2 (x+2)$
e) $1 + \log_2 x$
f) $1 - \log_2 x$.

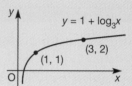

4 The graph of $y = \log_5 x$ is shown. Sketch the graph of:

a) $y = -\log_5 x$
b) $y = \log_5 (-x)$
c) $y = 2\log_5 x$
d) $y = \log_5 2x$.

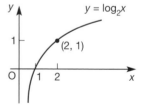

5 Find the values of a and b in each case:

a)

$y = \log_b(x + a)$

(11, 1)

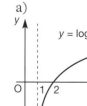

b)

$y = \log_b(x + a)$

(5, 1)

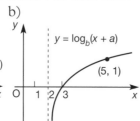

c)

$y = a - \log_b x$

(1, 1)

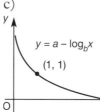

d)

$y = \log_b(a - x)$

(-6, 1)

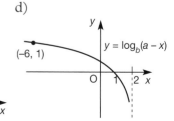

23 TOPIC TEST on Functions

⏱ Allow 45 minutes for this test (non-Calculator)

1 For the function shown in this arrow diagram, list the elements in

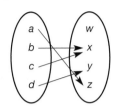

a) the domain
b) the co–domain
c) the range
d) What is the image of *d*?

2
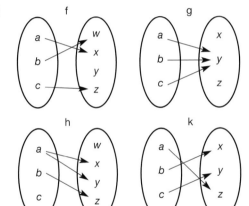

Which of these four arrow diagrams (f, g, h, or k)
a) does *NOT* represent a function? (and why?)
b) represents a function which has an inverse? (and why?)

3
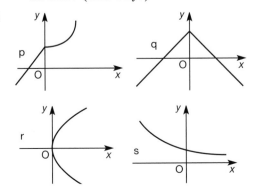

Which of these four graphs (p, q, r, or s)
a) does *NOT* represent the graph of a function? (and why?)
b) represents a function which has an inverse? (and why?)

4 For $f(x) = 2x + 1$ and $g(x) = 1 - 3x^2$, evaluate $f(g(-2))$, and find a formula for $f(g(x))$.

5 The graph of $y = f(x)$ is shown.

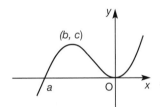

Make two copies of this graph and superimpose the graphs (one on each copy) of
(i) $y = f(-x)$
(ii) $y = f(x - 1)$

6 Given $f(x) = 4x + 5$ $g(x) = 1 + x^2$ $h(x) = \frac{1}{4}x - \frac{5}{4}$,
a) Find a formula for
(i) $g(f(x))$ (in its simplest form)
(ii) $f(h(x))$ (in its simplest form)
b) What is the connection between the functions f and h?
c) Sketch the graphs of f and h, and explain how these graphs are related.

33

DIFFERENTIATION

24 Optional Introductory Exercise for Class Discussion

Exercise 24

1 The diagram shows the tangent at the point P $(1, 3)$ to the curve with equation $y = 2x^2 + 1$. We wish to find the gradient of this tangent. Now the gradient of the chord PQ is greater than the gradient of the tangent, but as Q is moved closer to P, the gradient of the chord will decrease and get nearer to the gradient of the tangent.

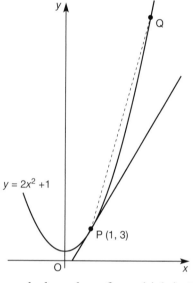

Suppose the x-coordinate of Q is 4.

Then $y = 2x^2 + 1 \Rightarrow y = 2 \times 4^2 + 1 = 33$

i.e. Q is $(4, 33)$

so $m_{PQ} = \dfrac{33 - 3}{4 - 1} = 10$

so the gradient of the tangent is less than 10.

As Q approaches P, x_Q, the x coordinate of Q will approach the value of x_P which is 1.

Copy and complete this table, and hence make an estimate of the value of the gradient of the tangent at P.

x_Q	4	3	2	$1\frac{1}{2}$	$1\frac{1}{4}$	1·1	1·01	1·001
y_Q	33	19						
m_{PQ}	10							

2 Now investigate what happens in question 1 if Q is to the left of P.
Copy and complete this second table, and hence make another estimate of the value of the gradient of the tangent at P.

x_Q	-2	-1	0	$\frac{1}{2}$	$\frac{3}{4}$	$0{\cdot}9$	$0{\cdot}99$	$0{\cdot}999$
y_Q	9	3						
m_{PQ}	-2							

3 All the numerical work in questions 1 and 2 can be generalised by using algebra:
   - Let the x-coordinate of Q be $(1 + h)$, work out the y-coordinate of Q, and hence the gradient of PQ.
   - Convince yourself that the numbers in your tables fit this formula.
     (Remember that h is negative in question 2.)
   - Finally let h take the value 0, and write down the value of the gradient of the tangent at P.

4 We now know the gradient of the curve at P $(1, 3)$, but we would like to know it at any point P (x, y). We can repeat the process of question 3:
   - Let the x-coordinate of Q be $(x + h)$, work out the y-coordinate of Q, and hence the gradient of PQ.
   - Check your formula : if $x = 1$ you should have the same result as question 3.
   - Finally let $h = 0$ and obtain a formula for the gradient of the curve at P (x, y).

5 In question 4 we established a formula for the gradient of the curve at any point on it. This formula is different from the formula, f, for the original function, but it has been derived from it, so it is called the derived function and denoted by f'.
   Thus we have $f(x) = 2x^2 + 1$, and $f'(x) = 4x$.
   a) Evaluate
       (i) $f(1)$ (ii) $f(2)$ (iii) $f(-1)$
       (iv) $f'(1)$ (v) $f'(-1)$ (vi) $f'(3)$
   b) What is the gradient of the curve $y = 2x^2 + 1$ at the point where x has the value
       (i) 1   (ii) 2   (iii) -2 (iv) 0?
   c) At what point on the curve is the gradient
       (i) 4   (ii) 8   (iii) -12 (iv) 0?
   d) Find the equation of the tangent to the curve at P $(1, 3)$.

25 Differentiation by Rule

> **Reminder**

The derivative of ax^n is nax^{n-1}

Example   Differentiate with respect to x

      a) $2x^4$ b) $5x^{-3}$ c) $8x^{-\frac{3}{4}}$ d) $\dfrac{(x + 1)(x - 2)}{\sqrt{x}}$.

> **Reminder** continued

Solution

a) $4 \times 2x^{4-1} = 8x^3$

b) $(-3) \times 5x^{-3-1} = -15x^{-4}$

c) $\left(-\frac{3}{4}\right)(8)x^{-\frac{3}{4}-1} = -6x^{-\frac{7}{4}}$

d) $f(x) = \dfrac{(x+1)(x-2)}{\sqrt{x}} = \dfrac{x^2 - x - 2}{x^{\frac{1}{2}}} = \dfrac{x^2}{x^{\frac{1}{2}}} - \dfrac{x}{x^{\frac{1}{2}}} - \dfrac{2}{x^{\frac{1}{2}}} = x^{\frac{3}{2}} - x^{\frac{1}{2}} - 2x^{-\frac{1}{2}}$

$$\Rightarrow \quad f'(x) = \frac{3}{2}x^{\frac{1}{2}} - \frac{1}{2}x^{-\frac{1}{2}} + x^{-\frac{3}{2}}.$$

Exercise 25

1 Write down the derivative of:

a) x^3 b) x^6 c) x^9 d) x^{20}

e) $4x^7$ f) $11x^4$ g) 15 h) $\frac{1}{2}x^3$

i) $\frac{2}{5}x^5$ j) $4x$ k) $\sqrt{2}$ l) $-3x^4$

m) $3x^5$ n) $-\frac{1}{4}x^4$ o) $\frac{3}{2}x^2$ p) $x^3 + 3x - 5$

q) $x^5 + 7x - 2$ r) $3x^2 + 2x + 5$ s) $1 - 2x + 3x^2 - x^4$ t) $4x + 3x^2$

u) $2 - 5x + 10x^2$ v) $\frac{1}{3}x^3 - 5x^2 + x$ w) x^{-4} x) x^{-7}

y) $2x^{-3}$ z) x^{-6}.

2 By expanding the brackets first, find the derivative of:

a) $(x + 2)^2$ b) $(x^2 - 3)^2$ c) $(x^3 + 1)^2$ d) $(2x + 1)^2$

e) $(2 + \frac{1}{2}\sqrt{x})^2$ f) $(3x - 2)^2$ g) $(7x + 4)^2$ h) $(4 - 5x)^2$.

3 Differentiate each of the following and express each answer with a positive index:

a) x^{-1} b) $3x^{-2}$ c) $\dfrac{1}{x^5}$ d) $\dfrac{3}{x^2}$

e) $\dfrac{1}{2x^3}$ f) $\dfrac{4}{5x^6}$ g) $\dfrac{1}{(x^2)^3}$ h) $x^{\frac{7}{3}}$

i) $x^{\frac{4}{5}}$ j) $3x^{\frac{2}{3}}$ k) $2x^{\frac{1}{2}}$ l) $3x^{\frac{1}{3}}$

m) $6\sqrt{x}$ n) $x\sqrt{x}$ o) $-x^{\frac{3}{4}}$ p) $\dfrac{-2}{\sqrt{x}}$

q) $6x^{\frac{-2}{3}}$ r) $\dfrac{3}{2x^{\frac{1}{4}}}$ s) $\dfrac{1}{\sqrt{\pi}}$ t) $\sqrt[3]{x}$

u) $\sqrt[3]{x^2}$ v) $\dfrac{1}{\sqrt[3]{x^2}}$ w) $\dfrac{5}{\sqrt{x^3}}$ y) $\dfrac{1}{x^2\sqrt{x}}$

4 Find the derivative of :

a) $5(x^4 + x^3)$ b) $x + \dfrac{1}{x}$ c) $\sqrt{x} + \dfrac{1}{\sqrt{x}}$ d) $2x^3 + 7x^2 - \dfrac{3}{x}$

e) $3x^5 + \dfrac{1}{2x^4}$ f) $2(x^5 - x^2 + 1)$ g) $x^{\frac{2}{3}} - x^{\frac{-3}{2}}$ h) $2(x^2\sqrt{x} - 3)$

i) $3x^2 - \dfrac{1}{4x^2}$ j) $x^2 + 5 - \dfrac{1}{x^2}$ k) $\dfrac{x}{3} + \dfrac{3}{x}$ l) $20x^{\frac{3}{4}} - \dfrac{12}{x^{\frac{2}{3}}}$.

5 For these functions of x, find the values of the derived function listed:

a) $f(x) = 5 + x - x^2$: $f'(0), f'\left(\dfrac{1}{2}\right), f'(1), f'(-2)$

b) $g(x) = (x^3 - 2)^2$: $g'(-1), g'(2)$

c) $h(x) = 4x^{\frac{3}{2}}$: $h'(0), h'(1), h'(4), h'\left(\dfrac{1}{9}\right)$

d) $u(x) = \dfrac{1}{x^2}$: $u'(1), u'(-1), u'(2), u'\left(-\dfrac{1}{2}\right)$

e) $v(x) = 3\sqrt{x} + \dfrac{1}{\sqrt[3]{x}}$: $v'(8)$.

6 a) For $f(x) = x^2 - 4x + 3$, find the value of x for which
   (i) $f'(x) = 2$
   (ii) $f'(x) = 0$.

b) For $g(x) = \dfrac{1}{3}x^3 + \dfrac{1}{2}x^2 - 6x$, find the value of x for which
   (i) $g'(x) = -4$
   (ii) $g'(x) = 0$.

7 Differentiate with respect to x, where $a, b, c, p, q,$ and r are constants:

a) ax^5 b) $px^2 + qx + r$ c) $b(x^3 - x^2)$

d) $\dfrac{c}{x}$ e) $\dfrac{\pi}{12}(x^4 + x^3)$ f) $3\pi x(x - a)$.

8 Differentiate with respect to x:

a) $\left(x + \dfrac{1}{x}\right)^2$ b) $\left(\sqrt{x} + \dfrac{1}{\sqrt{x}}\right)^2$ c) $\sqrt{x}\,(1 - \sqrt{x})$ d) $x^2(1 + \sqrt{x})$

e) $(x - 1)(x - 2)$ f) $(x + 3)(x - 4)$ g) $(3x + 1)(2x - 5)$ h) $(2x^3 - 1)^2$

i) $\left(x^2 - \dfrac{1}{x^2}\right)^2$ j) $\left(\dfrac{2}{x} + \dfrac{x}{2}\right)^2$ k) $\left(x + \dfrac{2}{x}\right)^2$ l) $\left(\sqrt{x} - \dfrac{3}{\sqrt{x}}\right)^2$

m) $3x\left(2 - \dfrac{5}{x^2}\right)$ n) $\sqrt{x}(2x - 1)$ o) $x^2(x + 2)$ p) $x^2(3x + 4)$

q) $x^{\frac{-1}{2}}(3x + 4)$ r) $x^{\frac{1}{3}}(x^2 + 3)$ s) $x^{\frac{3}{4}}(2x^2 - 1)$ t) $\left(2x^3 + \dfrac{1}{x}\right)^2$.

9 Differentiate with respect to x:

a) $x(x + 1)^2$ b) $x(x - 1)(x - 2)$ c) $x(x + 2)(x + 3)$

d) $(x^2 - 1)(x + 2)^2$ e) $(2 + x)^2 + (2 - x)^2$ f) $\left(x + 1 + \dfrac{1}{x}\right)\left(x + 1 - \dfrac{1}{x}\right)$.

10 Differentiate with respect to x:

a) $\dfrac{x - 3}{x}$
b) $\dfrac{x - 1}{\sqrt{x}}$
c) $\dfrac{3 + 5x}{x^2}$
d) $\dfrac{x^3 - 3x + 6}{x}$

e) $\dfrac{2x^3 - 3x^2 + 5}{x^2}$
f) $\dfrac{x^2 + 3x + 1}{x}$
g) $\dfrac{5x^3 - x^2 + 2}{x^3}$
h) $\dfrac{x + 1}{2x^{\frac{1}{3}}}$

i) $\dfrac{3x^4 - 11}{x^{\frac{3}{2}}}$
j) $\dfrac{3x^4 - x^2 + 5}{3x^2}$
k) $\dfrac{ax^2 + 2x + 9}{\sqrt{x}}$.

11 Show that for $f(x) = x^{\frac{1}{2}}\left(x + \dfrac{1}{x}\right)\left(x - \dfrac{1}{x}\right)$, $f'(x) = \dfrac{5x^4 + 3}{2x^{\frac{5}{2}}}$.

26 The Equation of a Tangent to a Curve

> **Reminder**

Example

Find the equation of the tangent to the curve with equation $y = \dfrac{2}{\sqrt{x}}$ at the point where $x = 4$.

Solution

Find the y–coordinate of the point: $y(4) = \dfrac{2}{\sqrt{4}} = 1 \Rightarrow (4,1)$.

Differentiate: $y = 2x^{-\frac{1}{2}} \Rightarrow y' = -x^{-\frac{3}{2}}$.

Find the gradient (m): $m = y'(4) = -(4)^{-\frac{3}{2}} = -(2^2)^{-\frac{3}{2}} = -2^{-3} = -\dfrac{1}{8}$.

Use $(y - y_1) = m(x - x_1)$: $y - 1 = -\dfrac{1}{8}(x - 4) \Rightarrow 8y - 8 = -x + 4$

hence $x + 8y = 12$.

Exercise 26

1 Find the equation of the tangent to the curve:

a) $y = 3x^2$ — where $x = 1$ b) $y = x^2 + 2$ — where $x = 2$

c) $y = \dfrac{1}{x}$ — where $x = -1$ d) $y = 2\sqrt{x}$ — where $x = 4$

e) $y = (x - 1)^2$ — where $x = 0$ f) $y = x^3$ — where $x = -1$

g) $y = 4 - x^2$ — where $x = 1$ h) $y = (x - 2)(x - 6)$ — where $x = 2$

i) $y = 2x + \dfrac{1}{2x}$ — where $x = \dfrac{1}{2}$ j) $y = 2x^3$ — where $x = -1$

k) $y = 6\sqrt{x} - 20$ — where $x = 16$ l) $y = \dfrac{3}{x^2}$ — where $x = 3$

m) $y = \sqrt[3]{x}$ — where $x = 8$ n) $y = \dfrac{2 - x}{\sqrt{x}}$ — where $x = 1$

o) $y = \dfrac{2}{\sqrt{x}}(1 + 2x)$ — where $x = 4$ p) $y = x^2 + \dfrac{2}{x}$ — where $x = 2$.

2 Find the equation of the normal to the curve:

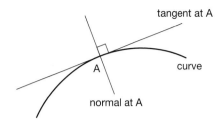

tangent at A

curve

A

normal at A

a) $y = \sqrt{x}$ at the point where $x = 4$
b) $y = 2x^2$ at the point where $x = 1$
c) $y = 3x + \dfrac{1}{x}$ at the point where $x = -1$
d) $y = (x + 1)^2$ at the point where $x = 3$
e) $4y = x^3 - 2$ at the point where $x = 2$.

3 Find the equation of the tangent to the curve $y = x^2$ at the point $(1, 1)$.
This tangent crosses the coordinate axes at the points K and L.
Show that the midpoint of KL is $\left(\dfrac{1}{4}, -\dfrac{1}{2}\right)$.

4 Find the equations of the tangents to the curve $y = \dfrac{1}{2}x^2$ at the points where $x = 2$ and $x = -2$.
Find also the coordinates of the point of intersection of these tangents.

5 Show that the tangents to the curve with equation $y = x^3 + 3x^2 + x + 1$ at the points where $x = 1$ and $x = -3$ are parallel, and find the coordinates of the points where they cut the y-axis.

6 Show that there is only one tangent whose gradient is -2 to the curve with equation $y = 2x^2 + 3$, and find its equation.

7 Find the equations of the tangents to the curve with equation $y = x^2 + 3$ at the points where $x = 2$ and $x = -\dfrac{3}{2}$, and show that they intersect on the x-axis.

8 Show that the tangent to the curve with equation $y = 3 - (x - 2)^2$ at the point where $x = 1$ passes through the origin.

9 The tangent at the point where $x = -\dfrac{1}{2}$ to the curve with equation $y = 1 - 2x - x^2$ cuts the coordinate axes at A and B. Find the length of AB.

10 Find the gradient of the curve with equation $y = x^3 - 2x^2$ at the point where $x = \dfrac{7}{3}$.
Find the other point on this curve which has the same gradient, and the equation of the tangent at that point.

11B The tangent at P to the curve with equation $y = x^2 + 4x + 5$ is parallel to the line with equation $12x - y + 17 = 0$. Find the coordinates of P.

12B Find the equation of the tangent to the curve with equation $y = x^2 - \dfrac{1}{x}$ at the point where it crosses the x-axis.

13B Find the equation of the tangent to the curve with equation $y = x^3 + 3x + 2$ at the point where it crosses the y-axis.

14B Show that the gradient of the curve with equation $y = 3x^3 + 6x^2 + 4x + 2$ is never negative, and find the equation of the normal at the point where it crosses the y-axis.

15B Find the coordinates of the point at which the curve with equation $y = 2x^2 + 5\sqrt{3}x + 1$ is inclined at $60°$ to the x-axis.

16B The line with equation $y = 7x - 1$ is a tangent to the curve with equation $y = x^2 + bx + c$ at the point $(3, 20)$. Find the values of b and c.

17B The line with equation $y = x + 16$ is a tangent to the curve with equation $y = a\sqrt{x} + b$ at the point $(4, 20)$. Find the values of a and b.

18B The line with equation $x + 6y = 31$ is a normal to the curve with equation $y = ax^3 + b$ at the point $(1, 5)$. Find the values of a and b.

27 Motion in a Straight Line

> **Reminder**

velocity (v) = rate of change of displacement (s) $\quad v = \dfrac{ds}{dt}$

acceleration (a) = rate of change of velocity (v) $\quad a = \dfrac{dv}{dt}$

Example

A particle moves along a straight line such that its displacement, s metres, after t seconds is given by $s = 2 + 3t^2 - t^3$.

Find its position, velocity and acceleration initially and after 2 seconds.

Solution

Since $\quad s = 2 + 3t^2 - t^3, \quad v = \dfrac{ds}{dt} = 6t - 3t^2 \quad$ and $\quad a = \dfrac{dv}{dt} = 6 - 6t$

$t = 0 \Rightarrow s = 2 \quad v = 0 \quad a = 6$

$t = 2 \Rightarrow s = 2 + (3 \times 4) - 8 = 6 \quad v = (6 \times 2) - (3 \times 4) = 0$
$\qquad\qquad a = 6 - (6 \times 2) = -6$

i.e. particle is initially 2 m to the right of the origin, at rest, and with an acceleration of 6 m/s² to the right.

After 2 seconds it is 6 m to the right of the origin, at rest, and with an acceleration of 6 m/s² to the left.

Notice that the particle is not always at rest. After 1 s, $v = 3$ m/s.

Exercise 27

1 A stone which has fallen s metres in the t seconds since it was dropped from rest has as its equation of motion $s = 5t^2$ (ignoring air resistance).

Find its speed after a) 1 s   b) $2\frac{1}{2}$ s   c) 3 s.

2 The motion of a ball projected vertically upwards with initial speed 10 m/s is described by the equation $s = 10t - 5t^2$, where s metres is the displacement after t seconds. Find the formula for its velocity and calculate the velocity after
a) 1 s   b) 2 s   c) 3 s.

3 The equation of motion of a body is $s = 6t^2 - 4t + 5$, where the displacement is s metres after t seconds. When is it at rest, and what is its displacement then?

4 The equation of motion of a particle is $s = 6t^2 - t^3$, where the displacement is s metres after t seconds. At what time does the particle have zero acceleration?

5 The equation of motion of a body is $s = 5 + 11t - t^3$, where the displacement is s metres after t seconds. Find the displacement, velocity, and acceleration after 3 s.

6 The equation of motion of a body is $s = 7 - 2t + t^3$, where the displacement is s metres after t seconds. Find the displacement, velocity and acceleration after 3 s.

7B The equation of motion of a particle is $s = 6t - 2t^2$, where the displacement is s metres after t seconds. Find the displacement and acceleration when the particle is at rest.

8B A particle moves in a straight line such that its displacement s metres, from a fixed point O after t seconds, is given by $s = 4 - 6t + t^2$.
a) How far is the particle from O when $t = 0$?
b) What is its position after 6 seconds?
c) What is its velocity after 5 seconds?
d) What is its initial acceleration?
e) When does the particle change its direction of motion?

9B A body starts at rest from O and moves in a straight line. Its equation of motion is $s = 3t^2 - 2t^3$, where the displacement is s metres after t seconds.
a) Find the time and position when it is again instantaneously at rest.
b) Find the displacement and velocity when the acceleration is zero.
c) When is the velocity at its maximum?
d) With what velocity does the particle pass through the origin again?

10B A ball is projected vertically upwards from a point A on a bridge with an initial velocity of 5 m/s. Its equation of motion is $s = 5t \, (1 - t)$, where s and t have their usual meanings.

Find its displacement, velocity and total distance travelled after $\frac{3}{4}$ s.

28 Increasing and Decreasing Functions

> **Reminder**

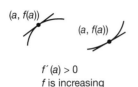

$f'(a) > 0$
f is increasing

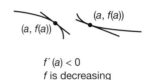

$f'(a) < 0$
f is decreasing

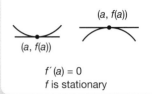

$f'(a) = 0$
f is stationary

Example Determine whether the function f defined by $f(x) = \dfrac{x^2 + 1}{x}$ is increasing, decreasing or stationary when $x = 2, 1, \dfrac{1}{2}$.

Solution

$f(x) = \dfrac{x^2 + 1}{x} = x + x^{-1}$ $\qquad \Rightarrow f'(x) = 1 - \dfrac{1}{x^2}$

$f'(2) = 1 - \dfrac{1}{4} = \dfrac{3}{4} > 0$ $\qquad \Rightarrow f$ is increasing at $x = 2$

$f'(1) = 1 - \dfrac{1}{1} = 0$ $\qquad \Rightarrow f$ is stationary at $x = 1$

$f'\!\left(\dfrac{1}{2}\right) = 1 - \dfrac{1}{\frac{1}{4}} = 1 - 4 = -3 < 0 \Rightarrow f$ is decreasing at $x = \dfrac{1}{2}$.

Exercise 28

1 If $y = 3x^2(x - 2)$, find whether y is increasing decreasing or stationary at
   a) $x = -1$ $\qquad\qquad$ b) $x = 0$ $\qquad\qquad$ c) $x = 1$.

2 If $y = (2x + 3)^2$, find whether y is increasing decreasing or stationary at
   a) $x = -2$ $\qquad\qquad$ b) $x = 0$ $\qquad\qquad$ c) $x = 2$.

3 Show that the curves with the following equations are never decreasing:
   a) $y = x^3$ $\qquad\qquad$ b) $y = 1 - \dfrac{1}{x}$ $\qquad\qquad$ c) $y = 4x^3 + 6x^2 + 3x + 5$.

4 Show that the curves with the following equations are never increasing:
   a) $y = \dfrac{16}{x}$ $\qquad\qquad$ b) $y = \dfrac{3}{x} - 2x$ $\qquad\qquad$ c) $y = 5 - 4x - x^3$.

5 Find the range of values of x where each of the following is increasing:
   a) $y = 3x^2$ $\qquad$ b) $y = 2x^3 - 3x^2 - 12x + 4$ $\qquad$ c) $y = x(x - 1)^2$.

6 Find the range of values of x where each of the following is decreasing:
   a) $y = 4 - x^2$ $\qquad$ b) $y = 5 + 2x - 2x^2$ $\qquad$ c) $y = x^3 + 3x^2 - 9x + 5$.

7B Find the interval in which $f(x)$ is (i) increasing and (ii) decreasing for $f(x)$ given by:
   a) $4x^2 + 3$ $\qquad\qquad$ b) $12x - x^3$ $\qquad\qquad$ c) $2x^3 - 10x^2 + 5$.

8B Show that $x^3 - 3x^2 + 4$ is positive for all $x > 2$.

9B Show that $27 + 4x^3 - x^4$ is negative for all $x > 3$.

10B Show that the function $\dfrac{x^2 + 2x - 3}{x}$ is increasing for all values of x except 0.

11B Show that the function $\dfrac{x^2 - 3x + 3}{x^3}$ is decreasing for all values of x except 0 and 3.

29 Stationary Points

> **Reminder**

There are four types of stationary point:

| minimum turning point | maximum turning point | rising point of inflection | falling point of inflection |

Example Find the stationary points on the curve with equation $y = \dfrac{x^3 + 2}{x}$ and determine their nature.

Solution
$$y = \frac{x^3 + 2}{x} = x^2 + 2x^{-1} \qquad \Rightarrow \qquad y' = 2x - \frac{2}{x^2} = \frac{2}{x^2}[x^3 - 1]$$

[It is generally advisable to factorise y' before proceeding.]

For stationary points $y' = 0$.

[Do not omit this line, it could be worth a mark.]

Hence $x^3 - 1 = 0 \Rightarrow x = 1 \Rightarrow y = 3$.

[If a fraction is zero, only the top line is zero.]

EITHER
$$x < 1 \Rightarrow x^3 < 1 \Rightarrow x^3 - 1 < 0$$
$$x > 1 \Rightarrow x^3 > 1 \Rightarrow x^3 - 1 > 0$$
$$\frac{2}{x^2} > 0 \text{ for all } x$$

x	1^-	1	1^+
$\dfrac{2(x^3-1)}{x^2} = y'$	$-$ve	0	$+$ve
tgt	↘	→	↗

OR
$$y'' = 2 + 4x^{-3} \Rightarrow y''(1) = 6 > 0$$
y' is increasing, from $-$ve through 0 to $+$ve
i.e. y is decreasing, stationary, increasing

$\Rightarrow (1, 3)$ is a minimum turning point.

[Note: make sure you label the rows of the nature table. It is useful to show the factorised form of y' in the second row, and use it to find the signs.]

1 Find the stationary points on the following curves and determine their nature:
a) $y = 3x^2$
b) $y = 6x - x^2$
c) $y = 2x^3$
d) $y = 2x^3 - 3x^2$.

2 Find the stationary values of the following functions and determine their nature:
a) $x(x - 2)^2$
b) $2x^3 - 9x^2 + 12x$
c) $x^4 - 50x^2$
d) $x + \dfrac{1}{x}$.

3 Find the stationary points on the following curves and determine their nature:
a) $y = x^2 - x - 1$
b) $y = 5 - x^2$
c) $y = (x - 3)(x + 7)$
d) $y = (x + 1)^2$.

4B Find the stationary values of the following functions and determine their nature:
a) $g(u) = u^3(8 - u)$
b) $h(t) = 4t(t^2 - 12)$
c) $w(x) = x^3 - 12x + 4$
d) $z(r) = 2r^2(r^2 - 1)$.

30 Curve Sketching

> **Reminder**

Example Sketch the curve with equation $y = x^3 - 9x$.

Solution First find the intersections with the axes:

$x = 0 \implies y = 0$

$y = 0 \implies x^3 - 9x = x(x^2 - 9) = x(x - 3)(x + 3) = 0 \implies x = -3, 0, 3$

i.e. the intersections with the axes are at $(-3, 0)$, $(0, 0)$ and $(3, 0)$.

Look for stationary points and determine their nature:

$y' = 3x^2 - 9 = 3(x^2 - 3) = 0$ for stationary points $\implies x^2 - 3 = 0$
$\implies x = \pm\sqrt{3}$

$x = \sqrt{3} \implies y = \sqrt{3}(3 - 9) = -6\sqrt{3} \implies (\sqrt{3}, -6\sqrt{3})$
$x = -\sqrt{3} \implies y = -\sqrt{3}(3 - 9) = 6\sqrt{3} \implies (-\sqrt{3}, 6\sqrt{3})$.

To find the nature:

EITHER

$y'' = 6x \implies$

$\begin{cases} y''(\sqrt{3}) = 6\sqrt{3} > 0 \implies y' \text{ is increasing} \implies \text{minimum turning point} \\ y''(-\sqrt{3}) = -6\sqrt{3} < 0 \implies y' \text{ is decreasing} \implies \text{maximum turning point} \end{cases}$

> **Reminder** continued

OR

$$x > \sqrt{3} \Rightarrow x^2 > 3 \Rightarrow x^2 - 3 > 0$$

$$x < -\sqrt{3} \Rightarrow x^2 > 3 \Rightarrow x^2 - 3 > 0$$

when $-\sqrt{3} < x < \sqrt{3}$

$$x < \sqrt{3} \Rightarrow x^2 < 3 \Rightarrow x^2 - 3 < 0 \qquad x > -\sqrt{3} \Rightarrow x^2 < 3 \Rightarrow x^2 - 3 < 0$$

x	$-\sqrt{3}^-$	$-\sqrt{3}$	$-\sqrt{3}^+$	$\sqrt{3}^-$	$\sqrt{3}$	$\sqrt{3}^+$
$3(x^2 - 3) = y'$	+ve	0	−ve	−ve	0	+ve
tgt	↗	→	↘	↘	→	↗

$$\Rightarrow (-\sqrt{3}, 6\sqrt{3}) \text{ max. t. pt. } (\sqrt{3}, -6\sqrt{3}) \text{ min. t. pt.}$$

When x is large y will behave as the leading term, x^3.
Thus as $x \to +\infty$, $y \to +\infty$, and as $x \to -\infty$, $y \to -\infty$.

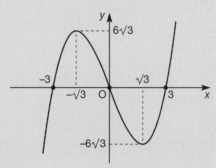

Exercise 30

Sketch the curves whose equations are:

1 $y = 9 - x^2$ 2 $y = x^2 - 16$ 3 $y = x(x - 6)$

4 $y = x^2 - 4x + 5$ 5 $y = (x - 2)^2$ 6 $y = x^3$

7 $y = x^4$ 8 $y = x(1 - x)^2$ 9 $y = 2x^3 - 3x^2 + 6$

10 $y = 1 - x^3$ 11 $y = x(x^2 + 4x - 3)$ 12 $y = x^3 - 3x$.

Sketch the curves whose equations are:

13B $y = x^3(4 - x)$ 14B $y = x^2(x^2 - 8)$

15B $y = x^4 - 2x^2 - 8$ 16B $y = 27 - 18x^2 - 8x^3 - x^4$.

31 Greatest and Least Values on a Closed Interval

> **Reminder**

Example

Find the greatest and least values of $x^3 - 9x$ in the interval

a) $-2 \leqslant x \leqslant -1$

b) $-1 \leqslant x \leqslant 4$.

Solution

The usual way is to sketch the curve, mark on the boundaries of the interval, and examine the extrema and end points of the interval. This is the same function as was used in the previous worked example, so the sketch is at hand.

a)

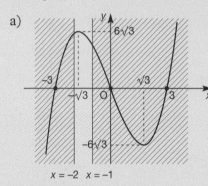

$f(x) = x^3 - 9x$

$f(-2) = -8 + 18 = 10$

$f(-\sqrt{3}) = 6\sqrt{3} \ (\approx 10 \cdot 4)$

$f(-1) = -1 + 9 = 8$

$\Rightarrow -2 \leqslant x \leqslant -1$

$\Rightarrow 8 \leqslant x^3 - 9x \leqslant 6\sqrt{3}$

b)

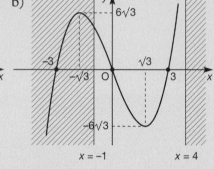

$f(x) = x^3 - 9x$

$f(-1) = -1 + 9 = 8$

$f(\sqrt{3}) = -6\sqrt{3} \ (\approx -10 \cdot 4)$

$f(4) = 64 - 36 = 28$

i.e. $-1 \leqslant x \leqslant 4 \Rightarrow -6\sqrt{3} \leqslant x^3 - 9x \leqslant 28$

Exercise 31

Find the greatest and least values of each function on the given closed interval :
[Illustrate each answer with a sketch and write each answer in the form $a \leqslant f(x) \leqslant b$.]

1 $f(x) = -x^2$ $-2 \leqslant x \leqslant 2$

2 $f(x) = x^2 - 4$ $-3 \leqslant x \leqslant 3$

3 $f(x) = x^3 - 2x$ $0 \leqslant x \leqslant 3$

4 $f(x) = 2x^3$ $-1 \leqslant x \leqslant 2$

5B $f(x) = 7 - 4x - x^2$ $-3 \leqslant x \leqslant 0$

6B $f(x) = x(6 - x)$ $2 \leqslant x \leqslant 7$

7B $f(x) = 6x^2 - x^3$ $-1 \leqslant x \leqslant 3$

8B $f(x) = x^4 - 2x^2$ $-\dfrac{1}{2} \leqslant x \leqslant \dfrac{1}{2}$.

32 Optimization

Example

A closed cylindrical oil drum is to be constructed to hold 25 litres. Find the dimensions of the drum which uses the least area of metal.

Solution

Let the drum have height h cm and base radius r cm.

Let the volume be V cm^3 and the surface area be A cm^2.

The volume is to be 25 000 cm^3.

Use the formula $V = \pi r^2 h$, to obtain

$$25\,000 = \pi r^2 h \quad \ldots\ldots\ldots\ldots (1)$$

This gives a connection between r and h.
We can use it to express r in terms of h or h in terms of r.

Since we have to minimise the surface area, we use the formula

$$A = 2\pi r^2 + 2\pi r h$$

In this formula, A depends on both r and h, so use equation (1) to express h in terms of r, and hence A in terms of the single variable r.

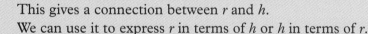

$$(1) \Rightarrow h = \frac{25\,000}{\pi r^2}$$

$$\Rightarrow A = 2\pi r^2 + 2\pi r \frac{25\,000}{\pi r^2} = 2\pi r^2 + \frac{50\,000}{r} = 2\pi r^2 + 50\,000 r^{-1}$$

$$\Rightarrow \frac{dA}{dr} = 4\pi r - 50\,000 r^{-2} = 4\pi r - \frac{50\,000}{r^2} = \frac{4\pi r^3 - 50\,000}{r^2} = 0$$

for stationary points

$$\Rightarrow r^3 = \frac{50\,000}{4\pi} = 3978 \cdot 87 \Rightarrow r = 15 \cdot 85 \text{ cm}$$

$$\Rightarrow h = \frac{25\,000}{\pi r^2} = \frac{25\,000}{\pi (15 \cdot 85)^2} = 31 \cdot 69 \text{ cm}.$$

To justify that these values for r and h give a minimum:

EITHER

$$A'' = 4\pi + 100\,000 r^{-3} \Rightarrow A'' \left(\sqrt[3]{\frac{50\,000}{4\pi}} \right) > 0 \Rightarrow \text{minimum}$$

OR

$$r < 15 \cdot 85 \Rightarrow 4\pi r^3 < 50\,000 \Rightarrow 4\pi r^3 - 50\,000 < 0$$
$$r > 15 \cdot 85 \Rightarrow 4\pi r^3 > 50\,000 \Rightarrow 4\pi r^3 - 50\,000 > 0$$

> **Reminder** continued

so

$$\frac{4\pi r^3 - 50\,000}{r^2} =$$

r	$<15{\cdot}85$	$15{\cdot}85$	$>15{\cdot}85$
A'	$-$ ve	0	$+$ ve
tgt	↘	→	↗

(hence minimum)

Strictly speaking $r \in [0, \infty]$, so we should check the 'end points'. When r is zero or infinite, A is infinite, so the minimum occurs at the stationary point.

Exercise 32

1 A farmer has 400 m of fencing available and wishes to create a rectangular pen in one of his fields. Find the length and breadth of the rectangle which will give the greatest area of pen when the pen is made
   a) somewhere in the middle of the field
   b) against a hedge at the side of the field (so requiring only 3 sides of fencing)
   c) in a right-angled corner of the field (so requiring only 2 sides of fencing).

   a)    b) 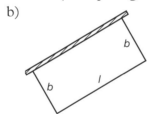   c)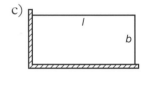

2 Two positive numbers x and y have a sum of 36. Find the maximum value of the product $P = xy$.

3 Two positive numbers x and y have a product of 36. Find the minimum value of the sum $S = x + y$.

4 Find the least possible value of the sum of a positive number x and its reciprocal $\frac{1}{x}$.

5 Find the least possible value of the sum of the square of a number and the square of its reciprocal.

6 A parallelogram is drawn inside a rectangle measuring 5 units by 3 units, as shown. Calculate the value of x for which the area of the parallelogram is least.

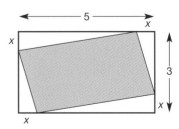

7 Repeat question 6 for a rectangle measuring 9 units by 7 units.

8 Find the value of x for which the area of this shaded triangle is a minimum.

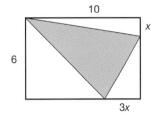

9 Find the value of x for which the area of this shaded triangle is a minimum.

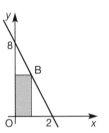

10 A rectangle with sides parallel to the coordinate axes is drawn with one vertex at the origin and the opposite vertex in the first quadrant and lying on the line with equation $y = 8 - 4x$.
Calculate the greatest possible area of such a rectangle, stating the corresponding coordinates of B.

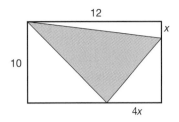

11 Repeat question 10 if the equation of the line is $3y = 18 - x$.

12B The point P lies in the first quadrant on the curve with equation $y = 3 - x^2$. Find the coordinates of P so that the shaded area shown is a maximum.

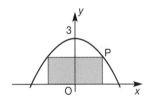

13B P is the point $(1 + \theta, 1 - \theta)$ and Q (θ, θ^2).
Express the gradient of PQ in terms of θ.
For what value of θ is the gradient of PQ a maximum?

14B A is the point $(a^3, a^3 - 2)$ and B $(a^2 + a^3, 2(1 + a^3))$.
For what value of a is the gradient of AB a minimum?

15B A steel strip mill has rolled a long strip of steel 1 metre wide. At each side, x cm are to be bent up as shown to create a water duct of rectangular cross section.
Find the value of x which will allow the duct to carry as much water as possible.

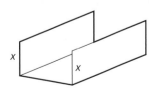

16B A sheet of steel 8 feet by 5 feet is to have a square of side x feet removed from each corner, and the remaining flaps bent up and the edges welded to form an open cuboid shaped storage tank. What value for x will provide the greatest volume for the tank?

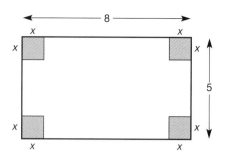

17B Repeat question 16 for a sheet of steel 1 m square with squares of side x cm removed.

18B Perspex sheeting is to be cut and glued together to form a fish tank in the shape of an open cuboid with a square base of side x cm and a volume of 62·5 litres.

a) Show that the required area of perspex, A cm^2, is given by $A = x^2 + \dfrac{250\,000}{x}$.

b) Find the value of x which uses the least perspex.

Use these two formulae (which you may have proved in Exercise 46 question 15) in questions 19 and 20: when θ is measured in radians,

the length of an arc of a circle   the area of a sector of a circle

$\ell = r\theta$

$A = \frac{1}{2} r^2 \theta$

19B The perimeter of a sector of a circle is to be 16 cm. What size of radius would give the maximum area?

20B The area of a sector of a circle is to be 16 cm^2. What size of radius would produce the minimum perimeter?

33 The Graph of the Derived Function

> **Reminder**

Example   For each of these functions draw the graph of the derived function.

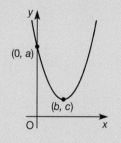

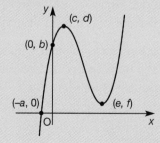

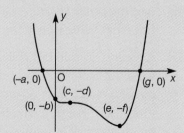

Solution

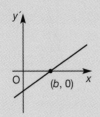 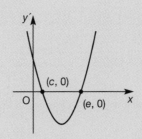 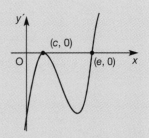

It is useful to draw the graph of y' directly underneath that of y. At each stationary point on y, y' is zero, so the x value at the stationary point is where the graph of y' crosses the x-axis. Observe that intersections of the original function with the axes are irrelevant, as are the stationary values (i.e. y coordinates). Complete the graph of y' by considering whether y is increasing or decreasing between (and outside) the roots of y'.

Notice that in the third example, which has a point of inflexion, y' is negative on both sides of it, so the graph of y' does not cross the x-axis at $(c, 0)$ but touches it.

Exercise 33

For each of the given functions, draw the graph of the derived function:

1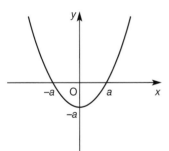

2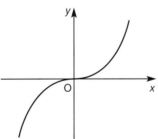

3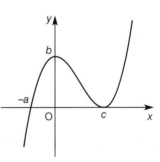

4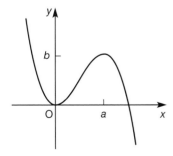

5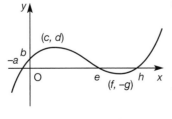

6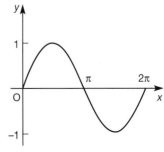

7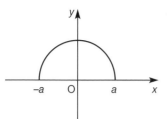

8B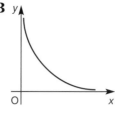

9B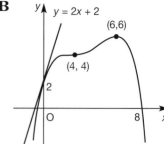

10B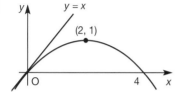

11B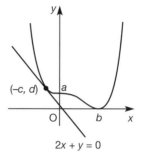

34 TOPIC TEST on Differentiation

⏱ Allow 45 minutes for this test

1 Differentiate

   a) $3x^{\frac{2}{3}}$

   b) $\dfrac{3}{x}$

   c) $\dfrac{4}{\sqrt{x}}$

   d) $\dfrac{1}{2x^2}$

2 Given that $f(x) = \dfrac{3x^4 + 5x^2 - 2}{x}$, evaluate $f'(-1)$.

3 Find (in its simplest form) the equation of the tangent to the curve

   $y = 3x^2 - 4x + 5$ at the point where $x = 2$.

   Calculate the angle between this tangent and the x-axis.

   Calculator required 🖩

4 Is the curve $y = 3x^2 - 9x + 11$ increasing decreasing or stationary at these points?

   a) $(1, 5)$

   b) $\left(\dfrac{3}{2}, \dfrac{17}{4}\right)$

5 Sketch the curve $y = x(x^2 - 12)$, showing how you obtained the stationary points, their nature, and the intersections with the axes.

   Hence determine the range of values of k for which the equation $x(x^2 - 12) = k$ has *three* real roots.

RECURRENCE RELATIONS

35 Introductory Examples for Discussion

> **Reminder**

Example
Last week I paid £1200 for a new hall carpet and another £1200 for a Macintosh Patrick print. I expect the carpet to depreciate by 3% and the print to appreciate by 3% each year. What will each be worth in 5 years' time?

Solution
To minimise the work in this topic, it is essential to calculate percentage changes by multiplying by a factor in a single step, rather than to calculate 3% and then add or subtract.

Carpet: $1200 \times (1 - 0{\cdot}03) = 1200 \times 0{\cdot}97$ after one year
$\therefore (1200 \times 0{\cdot}97) \times 0{\cdot}97 = 1200 \times (0{\cdot}97)^2$ after two years
$\therefore 1200 \times (0{\cdot}97)^5$ i.e. £1030·48   after five years.

Print: $1200 \times (1 + 0{\cdot}03) = 1200 \times 1{\cdot}03$ after one year
$\therefore (1200 \times 1{\cdot}03) \times 1{\cdot}03 = 1200 \times (1{\cdot}03)^2$ after two years
$\therefore 1200 \times (1{\cdot}03)^5$ i.e. £1391·13   after five years.

Exercise 35

1 Arthur contributes £100 on the first of every month to an I.S.A. The fund is growing at 0·5% per month and was worth £1000 on the first of June (after his June contribution). Show that it will be worth £1105 a month later, and calculate what it will be worth on the following 1 December (after his December contribution).

2 Betty pays off a loan of £2000 by monthly instalments of £250 on the first of each month. The interest is 1·5% per month on the outstanding balance. If she took out the loan on 1 February, show that on 1 March she was still due £1780. Find also the outstanding balance at 1 October and the payment required to clear off the loan at 1 November.

3 It has been estimated that when the total amount of a certain waste chemical in a particular sea loch reaches 6 tonnes, the water in the loch is sufficiently polluted to endanger marine life.
The natural flushing action of the tide is known to remove 40% of whatever amount of this waste chemical is in the loch every week.
A factory producing this waste chemical as a by–product seeks the permission of the local water authority to release a batch of 2 tonnes of it into the loch once a week.
Should this permission be granted?

4 If you invest £1000 for two years at a compound interest rate of 8% per annum, does it make any difference if the interest is added annually or quarterly?

36 The Arithmetic of Recurrence Relations

> **Reminder**

Example

A sequence is defined by the recurrence relation

$$u_{n+1} = 3u_n + 4; \quad u_0 = 2.$$

a) Write down the first 4 terms of the sequence.
b) Which is the first term of the sequence to exceed 2000?

Solution

a) Any term is 3 times the previous term, plus 4. Start at the beginning.

$$u_0 = 2 \quad u_1 = 3 \times 2 + 4 = 10$$
$$u_2 = 3 \times 10 + 4 = 34$$
$$u_3 = 3 \times 34 + 4 = 106 \qquad \therefore 2, 10, 34, 106.$$

b) Continuing
$$u_4 = 3 \times 106 + 4 = 322$$
$$u_5 = 3 \times 322 + 4 = 970$$
$$u_6 = 3 \times 970 + 4 = 2914 \qquad \therefore u_6 = 2914 \text{ is first} > 2000.$$

The following exercise is designed to help you deal efficiently and quickly with recurrence relations and to intoduce the idea of a limit. Your teacher may prefer to show you these things without the use of this exercise.

Exercise 36

1 Write down the first four terms of the sequence defined by the recurrence relation
a) $u_{n+1} = 2u_n + 3$ and $u_0 = 1$ b) $u_{n+1} = 3u_n - 2$ and $u_0 = 2$
c) $u_{n+1} = \frac{1}{2}u_n + 12$ and $u_0 = 16$ d) $u_{n+1} = \frac{1}{4}u_n - 16$ and $u_0 = 128$.

2 A sequence is defined by the recurrence relation $u_{n+1} = 3u_n + 1$ and $u_0 = 2$.
a) Calculate mentally the values of u_1, u_2, u_3 and u_4.
b) Check these values on your calculator and find u_5, u_6 and u_7, starting with
    $\boxed{2} \boxed{\times} \boxed{3} \boxed{+} \boxed{1}$ followed by $\boxed{\times} \boxed{3} \boxed{+} \boxed{1}$ as often as necessary.
c) This sequence can be found more easily by using the $\boxed{\text{ANS}}$ key on the calculator.
    Key in $\boxed{2} \boxed{=}$ (or $\boxed{\text{EXE}}$); $\boxed{3} \boxed{\times} \boxed{\text{ANS}} \boxed{+} \boxed{1} \boxed{=}$ followed by $\boxed{\text{EXE}}$ as often as necessary. It is essential that you can evaluate sequences quickly like this.
d) Use the procedure described in part (c) to find which term of this sequence is the first to exceed a million.

3 For the sequence defined by the recurrence relation $u_{n+1} = 2u_n - 1$ and $u_0 = 3$,
a) find the values of u_1, u_2, u_3, u_4, u_5 and u_6
b) find which term of the sequence is the first to exceed $50\,000$.

4 For the sequence defined by the recurrence relation $u_{n+1} = 5u_n - 3$ and $u_0 = 1$,
a) find the values of u_1, u_2, u_3 and u_9
b) find a simple reason why $123\,456\,789$ is not a member of this sequence.

5 a) Find the next term in each sequence given one particular term and the appropriate recurrence relation
(i) $u_{35} = 20$, $u_{n+1} = 0{\cdot}7u_n + 6$ (ii) $u_{29} = 10$, $u_{n+1} = 0{\cdot}3u_n + 7$
(iii) $u_{78} = 5$, $u_{n+1} = 0{\cdot}4u_n + 3$ (iv) $u_{41} = 2$, $u_{n+1} = 0{\cdot}5u_n + 1$
(v) $u_n = 4$, $u_{n+1} = 0{\cdot}25u_n + 3$ (vi) $u_n = 110$, $u_{n+1} = 0{\cdot}9u_n + 11$
b) Write down the limit of each sequence.
c) Check these values for the limits by solving the equation obtained by replacing both u_{n+1} and u_n by L in the recurrence relation equation.
d) Apply this process to $u_{n+1} = au_n + b$ to obtain a formula for the limit.
e) Under what circumstances is this formula valid?

6B Find the values of u_1, u_2, u_3, u_4 and u_5 for the sequence defined by:
a) $u_{n+1} = -2u_n + 1$; $u_0 = 1$
b) $u_{n+1} = -2u_n + 1$; $u_0 = 4$
c) $u_{n+1} = -3u_n + 2$; $u_0 = 1$
d) $u_{n+1} = 4u_n + 3$; $u_0 = -3$
e) $u_{n+1} = 6u_n - 2$; $u_0 = -1$
Observe the effects in $u_{n+1} = au_n + b$ of a or b being negative.

7B a) Find u_{15}, u_{16}, u_{17}, for the sequence defined by $u_{n+1} = -0{\cdot}2u_n + 12$; $u_0 = 5$.
b) Find u_{35}, u_{36}, u_{37}, for the sequence defined by $u_{n+1} = -0{\cdot}5u_n + 3$; $u_0 = 5$.
c) If the sequence defined by the recurrence relation $u_{n+1} = au_n + b$ approaches a limit, it does so in different ways depending on whether $a > 0$ or $a < 0$. Explain.

37 Using Limits of Recurrence Relations

> **Reminder**

When $|a| < 1$, the recurrence relation $u_{n+1} = au_n + b$ has a limit as $n \to \infty$.
There are two algebraic methods for finding the limit.

a) 'at ∞', $u_{n+1} = u_n = l$; solve this equation for l

b) use the result of solving this equation, which is the formula $l = \dfrac{b}{1 - a}$

The limit is independent of u_0, but the relative sizes of l and u_0 determine whether the sequence approaches its limit from above or below.

The quantity $\dfrac{b}{1 - a}$ exists when $|a| > 1$, but it has no significance.

> **Reminder** continued

Example

A hospital patient suffering from a chronic disorder is to be given 250 mg of a painkiller every 4 hours.

In any 4-hour period, the amount of this painkiller in the body reduces by 20%.

The painkiller does not become effective until there is 500 mg continuously in the body.

The painkiller is known to have dangerous side effects if there is more than 1500 mg of it in the body.

a) After how many doses will the painkiller become effective?

b) Will the patient suffer the side effects if this dose of painkiller is administered for a long time?

Solution

a) This part can be done without direct reference to recurrence relations.

It is useful to construct a saw tooth diagram (not necessarily to scale) to represent the amounts of painkiller in the body.

The vertical lines represent the 250 mg doses.

Losing 20% is the same as retaining 80%, i.e. reduction by a factor of 0.8

$250 \times 0.8 = 200 \quad 200 + 250 = 450$
$450 \times 0.8 = 360 \quad 360 + 250 = 610$
$610 \times 0.8 = 488 \quad 488 + 250 = 738$
$738 \times 0.8 = 590$

Thus it is only after the 4th dose that the painkiller becomes effective.

b) To look at the long term effects, a recurrence relation is required to generate the sequence of maximum amounts of painkiller in the body.

This more general saw tooth diagram shows that

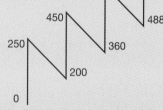

$$u_{n+1} = 0.8u_n + 250.$$

Although a sequence is not well-defined by a recurrence relation unless we have a starting value, the starting value does not affect any limit which may exist.

Since $-1 < 0.8 < 1$, this sequence has a limit, call it L.

[Don't miss out this line in your exam.]

Reminder continued

Then $L = 0.8L + 250$ OR $L = \dfrac{b}{1-a} = \dfrac{250}{1-0.8} = 1250 \; (< 1500)$

$\Rightarrow 0.2L = 250$

$\Rightarrow L = 1250 \; (< 1500)$ Hence *no side effects.*

Exercise 37

1   A bird feeder is initially filled with 200 g of bird seed. The birds eat 60% of whatever seed is in the feeder every day. Every morning thereafter, the feeder is topped-up with 60 g of bird seed. If this pattern continues, how much seed is eventually in the feeder each morning after it has been topped-up?
[Hint : Let u_n be the number of grams of seed in the feeder after it has been topped-up on the nth morning, and show that $u_{n+1} = 0.4u_n + 60$.]

2   The population of the Isle of Scrabley was 250 ten years ago. Since then a pattern has developed of 10% of the population leaving each year to seek work on the mainland, and 30 city escapees from the 'rat–race' retiring to the island. If this pattern continues for many years, what will the population of the island eventually be? [Obtain an appropriate recurrence relation.]

3   The tea stain on the inside of the bottom of Granny's tea pot is 150 units thick. On each wash, her dishwasher removes half of whatever thickness of stain there is. Each time Granny makes a pot of tea, the stain becomes 25 units thicker. If she only washes the tea pot once after each use, what will the thickness of the stain eventually become?

4   An angina sufferer is prescribed one capsule containing 250 mg of a certain drug per day. Over any 24 hour period the human body loses half of the amount of drug it had initially. If the patient takes this medicine regularly at the same time each day over a long period of time, what is the least amount of drug present in the body?
[Interpret the limit of your recurrence relation sensibly.]

5   A schoolboy, whose piggy bank is empty, negotiates with his parents to receive £10 pocket money each Friday night. He decides to spend 80% of the contents of his piggy bank each week. If he maintains this arrangement over a long time, what are the greatest and least amounts of money he ever has in his piggy bank?
If, on the other hand, he decided to save up for his holidays by only spending 20% of the bank's contents every week, what difference would this make?

6   The rear tyre on a tractor has a slow puncture which reduces the pressure in the tyre by 20% each day. The tractor driver uses a foot pump every morning to add 5 units to the tyre pressure. If the puncture gets no worse over a long period, what will the pressure in the tyre be each morning after it has been re–inflated?

7 Algae is growing in a fish tank at a rate of 100 g per week. The tank is cleaned every week using a process which removes only 35% of any algae present. Is this cleaning process adequate, if 300 g of algae in the tank is thought to be too much for the fish?

8 Victoria Park Gardens are combed for litter every day, resulting in 80% of all litter being removed. Every day however, 20 kg of litter is dropped in the gardens. What can be said about the mass of litter in the gardens after several weeks?

9 The sequences generated by the recurrence relations

$$u_{n+1} = au_n + 12 \text{ and } u_0 = 1, \text{ and } v_{n+1} = a^2v_n + 16 \text{ and } v_0 = 1,$$

have the same limit. Find this limit and the value of a.

10 Two sequences are generated by the recurrence relations

$$u_{n+1} = pu_n + 2 \text{ and } u_0 = a, \text{ and } v_{n+1} = qv_n + 3 \text{ and } v_0 = b.$$

The limit of $\{u_n\}$ is twice the limit of $\{v_n\}$. Express q in terms of p.

11B A gardener is feeding her conifer saplings weekly with 'Bioforce' (the wonder plant food). It is known that the amount of plant food in the sap of the young trees falls by 4% each day.
a) Show that over a week the level of plant food in the sap will have fallen by about 25%.
b) 'Bioforce' is only effective in trees if there is continuously more than 2 g of it in the sap. Each tree is receiving 1 g of 'Bioforce' each week. Given that the trees had no food in their sap originally, after how many feeds does it become effective?
c) If the level of 'Bioforce' in the sap exceeds 5 g, it will cause leaf curl. Is it safe to continue feeding the trees at this level indefinitely?

12B A bank offers customers loans on the basis of collecting monthly repayments by direct debit from the borrower's account equal to $\frac{1}{24}$ of the debt outstanding at the start of the month. Interest charges are 2% per month. Mr. and Mrs. Cook borrowed £500 to install a new washing machine, thinking, 'If we pay $\frac{1}{24}$ each month, it'll be paid up in two years'.
a) How much will the Cooks still owe after two years (i.e. 24 instalments)?
b) If the minimum direct debit is £5, when will the debt be repaid?

[The second part of this question should just be done using the answer key on your calculator, but be careful, the answer is not 211 payments. A more efficient way of solving the problem will be available after you have studied logarithms.]

13B There are 100 residents in Achnatarry Nursing Home. They all pay their monthly account by credit card. The bursar examined these payments and noticed that
(i) 10% of those who paid by Access one month used Visa the next.
(ii) 15% of those who paid by Visa one month used Access the next.
The bursar wondered if they would ever all end up using the same credit card. Explain to the bursar what would happen if this pattern continued indefinitely.
[Hint: let there be x% using Access one month and show that $(0 \cdot 75x + 15)$% are using it the following month.]

14B A tractor engine holds 3 litres of oil when full. It will just run satisfactorily on 2 litres. Experience shows that 0·1 litres of oil must be added each week to maintain the level at full. To economise, the owner decides to add only 0.05 litres each week. Is this plan safe?
Would 'add half the amount of oil needed to top it up' be safe?

15B It is observed that because of silting up, the depth of water in a harbour at the end of each year is only seven eighths of what it was at the end of the previous year. A depth of 6 m is needed to allow the passage of ships. If ships have had access to the harbour for the last three years, would it be satisfactory to dredge 2 m of silt now and every three years thereafter?

38 TOPIC TEST on Recurrence Relations

⏱ Allow 45 minutes for this test (Calculator permitted)

1 A sequence is defined by the recurrence relation

$$u_{n+1} = 2·7\,u_n - 3 \text{ and } u_0 = 10$$

a) Find the values of u_1, u_2, and u_3
b) Which is the first term of this sequence to exceed 1 million?

2 A sequence is defined by the recurrence relation

$$u_{n+1} = 0·3u_n + 1·4 \text{ and } u_0 = 10$$

a) Find the values of u_1, u_2 and u_3
b) Discuss the value of u_n as n becomes very large.

3 A sequence is defined by the recurrence relation

$$u_{n+1} = 6 - 0·2u_n \text{ and } u_0 = 0$$

a) Find the values of u_1, u_2 and u_3
b) Discuss the value of u_n as $n \to \infty$.

4 a) Find the limit of each of these sequences:
   (i) $u_{n+1} = 3 - 0·5u_n$ $u_0 = 1$
   (ii) $u_{n+1} = 3 + 0·5u_n$ $u_0 = 1$
   b) What is the difference between the ways these two sequences approach their limits?

5 You have £45 saved up to spend at the annual fair.
Your Dad has agreed to give you £5 each night as well.
You decide to spend one third of whatever cash you have available each night.
So, starting with the £50 on the Wednesday night, and going down to the fair every night until Monday, how much money do you have left on the following Tuesday morning after the fair is gone?

If your Dad continues to give you £5 every night and you keep spending one third of your assets, how much would you eventually end up with in your pocket every morning?

IDENTITIES AND RADIANS

39 Revision of the Triangle Formulae

> **Reminder**

Example

In triangle ABC, AB = 7 units, AC = 6 units, $\hat{A}$ = 50°.

Find a) the size of $\hat{B}$
      b) the area of triangle ABC.

Solution

a) If we try to find $\hat{B}$ by the sine rule, we need to know either BC or $\hat{C}$. So we use the cosine rule for BC first.

$$BC^2 = 7^2 + 6^2 - 2 \times 7 \times 6 \times \cos 50° \Rightarrow BC = 5\cdot568\ldots$$

(Keep this number in your calculator to avoid premature rounding.)

Hence $\dfrac{6}{\sin \hat{B}} = \dfrac{BC}{\sin 50°} \Rightarrow \sin \hat{B} = \dfrac{6 \sin 50°}{BC} = 0\cdot825\ldots \Rightarrow \hat{B} = 55\cdot6°.$

b) Area = $\dfrac{1}{2} bc \sin \hat{A} = \dfrac{1}{2} \times 7 \times 6 \times \sin 50° = 16\cdot1$ units².

Exercise 39

1 From the points A and B, 41·5 m apart, the angles of elevation of the point C, the tip of the church spire, are 27° and 49° respectively, as shown.
Calculate the height of the spire.

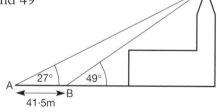

2 A farmer wishes to know the area of his triangular field in order to know how much fertiliser to apply to it. He has measured the lengths of the sides, as shown.
Calculate the area for him.

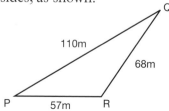

3 Calculate the perimeter of triangle ABC.

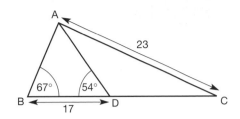

4 Calculate the size of the largest angle in a triangle with sides 7·5, 9·5 and 15·5 cm.

40 Three Dimensions

> **Reminder**

Example

ABCD, EFGH is a cuboid with AB = 8 units BC = 12 units and CG = 5 units. K is the midpoint of EH.

Calculate the size of the angle between
a) KB and the base ABCD
b) the plane KBC and the base ABCD.

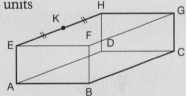

Solution

a) If L is the midpoint of AD, then the projection of KB on ABCD is LB.

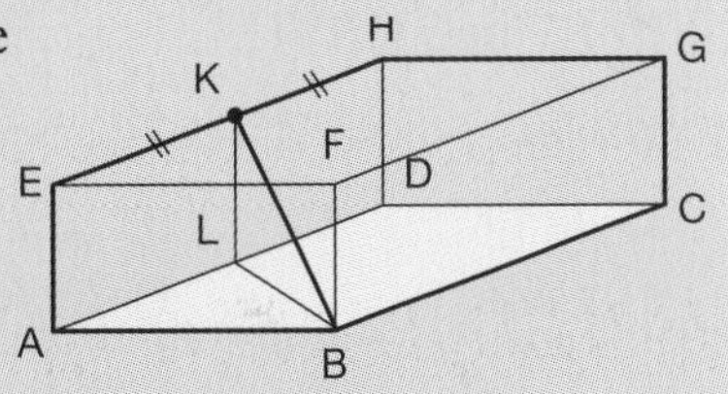

So the angle required is $K\hat{B}L$.

Make an auxiliary diagram of $K\hat{B}L$. Thus:

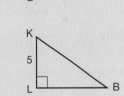

In triangle KBL, $\hat{L} = 90°$ and KL = 5, so we need to know another length. LB can be found from triangle ALB, so make another auxiliary diagram of triangle LAB.

Notice how $L\hat{A}B$ is a right angle, even though it does not appear as a right angle in the given sketch.

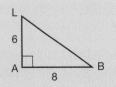

By Pythagoras' Theorem, LB = 10.

Now add this information to your first auxiliary diagram.

Now tan $K\hat{B}L = \frac{5}{10}$, so $K\hat{B}L = 26.6°$.

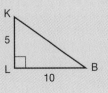

> **Reminder** continued

b) If M is the midpoint of BC, then the projection of KM on ABCD is LM.

So the angle required is $K\hat{M}L$.

Make an auxiliary diagram of $K\hat{M}L$.

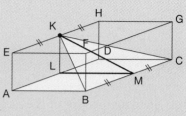

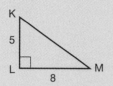

$\tan K\hat{M}L = \dfrac{5}{8} \Rightarrow K\hat{M}L = 32{\cdot}0°.$

Exercise 40

Questions 1 to 4 refer to this diagram of the cuboid PQRS,TUVW.

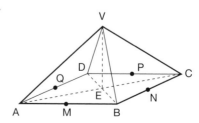

1 Name the angle between
a) PV and PQRS
b) TR and WVUT
c) TV and TWSP
d) SV and QRVU.

2 Which of these angles are NOT right angles?
a) $S\hat{P}Q$ b) $S\hat{V}U$ c) $W\hat{V}R$ d) $T\hat{W}U$
e) $P\hat{S}W$ f) $S\hat{T}R$ g) $S\hat{Q}U$ h) $P\hat{U}V$.

3 Name the angle between the planes
a) PQRS and PQVW   b) TUVW and SVUP
c) TUQP and TVRP   d) PUVS and TUVW.

4 Which of these pairs of planes are not at right angles to each other?
a) PQRS and PQUT   b) TVRP and TUVW   c) TPRV and WUQS
d) PQRS and SQUW   e) PUVS and SRVW   f) TUQP and WVRS
g) TUQP and WVQP   h) PTWS and QRVU.

5 V, ABCD is a rectangular pyramid.
E is the point of intersection of AC and BD.
M, N, P, Q are midpoints as shown.

Name the angle between
a) AV and ABCD
b) PV and ABCD
c) VBC and ABCD
d) VBD and VAC.

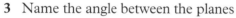

6 This figure represents a cuboid with AB = 16 cm
BC = 12 cm and CG = 6 cm.
Calculate the angle between
(i) HB and ABCD
(ii) HB and AB.

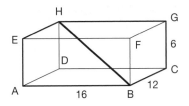

7 This figure represents a cuboid with a square base of side 16 cm and height 12 cm.
Calculate the angle between
(i) HB and the base ABCD
(ii) the planes AHC and ABCD.

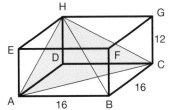

8 ABCD is a horizontal rectangle measuring 30ft x 7ft.
E is the midpoint of BC.
EF is vertical and of length 12ft.
Calculate the angle between the plane AFD and the
base ABCD.

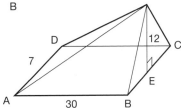

41 Exact Values, Identities, and Relationships between Angles

> **Reminder**

Memorise these
exact values

angle	0°	30°	45°	60°	90°
sin	0	$\frac{1}{2}$	$\frac{1}{\sqrt{2}}$	$\frac{\sqrt{3}}{2}$	1
cos	1	$\frac{\sqrt{3}}{2}$	$\frac{1}{\sqrt{2}}$	$\frac{1}{2}$	0
tan	0	$\frac{1}{\sqrt{3}}$	1	$\sqrt{3}$	∞

Example   Find the exact value of sin 330°.

Solution   330° is in the fourth quadrant,
30° below the x-axis,
so $|\sin 330°| = |\sin 30°|$.

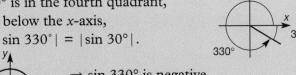

⇒ sin 330° is negative
so sin 330° = − sin 30°

> **Reminder** continued

Recall the exact value of sin 30° from this diagram, or better still, learn it.

Hence $\sin 330° = -\dfrac{1}{2}$.

This is how you think it out, but do it all mentally.

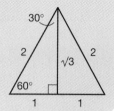

Exercise 41

1 Write down the exact values of
   a) $\sin 120°$ b) $\cos 330°$ c) $\tan 135°$ d) $\sin 210°$
   e) $\cos 315°$ f) $\tan 240°$ g) $\sin 300°$ h) $\cos 225°$
   i) $\tan 150°$ j) $\sin 270°$.

2 Calculate the exact value of
   a) $\sin^2 30° + \cos^2 60°$ b) $1 - \tan^2 60°$ c) $1 + 2\sin^2 60°$
   d) $2\cos^2 30° - 1$ e) $2\sin 45°\cos 45°$ f) $1 + \tan 45°$.

3 Solve for x: $\dfrac{x + \tan 45°}{1 - x \tan 45°} = \dfrac{1}{2}$.

> **Reminder**

$$\sin^2 \theta + \cos^2 \theta = 1; \quad \tan \theta = \frac{\sin \theta}{\cos \theta}$$

Example   Using triangle PQR as shown, verify that

a) $\cos^2 36\cdot9° + \sin^2 36\cdot9° = 1$

b) $\tan 36\cdot9° = \dfrac{\sin 36\cdot9°}{\cos 36\cdot9°}$

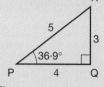

Proof   a)   l.h.s.$= \left(\dfrac{4}{5}\right)^2 + \left(\dfrac{3}{5}\right)^2 = \dfrac{16 + 9}{25} = 1 =$ r.h.s. (q.e.d).

   b)   l.h.s. $= \dfrac{3}{4}$

   r.h.s. $= \dfrac{\frac{3}{5}}{\frac{4}{5}} = \dfrac{3}{4} =$ l.h.s (q.e.d).

4 Using triangle ABC as shown, verify that

a) $\cos^2 45° + \sin^2 45° = 1$

b) $\tan 45° = \dfrac{\sin 45°}{\cos 45°}$.

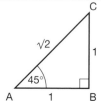

5 Using this diagram, verify that

a) $\sin^2 150° + \cos^2 150° = 1$

b) $\tan 150° = \dfrac{\sin 150°}{\cos 150°}$.

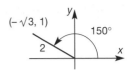
$(-\sqrt{3}, 1)$
150°
2

> **Reminder**

Example Solve $\begin{cases} k\cos a° = -4 \\ k\sin a° = 7 \end{cases}$ for $k > 0$ and $0 \le a \le 360$.

Solution It is customary to solve these simultaneous equations by solving for each variable separately, rather than substituting the first value to obtain the second.

to find k:

square both equations and add
$$k^2 \cos^2 a° = 16$$
$$k^2 \sin^2 a° = 49$$
$$\Rightarrow k^2(\cos^2 a° + \sin^2 a°) = 65$$

$$\Rightarrow k = \sqrt{65}.$$

to find $a°$:

divide the equations
to eliminate k

$$\tan a° = \frac{k \sin a°}{k \cos a°} = \frac{7}{-4}$$

$$\Rightarrow a = 180 - \tan^{-1}\left(\frac{7}{4}\right)$$

$$= 119.7 \text{ as } 90 < a < 180$$

c s	s
✓ ✓	✓
✓ c	

---

6 Use the identities $\tan a = \dfrac{\sin a°}{\cos a°}$ and $\sin^2 a° + \cos^2 a° = 1$ to solve these pairs of simultaneous equations for k and a ($k > 0$ and $0 \le a \le 360$).

a) $k \cos a = 3$
   $k \sin a = 4$

b) $k \cos a = 5$
   $k \sin a = 12$

c) $k \sin a = -1$
   $k \cos a = 1$

d) $k \cos a = -1$
   $k \sin a = 1$

e) $k \sin a = -15$
   $k \cos a = -8$

f) $k \sin a = 2$
   $k \cos a = 4$.

> **Reminder**

Example Express $\sin 160°$, $\cos 160°$, $\sin 245°$, $\cos 245°$, $\sin 280°$ and $\cos 280°$ in terms of sines and cosines of acute angles.

Solution

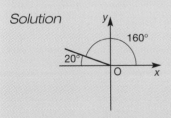
160°
20°

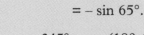
245°
65°

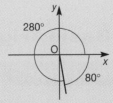
280°
80°

$\sin 160° = \sin(180 - 20)°$
$\quad = \sin 20°.$

$\sin 245° = \sin(180 + 65)°$
$\quad = -\sin 65°.$

$\sin 280° = \sin(360 - 80)°$
$\quad = -\sin 80°.$

$\cos 160° = \cos(180 - 20)°$
$\quad = -\cos 20°.$

$\cos 245° = \cos(180 + 65)°$
$\quad = -\cos 65°.$

$\cos 280° = \cos(360 - 80)°$
$\quad = \cos 80°.$

7 (i) Express in terms of the sine of an acute angle:

    a) sin120°   b) sin 95°   c) sin 300°   d) sin 260°

(ii) Express in terms of the cosine of an acute angle:

    a) cos 100°   b) cos 179°   c) cos 200°   d) cos 310°

(iii) Express as the cosine of an acute angle:

    a) sin 50°   b) sin 10°   c) sin 72°

(iv) Express as the sine of an acute angle:

    a) cos 20°   b) cos 65°   c) cos 33°

(v) Express as cos $x°$ and as sin $y°$ where x and y are acute:

    a) sin100°   b) cos300°   c) sin200°.

> **Reminder**

Example   Simplify

     a) sin $(180 + A)°$ b) cos $(180 + A)°$

Solution $(180 + A)°$ is in the third quadrant

     $A°$ below the x-axis

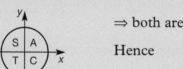

     $\Rightarrow$ both are negative

     Hence   sin $(180 + A)° = -$ sin$A$

                    cos $(180 + A)° = -$ cos$A$.

     This is a mental, one-line calculation.

8 Simplify:

    a) sin$(180 - p)°$ b) cos$(180 - q)°$ c) cos$(180 + r)°$ d) cos$(90 - s)°$

    e) sin$(90 - t)°$ f) cos$(-u)°$ g) sin$(180 - v)°$ h) sin$(-w)°$

    i) cos$(90 - x)°$ j) sin$(360 - y)°$ k) cos$(90 - z)°$ l) cos$(180 - x)°$.

9 Simplify:

    a) cos$^2a° +$ cos$^2(90 - a)°$ b) $\dfrac{\sin(180 - a)°}{\cos(180 - a)°}$ c) $\dfrac{\cos(90 - a)°}{\sin(90 - a)°}$

    d) cos$^2(180 - a)° +$ sin$^2(180 - a)°$ e) sin$^2a° +$ cos$^2(180 - a)°$.

42 Basic Trig Equations

> **Reminder**

Example   Find the exact values of t for which tan $t° = \sqrt{3}$ for $0 \leqslant t \leqslant 360$.

Solution   Use tan 60° $= \sqrt{3}$ and

     'All Sine Tan Cos' to deduce t lies in first and third quadrants.

     Hence $t = 60$ or $t = 180 + 60 = 240 \Rightarrow t = 60, 240$.

Exercise 42

1 Find the EXACT solutions (between 0° and 360°) of each of the following equations:
   a) $\sin p° = 0\cdot5$ b) $\tan q° = 1$ c) $\cos r° = -0\cdot5$ d) $\tan s° = -\sqrt{3}$
   e) $1 - 2\cos x° = 0$ f) $2\sin y° + 1 = 0$ g) $4\sin^2 t° = 1$ h) $3\tan^2 z° - 1 = 0$.

2 Use your calculator to solve correct to 1 decimal place the following equations for angles between 0° and 360°:
   a) $\cos p° = 0\cdot729$ b) $\tan q° = 2\cdot593$ c) $\sin r° = 0\cdot777$ d) $\cos s° = -0\cdot892$
   e) $\sin t° = -0\cdot215$ f) $\tan x° = -3\cdot428$ g) $\sin^2 y° = 0\cdot123$ h) $2 \tan z° = 5$.

43 Quadratic Trig Equations

> **Reminder**

Example Solve $2\cos^2 x° + \cos x° - 1 = 0$ for $0 \leqslant x \leqslant 360$.

Solution It is absolutely vital to realise that this is a quadratic equation in $\cos x°$.
Therefore try to factorise the left hand side.
If not possible, use the quadratic formula.

$$(2 \cos x° - 1)(\cos x° + 1) = 0 \quad \Rightarrow \quad \cos x° = \frac{1}{2}, -1$$

$$\cos x° = \frac{1}{2} \quad \Rightarrow \quad x = 60, 300$$

$$\cos x° = -1 \quad \Rightarrow \quad x = 180 \quad \text{hence} \quad x \in \{60, 180, 300\}.$$

Exercise 43

Find the values of the angles between 0° and 360° which satisfy the following equations:

1 $2\sin^2 r° + \sin r° = 1$ 2 $12 \cos^2 s° + \cos s° - 6 = 0$
3 $14 \tan^2 t° = 11 \tan t° + 15$ 4 $5 \cos^2 v° - 2 \cos v° = 3 \sin^2 v°$
5 $6 \cos^2 w° - 7 \sin w° = 8$ 6 $10 \sin^2 x° + 3 \cos x° = 6$.

44 Trig Equations with Multiple Angles

> **Reminder**

Example Solve $2 \sin 2x° = 1$ for $0 \leqslant x \leqslant 360$.

Solution $0 \leqslant x \leqslant 360 \Rightarrow 0 \leqslant 2x \leqslant 720$

Thus we need all the solutions for $2x°$ up to 720°, i.e.

$\sin 2x° = \frac{1}{2} \Rightarrow 2x = 30, 150, 390, 510$ If we only take the solution up to 360° in this line, then we will only get the solutions up to 180° in the last line.

$$\Rightarrow \quad x = 15, 75, 195, 255.$$

Exercise 44

1 Find **all** the EXACT solutions (between $0°$ and $360°$) of these equations:
   a) $\sin 2p° = 1$
   b) $\cos 3w° = -1$
   c) $\tan 4x° = 1$
   d) $\sin 2y° = 0.5$
   e) $2 \cos 3z° = 1$.

2 Solve the following equations correct to one decimal place for $0 \leqslant x \leqslant 360$:
   a) $\sin 2x° = 0.345$
   b) $\cos 2x° = -0.783$
   c) $\cos 3x° = 0.486$
   d) $\sin \dfrac{x°}{2} = 0.587$
   e) $\cos \dfrac{x°}{2} = -0.897$.

45 Related Trig Graphs

> **Reminder**

Example   Make 3 copies of the graph of $y = \cos x°$ for $0 \leqslant x \leqslant 360$, and superimpose these graphs on the copies:

   a) $y = 2 \cos x°$
   b) $y = \cos 2x°$
   c) $y = \cos (x - 45)°$.

Solution   a)

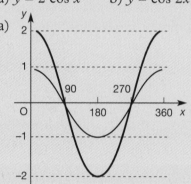

b)

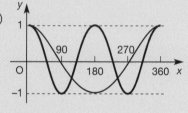

c)

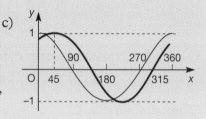

Observe that these are the same transformation as in 'Functions' Section 20 Exercise 20.

Exercise 45

1 Sketch the following graphs on plain paper for $0 \leqslant x \leqslant 360$: show each pair on the same diagram.
   a) $y = \sin x°$ and $y = 2 \sin x°$
   b) $y = \sin x°$ and $y = \sin x° + 2$
   c) $y = \sin x°$ and $y = \sin 2x°$
   d) $y = \cos x°$ and $y = 4 \cos x°$
   e) $y = \cos x°$ and $y = 2 \cos 2x°$
   f) $y = \sin x°$ and $y = 1 - 3 \sin x°$
   g) $y = \sin x°$ and $y = \sin(x - 30)°$
   h) $y = \cos x°$ and $y = \cos(x + 40)°$.

2 Sketch the graph of $y = 2 \sin 20t°$ for $0 \leqslant t \leqslant 18$.

3 Sketch the graph of $y = 3 \cos 15t°$ for $0 \leqslant t \leqslant 24$.

4 Write down the coordinates of the turning points on these graphs for $0 \leqslant x \leqslant 360$, stating the nature (maximum or minimum) of each:
   a) $y = 3 \cos x°$
   b) $y = -2 \sin x°$
   c) $y = 4 \sin(x + 60)°$
   d) $y = 3 \cos(x - 30)°$.

5   An ocean tide is modelled by the equation $y = 3\sin 30t°$, where y is the height in metres above mean sea level after t hours.
    a) What is the difference in level between high and low tide?
    b) Sketch the graph of y against t for $0 \leqslant t \leqslant 12$.

6   A toy spider oscillating on a spring starts from a rest position 1 metre above the floor. Its height after t seconds is given by $h = 1 + \frac{1}{3}\cos 3t°$. Sketch the graph of h against t for $0 \leqslant t \leqslant 120$.

46 Radians

> ### Reminder

One radian is the angle subtended at the centre of a circle by an arc equal in length to the radius.

Hence π radians = 180°

or $360° = 2\pi^c$ (c denotes circular measure i.e. radians)

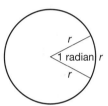

Example   Express a) 330° in radians   b) $\frac{5\pi}{9}$ radians in degrees

Solution   a) $330° = \frac{330}{360} \times 2\pi^c = \frac{11\pi}{6}$ radians

   b) $\frac{5\pi^c}{9} = \frac{5}{9} \cdot 180° = 100\%$

Exercise 46

1   Copy and complete the following table:

degrees	0	30	45	60	90	120	135	150	180	210	270	300	360
radians									π				2π

2   Express in degrees the angles whose radian measures are:
   $$\frac{\pi}{3}, \frac{\pi}{6}, \frac{5\pi}{6}, \frac{3\pi}{4}, \frac{5\pi}{4}, \frac{3\pi}{2}, \frac{4\pi}{5}, \frac{5\pi}{3}$$

3   Complete this table of exact values:

θ	0	$\frac{\pi}{6}$	$\frac{\pi}{4}$	$\frac{\pi}{3}$	$\frac{\pi}{2}$
$\sin \theta$					
$\cos \theta$					
$\tan \theta$					

4 Two angles of a triangle are $\frac{\pi}{6}$ and $\frac{2\pi}{3}$. Calculate the size of the third angle in radians, and hence in degrees.

5 Write down both in radians and degrees
   a) the complement of $\frac{\pi}{6}$ radians
   b) the supplement of $\frac{\pi}{6}$ radians.

6 Angle x is bigger than angle y. The angles x and y have a sum of $\frac{11\pi}{9}$ and a difference of $\frac{\pi}{8}$.
   Working in radians, form a pair of simultaneous equations in x and y and hence find their values.

7 Simplify
   a) $\sin(\pi - \theta)$
   b) $\cos\left(\frac{\pi}{2} - \theta\right)$
   c) $\sin(2\pi + \alpha)$
   d) $\cos(\pi + \text{ø})$

▶ **Reminder**

Example Find a) the EXACT solution of $2\cos\theta + 1 = 0$
and   b) the solution of $3\cos\theta + 2 = 0$ correct to 2 decimal places.

Solution
   a) $\cos\theta = -\frac{1}{2}$

   [Think $\cos\frac{\pi}{3} = \frac{1}{2}$ and cosine is negative in 2nd, 3rd quadrants]

   $\Rightarrow \theta = \pi \pm \frac{\pi}{3} = \frac{2\pi}{3}, \frac{4\pi}{3}$.

   b) $\cos\theta = -\frac{2}{3}$

   [Put your calculator into radian mode and remember that cosine is negative in 2nd, 3rd quadrants]

   $\Rightarrow \theta = \pi \pm \cos^{-1}\left(\frac{2}{3}\right) = 2.30, 3.98$.

---

8 Find the EXACT solutions of the following equations for angles between 0 and 2π:
   a) $\sin a = \frac{-1}{\sqrt{2}}$
   b) $\tan b = -1$
   c) $\cos c = \frac{1}{2}$
   d) $3\tan d = \sqrt{3}$
   e) $4\sin^2 e = 3$
   f) $2\cos^2 f = 1$
   g) $3\tan^2 g = 1$.

9 Find the EXACT solutions between 0 and 2π for the equation:
   a) $2\sin 2x = \sqrt{3}$
   b) $2\cos 3x + \sqrt{3} = 0$.

10 Find the EXACT solutions between 0 and 2π for the equation:
   a) $2\sin^2 x - \sin x - 1 = 0$
   b) $2\cos^2 x + 3\cos x = 2$.

11 For the equations in question 10, write down the decimal approximation to each of the exact roots found (correct to 3 decimal places).

12 Solve the following equations correct to three decimal places for $0 \leqslant x \leqslant 2\pi$:
  a) $\sin x = 0.4$
  b) $3 \cos x + 0.63 = 0$
  c) $6 \sin^2 x + 5 \sin x - 6 = 0$
  d) $\tan 2x = 1\cdot5$.

13B Sketch the graph of $y = 3 \cos \dfrac{\pi t}{6}$ for $0 \leqslant t \leqslant 12$.

14B Sketch the graph of $y = 2 \sin \dfrac{\pi t}{12}$ for $0 \leqslant t \leqslant 24$.

15B Remembering that the length of an arc and the area of a sector are proportional to the angle (θ radians) that they subtend at the centre of the circle of radius r, prove that:
  a) the length of the arc is given by $r\theta$
  b) the area of the sector is given by $\dfrac{1}{2} r^2 \theta$.

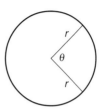

47 TOPIC TEST on Identities & Radians

⏱ Allow 45 minutes for this test (Calculator required)

1 a) Express 330° in radians (in terms of π).
  b) Write down the EXACT value of $\sin \dfrac{3\pi}{4}$.
  c) Simplify $\sin (\pi - x)$.
  d) Simplify $\sin^2 7x + \cos^2 7x$.
  e) Simplify $\dfrac{\sin 4y}{\cos 4y}$.

2 Draw the graph of $y = 2 \sin \dfrac{\pi t}{6}$ for $0 \leqslant t \leqslant 12$.

3 Calculate the size of the angle between DF and the base ABCD, given AB = 8, AD = 6, and BF = 5.

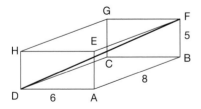

4 Solve for $0 \leqslant \theta \leqslant 2\pi$
  a) $2 \sin \theta + 1 = 0$
  b) $2 \cos^2 \theta = \cos \theta + 1$.

5 The displacement, W cm, of the piston of a model steam railway engine t tenths of a second after attaining its maximum speed is given by the formula:

$$W(t) = 5 + 3 \sin \left(\dfrac{\pi t}{10} + \dfrac{\pi}{5} \right).$$

The diagram shows the graph of this function W for $0 \leqslant t \leqslant 20$ and the line with equation $y = 6\cdot5$.

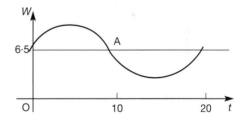

a) State the maximum value of W and find (non-graphically) the value of t between 0 and 20 at which it occurs.
b) State the minimum value of W and find (non-graphically) the value of t between 0 and 20 at which it occurs.
c) Evaluate $W(20)$ correct to 3 significant figures.
d) Find the **exact** coordinates of the point A
  (i.e. find the smallest value of t for which W is 6·5).

71

PRACTICE UNIT TESTS

48 Practice Unit Test on Unit 1

Calculator may be used

marks

1 Find the equation of the straight line passing through A $(-2, 3)$ and B $(2, 11)$. (3)

2 Write down the gradient of a line which makes an angle of $40°$ with the x-axis. (2)

3 Write down the gradient of a line
   a) parallel to $y = 3x - 2$ (1)
   b) perpendicular to $y = 3x - 2$ (1)

4 Make two copies of this graph of $y = f(x)$.
   a) On one copy show the graph of $y = -f(x)$. (1)
   b) On the other, show the graph of $y = f(x - 1)$. (1)

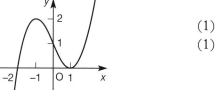

5 This diagram shows the graph of
   $y = \cos x°$ and two other related graphs.
   Identify the two related graphs. (2)

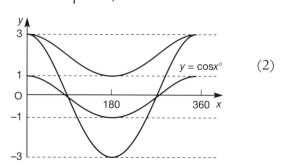

6 Identify these graphs:
   a) 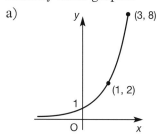 b) 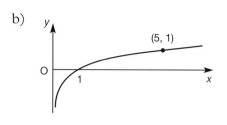 (2)

7 Three functions f, g, h, defined on suitable domains, are defined by:

   $f(x) = x^3$, $g(x) = 3x - 1$, $h(x) = \cos x°$

   Find formulae for a) $g(f(x))$ b) $f(h(x))$. (2)

8 Find $\frac{dy}{dx}$ where $y = \frac{2x + 1}{x^2}$. (4)

9 Find the gradient of the tangent to the curve with equation
$y = (x + 2)(x - 3)$ at the point $(3, 0)$. (4)

10 Find the stationary points on the curve with equation
$y = 2x^3 - 3x^2 - 12x + 1$, and determine their nature. (8)

11 Granny Murphy keeps a tin of mini Mars Bars for her grandchildren,
who visit her every Saturday. She buys a pack of 48 bars every Thursday with
her shopping and puts them in her tin. The grandchildren eat two thirds of
whatever is in the tin every visit.
a) If there are u_n bars in the tin one Friday, write down a recurrence relation
for u_{n+1}, the number of bars in the tin on the following Friday. (1)
b) Find the limit of the sequence generated by this recurrence relation and
explain what it means. (3)

49 Revision (Non-calculator) Tests on Unit 1

TEST 1

⏱ **Allow 45 minutes for this test**

1 In triangle OAB, A is the point $(2, 5)$
and B$(6, 4)$.

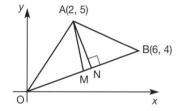

Find the equation of
a) the median AM,
b) the altitude AN.

2 A is the point $(-2, -3)$, B$(5, 1)$ and
C$(-1, 3)$.

Find the equation of the line through C
perpendicular to AB, expressing your
answer in its simplest form without
fractions.

3 Find the value of t if the points A$(-1, 2)$
B$(2, 9)$ and C$(t, 30)$ are collinear.

4 Find the equation of the tangent to the
curve $y = x^{\frac{2}{3}}$ at the point where $x = 8$.

5 a) Write down the exact value of
$$\frac{\sin 60°}{\tan 60° + \tan 45°}$$
b) Express your answer with a rational
denominator.

6 In triangle PQR, PQ $= (2 + \sqrt{2})$ cm,
QR $= (2\sqrt{2} - 2)$ cm, and angle PQR $= \frac{\pi}{4}$.

Show that the area of triangle
PQR is 1 cm².

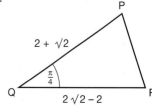

7 a) Find the gradient of the tangent at P(1,10) to the curve with equation $y = -x^3 + 2x^2 + 4x + 5$.

b) If this tangent is also a tangent at P to the parabola with equation $y = x^2 + bx + c$, find the values of b and c.

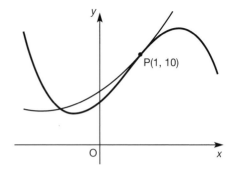

TEST 2

🕐 Allow 45 minutes for this test

1 Triangle ABC has vertices A(6,10) B(3,4) and C(9,4).
The altitudes AD and BE meet at H.

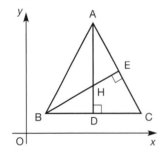

a) Show that triangle ABC is isosceles.
b) Write down the equation of the altitude AD.
c) Find the equation of the altitude BE.
d) Find the coordinates of H.
e) Show that H lies one quarter of the way along DA.

2 A householder has a triangular piece of garden in the shape of half of a 10m × 10m square, adjacent to one wall of his house. He would like to build a rectangular lean-to greenhouse in this space.

Let the greenhouse have length y metres and breadth x metres, as shown in the second diagram.

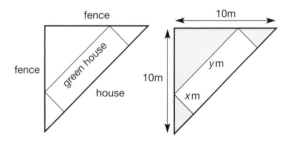

a) What shape is each shaded triangle?
b) Show that the area, A m², of the greenhouse is given by $A = 10\sqrt{2}\, x - 2x^2$.
c) Calculate the greatest possible area of the greenhouse.

3 The diagram below shows the graph of a curve with equation $y = a + b\sin\dfrac{\pi t}{c}$ for the interval $0 \leqslant t \leqslant 18$.

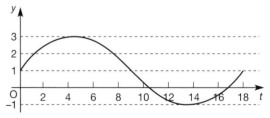

a) State the values of a, b and c.
b) The points $(0, 3)$ and $(18, -1)$ are joined by a straight line ℓ. At how many points does ℓ intersect this curve?
c) Does the point on the curve where $t = 9$ lie above, on, or below ℓ?

QUADRATIC THEORY

50 Factorising Quadratic Expressions

▶ **Reminder**

Example Factorise:
a) $k^2 - 7k$ b) $y^2 - 9$ c) $2t^2 + 5t - 3$.

Solution
a) Take out the common factor k: $k^2 - 7k = k(k - 7)$.
b) Recognise the difference of two squares:
$y^2 - 9 = y^2 - 3^2 = (y - 3)(y + 3)$.

c) List the factors of 2 and 3:
$$\begin{array}{c|cc} 2 & 1 & 3 \\ 1 & 3 & 1 \end{array}$$

Look for products with a difference of 5:
$$\begin{array}{c|cc} 2 & 1 & 3 \\ 1 & 3 & 1 \end{array}$$

$2 \times 3 - 1 \times 1 = 5$ so $2t \times (3) + 1t \times (-1) = 5t$

Hence $(2t - 1)(t + 3)$.

Exercise 50

Factorise :

1 $t^2 - 6t$ 2 $u^2 + 7u$ 3 $5v - v^2$ 4 $6y - 2y^2$

5 $x^2 - 1$ 6 $y^2 - 16$ 7 $4x^2 - 25$ 8 $2t^2 - 18$

9 $x^2 + 4x + 3$ 10 $x^2 - 6x + 8$ 11 $x^2 + 2x - 15$ 12 $x^2 - 6x - 16$

13 $2k^2 - k - 3$ 14 $2w^2 + 3w - 35$ 15 $6x^2 + 11x - 10$ 16 $14x^2 - 29x - 15$.

51 Solving Quadratic Equations by Factorising

▶ **Reminder**

Example Solve:
a) $k^2 - 7k = 0$ b) $y^2 - 9 = 0$ c) $2t^2 + 5t - 3 = 0$.

Solution a) $k^2 - 7k = 0$ $\Rightarrow$ $k(k - 7) = 0$ $\Rightarrow$ $k = 0, 7$.
Alternatively, $k^2 = 7k$ $\Rightarrow$ $k = 0$ is a solution by inspection.
If $k \neq 0$, we can divide both sides by k and obtain $k = 7$.

▶ **Reminder** continued

b) $y^2 - 9 = 0 \implies (y-3)(y+3) = 0 \implies y = 3, -3$.

Alternatively, $y^2 = 9 \implies y = \pm 3$.

[$\pm$ appears whenever you take the square root of both sides of an equation]

c) $2t^2 + 5t - 3 = 0 \implies (2t-1)(t+3) = 0 \implies t = -3, \frac{1}{2}$.

[NEVER do '$t(2t+5) = 3$']

Exercise 51

Solve these equations by factorising:

1 $k^2 - 2k = 0$ **2** $m^2 + 7m = 0$ **3** $r^2 - 9 = 0$

4 $4s^2 - 25 = 0$ **5** $x^2 - 5x + 6 = 0$ **6** $x^2 + 5x + 4 = 0$

7 $y^2 + y - 20 = 0$ **8** $z^2 + 6z + 8 = 0$ **9** $2x^2 - 5x - 3 = 0$

10 $6x^2 + 11x - 10 = 0$ **11** $x(x-1) = 12$ **12** $y(y+2) = 3$

13 $z - 1 = \dfrac{2}{z}$ **14** $\dfrac{x+1}{x+3} = \dfrac{2x-1}{x+7}$.

52 Intersection of a Line and a Parabola

▶ **Reminder**

Example

Consider the parabola with equation $y = x^2$ and the family of straight lines with equation $y = 4x + c$.

Investigate the intersection of the line and the parabola when c is

a) 5 b) –4 c) –7.

Solution

a) $\left.\begin{array}{l} y = x^2 \\ y = 4x + 5 \end{array}\right\} \implies 4x + 5 = x^2$

This equation is obtained by equating the two expressions for y, but it is generally more useful to think of substituting the linear expression for y into the higher degree equation.

$x^2 - 4x - 5 = (x+1)(x-5) = 0 \implies x = -1, 5$
$ \implies y = 1, 25$

$\implies$ The line intersects the parabola at the two points $(-1, 1)$ and $(5, 25)$.

Reminder continued

b) $\left.\begin{array}{l} y = x^2 \\ y = 4x - 4 \end{array}\right\} \Rightarrow 4x - 4 = x^2 \Rightarrow x^2 - 4x + 4 = (x - 2)^2 = 0$

$\Rightarrow x = 2, 2 \Rightarrow y = 4, 4$

The equal roots show that the line is a tangent to the parabola at the point $(2, 4)$.

c) $\left.\begin{array}{l} y = x^2 \\ y = 4x - 7 \end{array}\right\} \Rightarrow 4x - 7 = x^2 \Rightarrow x^2 - 4x + 7 = 0$

$\Rightarrow x = \dfrac{4 \pm \sqrt{-12}}{2} \Rightarrow$ no real solutions of this equation

$\Rightarrow$ no intersection of the line and parabola.

Exercise 52

Find in each case the point of intersection of the line and the parabola:

1 $\begin{cases} y = x + 6 \\ y = x^2 \end{cases}$ **2** $\begin{cases} y = 3 - 2x \\ y = x^2 \end{cases}$ **3** $\begin{cases} y = 2x \\ y = 8x - x^2 \end{cases}$ **4** $\begin{cases} y = x - 1 \\ y = x^2 - 6x + 5. \end{cases}$

Show in each case that the line is a tangent to the parabola, stating the coordinates of the point of contact:

5 $\begin{cases} y = 4(x - 1) \\ y = x^2 \end{cases}$ **6** $\begin{cases} y = 3(2x - 3) \\ y = x^2 \end{cases}$ **7** $\begin{cases} y = 2x + 1 \\ y = 4x - x^2 \end{cases}$ **8** $\begin{cases} y = 6 + 2x \\ y = 5 - x^2. \end{cases}$

Determine in each case whether or not the line is a tangent to the parabola:

9 $\begin{cases} 4x + y + 4 = 0 \\ y = x^2 \end{cases}$ **10** $\begin{cases} y = 2x - 1 \\ y = x^2 - 4 \end{cases}$ **11** $\begin{cases} y = 4x \\ y = x^2 + 4 \end{cases}$ **12** $\begin{cases} y = 2x \\ y = x^2 + 2. \end{cases}$

53 Solving Quadratic Equations by Completing the Square

Reminder

Example

Solve by completing the square:
a) $x^2 + 4x + 3 = 0$ b) $x^2 + 6x + 1 = 0$ c) $2x^2 - 5x - 33 = 0$.

Solution

a) $x^2 + 4x + 3 = 0$

$\Rightarrow x^2 + 4x = -3$ [x terms on the left, number on the right]

$\Rightarrow x^2 + 4x + 4 = 4 - 3$ [halve the coefficient of x and square it, add to each side]

$\Rightarrow (x + 2)^2 = 1$ [the left hand side is now always a square]

$\Rightarrow x + 2 = \pm 1$ [as in §51 worked example part (*b*)]

$\Rightarrow x = -3, -1$ [in this case, more work than factorising].

⟩ ***Reminder*** continued

b) $x^2 + 6x + 1 = 0$ [This equation does <u>not</u> factorise.]

$\Rightarrow x^2 + 6x = -1$

$\Rightarrow x^2 + 6x + 9 = 9 - 1$

$\Rightarrow (x + 3)^2 = 8$

$\Rightarrow x + 3 = \pm 2\sqrt{2}$

$\Rightarrow x = -3 \pm 2\sqrt{2}$

These roots are exact solutions. Decimal approximations may be obtained where appropriate.

c) $2x^2 - 5x - 33 = 0$

$\Rightarrow 2x^2 - 5x = 33$

$\Rightarrow x^2 - \dfrac{5}{2}x + \left(\dfrac{5}{4}\right)^2 = \dfrac{25}{16} + \dfrac{33}{2}$ [We must have $1x^2$ on the l.h.s.]

$\Rightarrow \left(x - \dfrac{5}{4}\right)^2 = \dfrac{25 + 264}{16} = \dfrac{289}{16} \Rightarrow x - \dfrac{5}{4} = \pm \dfrac{17}{4}$

$\Rightarrow x = \dfrac{5}{4} \pm \dfrac{17}{4} = -3, \dfrac{11}{2}.$

Exercise 53

Solve these equations by completing the square :

1 $x^2 - 2x - 3 = 0$ **2** $x^2 + 6x + 5 = 0$ **3** $x^2 + 10x + 16 = 0$

4 $x^2 - x - 2 = 0$ **5** $2x^2 + x - 6 = 0$ **6** $3x^2 - 4x - 4 = 0.$

Solve these equations by completing the square, leaving your answers as compound surds :

7 $x^2 + 4x + 2 = 0$ **8** $x^2 - 6x + 7 = 0$

9 $x^2 + 10x + 5 = 0$ **10** $2x^2 - 7x - 1 = 0.$

Use completing the square to prove that the following equations have no real roots :

11 $x^2 + 2x + 1 = -1$ **12** $x^2 - 2x + 3 = 0$

13 $x^2 + 3x + 3 = 0$ **14** $2x^2 - x + 5 = 0.$

54 Solving Quadratic Equations by the Formula

⟩ ***Reminder***

Example   Solve $3x^2 + 4x - 5 = 0$ by the formula, giving your answers correct to 2 decimal places.

Solution $x = \dfrac{-4 \pm \sqrt{4^2 - 4 \times 3 \times (-5)}}{2 \times 3} = \dfrac{-4 \pm \sqrt{76}}{6} = -2 \cdot 12, 0 \cdot 79.$

Exercise 54

1 Solve the equation $ax^2 + bx + c = 0$ by completing the square.

2 Use the quadratic formula (i.e. the answer to question 1) to solve these equations, leaving your answers to parts c) and d) as compound surds:
a) $x^2 - 4x + 3 = 0$
b) $2x^2 - x - 3 = 0$
c) $x^2 + x - 1 = 0$
d) $2x^2 - 3x - 4 = 0$.

3 Use the quadratic formula to prove that these equations have no real roots:
a) $x^2 + x + 1 = 0$
b) $2x^2 + 3x + 4 = 0$.

55 Sketching Parabolae by completing the Square

> **Reminder**

Example

Sketch the parabola with equation:
a) $y = x^2 + 6x + 5$
b) $y = x^2 - 8x + 19$.

Solution

a) $y = x^2 + 6x + 5$
$\quad = x^2 + 6x + 9 - 9 + 5$
$\quad = (x + 3)^2 - 4$

$\Rightarrow$ minimum turning point at $(-3, -4)$

$y = 0 \;\Rightarrow\; (x + 3)^2 = 4$
$\quad\quad \Rightarrow\; x + 3 = \pm 2$
$\quad\quad \Rightarrow\; x = -5, -1$
$x = 0 \;\Rightarrow\; y = 5$
[use the first line].

b) $y = x^2 - 8x + 19$
$\quad = x^2 - 8x + 16 - 16 + 19$
$\quad = (x - 4)^2 + 3$

$\Rightarrow$ minimum turning point at $(4, 3)$

$y = (x - 4)^2 + 3 \geqslant 3 > 0$
(no intersections with x-axis)

$x = 0 \;\Rightarrow\; y = 19$.

Note:
a) is $y = x^2$ moved 3 left and 4 down.

b) is $y = x^2$ moved 4 right and 3 up.

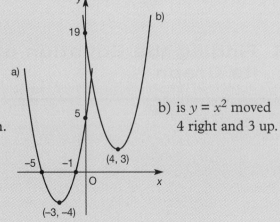

Exercise 55

1 Write down the coordinates of the turning point on each parabola, stating its nature:
   a) $y = (x + 1)^2 - 3$
   b) $y = 2 - (x - 3)^2$
   c) $y = 2(x + 3)^2 + 1$
   d) $y = 5 - 2(x - 1)^2$
   e) $y = 3(x - 2)^2 + 7$
   f) $y = 4 - 3(x + 2)^2$.

2 Express each of the following in the form $(x + a)^2 + b$:
   a) $x^2 - 6x$
   b) $x^2 + 8x$
   c) $x^2 - 10x + 21$
   d) $x^2 - 12x - 13$
   e) $x^2 + 4x + 5$
   f) $x^2 + 6x + 2$
   g) $x^2 + 3x + 1$
   h) $x^2 + 5x + 3$.

3B Express each of the following in the form $a(x + b)^2 + c$:
   a) $2x^2 + 8x + 1$
   b) $3x^2 - 6x - 5$
   c) $2x^2 + 4x + 3$
   d) $5x^2 - 20x + 11$.

4B Express each of the following in the form $c - a(x + b)^2$:
   a) $8 - 2x - x^2$
   b) $7 - 6x - x^2$
   c) $11 - 4x - 2x^2$
   d) $5 + 6x - 2x^2$.

5 In question 2(c) you showed that $f(x) = x^2 - 10x + 21 = (x - 5)^2 - 4$. Writing $f(x)$ in this form is helpful for sketching the graph of f, by thinking of moving the graph of $y = x^2$.

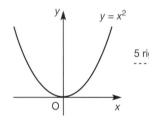
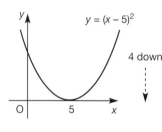
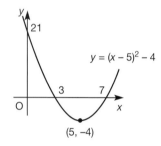

The intersections with the axes are found as follows:
$$x = 0 \implies y = 0^2 - 10 \times 0 + 21 = 21$$
$$y = 0 \implies (x - 5)^2 - 4 = 0 \implies (x - 5)^2 = 4 \implies x - 5 = \pm 2 \implies x = 3, 7.$$

Similarly sketch the graph of
   a) $x^2 - 12x - 13$ see qu. 2 (d)
   b) $x^2 + 4x + 5$ see qu. 2 (e)
   c) $8 - 2x - x^2$ see qu. 4 (a).

56 Finding the Equation of a Parabola from its Graph

> **Reminder**

Example   Find the equation of the parabola shown.

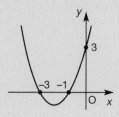

> **Reminder** continued

Solution   roots at −1 and −3
$$\Rightarrow\; y = k(x + 1)(x + 3)$$

$y = 3$ when $x = 0$
$$\Rightarrow\; 3 = k(1)(3)$$
$$\Rightarrow\; k = 1$$
$$\Rightarrow\; y = 1(x + 1)(x + 3)$$
i.e. $y = x^2 + 4x + 3$

Exercise 56

1 Find the equation of each of the parabolae shown.

a) 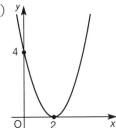   b) 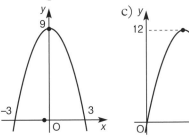   c) 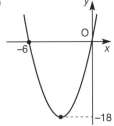   d)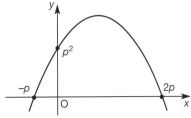

e) 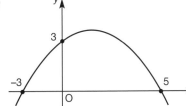   f)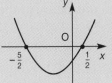

57 Solving Quadratic Inequalities

> **Reminder**

Example   Solve $4x^2 + 8x − 5 > 0$.

Solution   Note: for a quadratic equation, the solution set is at most two values of x.
For a quadratic inequality, the solution set is an interval of the number line.

First find the roots of the function:
$$4x^2 + 8x − 5 = (2x − 1)(2x + 5)$$

This has roots at $\dfrac{1}{2}, \dfrac{-5}{2}$.

> ### Reminder continued

The $(+)4$ in front of x^2 indicates a minimum turning point. We do not need to know the coordinates of this point to obtain this rough sketch.

The function is positive when the graph is above the x-axis,

hence $x \in \left\{ x : x < -\frac{5}{2} \right\} \cup \left\{ x : x > \frac{1}{2} \right\}$

Exercise 57

Solve the following inequalities:

1. $x^2 - 2x - 3 < 0$
2. $4 + 5x + x^2 \geqslant 0$
3. $x^2 - 16 \geqslant 0$
4. $25 - x^2 < 0$
5. $x^2 - 5x < 0$
6. $x^2 - 5x + 4 \geqslant 0$
7. $2x^2 - x - 3 \leqslant 0$
8. $4x^2 - 24x + 35 > 0$
9. $x - x^2 > 0$
10. $x^2 - 2x + 1 < 0.$

58 The Discriminant and the Nature of the Roots of a Quadratic Equation

> ### Reminder

$ax^2 + bx + c = 0 \implies$ discriminant $= \Delta = b^2 - 4ac$

$\Delta < 0 \implies$ no real roots
$\Delta = 0 \implies$ equal real roots
$\Delta > 0 \implies$ distinct real roots

Furthermore, if $\Delta > 0$ and Δ is a perfect square, then $ax^2 + bx + c$ will factorise.

Example Prove that the equation $x^2 + 2kx + (k - 1) = 0$ has real roots for all k.

Solution
$$x^2 + 2kx + (k - 1) = 0$$
$$\implies \Delta = (2k)^2 - 4(1)(k - 1) = 4k^2 - 4(k - 1) = 4[k^2 - k + 1]$$
$$= 4\left[k^2 - k + \frac{1}{4} + \frac{3}{4}\right] = 4\left[\left(k - \frac{1}{2}\right)^2 + \frac{3}{4}\right] \geqslant 3 > 0 \text{ for all values of } k$$

hence real roots for all k.

Exercise 58

1. Discuss the nature of the roots of the following quadratic equations:
   a) $x^2 + 5x + 2 = 0$
   b) $x^2 + 5x + 4 = 0$
   c) $x^2 + 5x + 7 = 0$
   d) $3x^2 - x + 4 = 0$
   e) $4x^2 + 12x + 9 = 0$
   f) $x^2 - x - 1 = 0$
   g) $x(x - 3) = 2$
   h) $(x + 3)(x - 3) = 2x - 10$
   i) $2(x^2 + a^2) = 5ax$
   j) $x^2 - 2ax + 4a^2 = 0$
   k) $x^2 - a^2 = 2ax$
   l) $x(a^2 - 1) = a(x^2 - 1).$

2 Show that the roots of $x^2 - 2ax - b^2 = 0$ are always real.

3 Find the value of k or p for which the following equations have equal roots:
a) $x^2 - 8x + k = 0$ b) $kx^2 - 12x + 9 = 0$ c) $x^2 + kx + 16 = 0$
d) $x^2 + 2px + 9 = 0$ e) $x^2 - 2x + p = 0$ f) $x^2 + (p + 1)x + 9 = 0$
g) $x^2 = k(2x - 5)$ h) $(p + 1)x^2 - 2(p + 3)x + 3p = 0$.

4 For what range of values of q does the equation $qx^2 + 2x + q = 0$ have distinct real roots?

5 Find the condition for each of the following equations to have equal roots:
a) $(px + q)^2 = 8x$ b) $x^2 + (x + c)^2 = 8$ c) $x^2 - 2ax + b^2 = 0$.

6B For what range of values of k does the equation $k(x + 1)(x + 4) = x$ have no real roots?

7B a) Find two values of m for which the equation $(2m - 1)x^2 + (m + 1)x + 1 = 0$ has equal roots.
b) State the nature of the roots when m lies between these values.

8B The equation $5x^2 - 12x + k = 0$ has no real roots. What are the permissible values for k?

9B Find two values of a for which the equation $a^2x^2 + 2(a + 1)x + 4 = 0$ has equal roots, and solve the equation in each case.

59 Using the Discriminant for Tangency

> **Reminder**

Example

Find the equation of the tangent with gradient 2 to the parabola with equation $y = x^2 - 4x$, stating the coordinates of the point of contact.

Solution

Any line with gradient 2 has an equation of the form $y = 2x + c$.

$$\left. \begin{array}{l} y = x^2 - 4x \\ y = 2x + c \end{array} \right\} \Rightarrow 2x + c = x^2 - 4x \Rightarrow x^2 - 6x - c = 0$$

when the line is a tangent, this equation has equal roots

i.e. $\Delta = 0 \Rightarrow (-6)^2 - 4 \times 1 \times (-c) = 0 \Rightarrow c = -9$

hence the line is $y = 2x - 9$

$c = -9 \Rightarrow x^2 - 6x + 9 = 0 = (x - 3)^2 \Rightarrow x = 3, 3$
$\Rightarrow y = (2 \times 3) - 9 = -3 \Rightarrow (3, -3)$

Exercise 59

1B Find the equation(s) of the tangent(s) with gradient

a) 1 to the curve $y^2 = 4x$

b) 4 to the curve $xy = -1$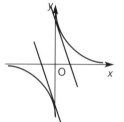

c) −1 to the curve $x^2 + y^2 = 8$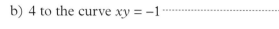

d) −4 to the curve $xy = 4$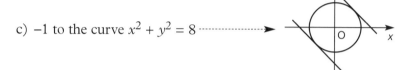

e) 2 to the curve $y = x^2$

f) −8 to the curve $y = 2x^2$.

2B Find the equation(s) of the tangent(s) to the curve

a) $y = x^2$ from the point $(0, -4)$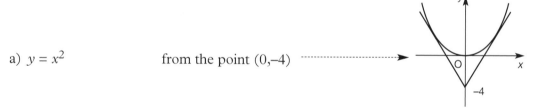

b) $y^2 = x^2 - 1$ from the point $(0, -5)$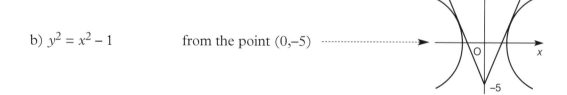

c) $x^2 + y^2 - 4x - 2y = 0$ from the point $(0, -8)$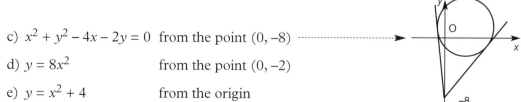

d) $y = 8x^2$ from the point $(0, -2)$

e) $y = x^2 + 4$ from the origin

f) $x^2 + y^2 = 9$ from the point $(0, 5)$.

3B a) Find the equations of the tangents from the point $(4,0)$ to the circle $x^2 + y^2 = 8$, and show that they are perpendicular.

b) Find the equations of the tangents from the point $(5,0)$ to the circle $x^2 + y^2 = 16$, and show that they are inclined equally to the x-axis.

c) Find the equations of the tangents from the point $(2,4)$ to the circle $x^2 + y^2 = 10$, and show that they are perpendicular.

60 TOPIC TEST on Quadratic Theory

Allow 45 minutes for this test (Non-calculator)

1 Labelling all turning points and intersections with axes, sketch the parabolae:
a) $y = x^2$
b) $y = (x - 2)^2$
c) $y = (x - 2)^2 + 1$.

2 Show that the line $2x + y = 5$ is a tangent to the parabola $y = 4 - x^2$, and find the coordinates of the point of contact.

3 For what range of values of k does the equation $x^2 - 3x + k = 0$ have real roots?

4 Solve $x^2 + x - 2 \geqslant 0$.

5 a) Express $x^2 - 4x + 7$ in the form $(x - a)^2 + b$

b) Write down the least possible value of $x^2 - 4x + 7$

c) Write down the greatest possible value of $\dfrac{1}{x^2 - 4x + 7}$.

6 Find the equations of tangents to the circle $x^2 + y^2 = 10$ which have gradient 3, stating the coordinates of the point of contact of each.

THE REMAINDER THEOREM

61 The Vocabulary of Polynomials

> **Reminder**

A polynomial is of the form $a + bx + cx^2 + dx^3 + ex^4 + \ldots\ldots + \alpha x^n$
where a, b, c, d, e, etc are numbers. They are called coefficients.

e.g. in $3 + 4x^2 + 7x^3 - x^4$, the coefficient of x^2 is 4.

Functional notation is often used, e.g. $f(x) = 4 + 2x - 3x^2$.
The degree of the polynomial is the highest power which appears

e.g. $g(x) = 4x^3 - x + 1$ has degree 3.

Note that $f(x)$ (above) has been arranged in ascending powers, but
$g(x)$ (above) has been arranged in descending powers.

Exercise 61

1 State the coefficient of x^2 in:
   a) $3x^3 + 5x^2 - 2x + 1$ b) $4x - 3x^2 + 5x^3$
   c) $7x^3 - 1$ d) $(2x^2 - 1)^2$.

2 State the coefficient of x in:
   a) $2x^3 + 3x - 4$ b) $5x^2 - 2x + 7$
   c) $x^3 - 13$ d) $x(3x - 2)$.

3 State the degree of the polynomial:
   a) $5x^4 - 11x^5 + x^6$ b) $6x^2 - 2x + 5$
   c) $(x - 1)^3$ d) $x(x + 1)^2$.

4 Arrange in ascending powers of x:
   a) $x^2 - 1 + 2x$ b) $(2x - 1)^2$.

5 Arrange in descending powers of x:
   a) $(2 + 3x)^2$ b) $x(4 - x)^2$.

6 State the coefficient of
   a) x in $(1 + x)(2 - x)$ b) x^2 in $(2 - x)(3 + x)$
   c) x^3 in $x(3x - 1)^2$ d) x in $x^2(x - 1)$.

62 Evaluation of Polynomials

> **Reminder**

Example   Evaluate $f(2)$ where $f(x) = 3x^3 - 4x^2 + 5x - 6$.

Solution

(i) By direct substitution: $f(2) = 3(2)^3 - 4(2)^2 + 5(2) - 6$
$$= 24 - 16 + 10 - 6 = 12.$$

(ii) By programmable calculator: refer to the instruction manual of your calculator to see how to do so. You will find this method most useful when you reach Exercise 67.

(iii) By nesting: $f(x) = 3x^3 - 4x^2 + 5x - 6$
$$= (3x^2 - 4x + 5)x - 6$$
$$= [(3x - 4)x + 5]x - 6$$
$$\Rightarrow f(2) = [(3 \times 2 - 4) \times 2 + 5] \times 2 - 6$$
$$= [2 \times 2 + 5] \times 2 - 6 = 12.$$

This is not a layout that is often used in practice, but it lays the theoretical foundation for the following method, synthetic division.

(iv) By synthetic division:

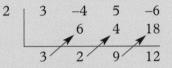

$$2 \,\bigg|\; \begin{array}{cccc} 3 & -4 & 5 & -6 \\ & 6 & 4 & 18 \\ \hline 3 & 2 & 9 & 12 \end{array}$$

1 to find $f(2)$, 2 goes on the left, as shown
2 copy down 3, the leading coefficient, from the top to bottom row
3 multiply diagonally by 2 as shown to obtain the 6 in the middle row
4 add the -4 in the first row and the 6 in the second row to get the 2 in the third row
5 Similarly, multiply and add another twice, and the remainder is the last number in the third row
6 include a zero in the top row for any 'missing' term, e.g. in $x^5 - 4x^3$ ... .

Exercise 62

1 Use direct substitution (without your calculator) to evaluate:
    a) $f(1)$ where $f(x) = 3x^2 + 4x + 5$ b) $f(-1)$ where $f(x) = 3x^2 - 4x + 5$
    c) $f(2)$ where $f(x) = x^3 - 3$ d) $f(-2)$ where $f(x) = 7x^3 - 11$.

2 Use a programmable calculator to evaluate:
    a) $f(1 \cdot 1)$ where $f(x) = x^2 + 2x + 3$ b) $g(1 \cdot 2)$ where $g(t) = 2t^2 - t + 1$
    c) $h(-3 \cdot 6)$ where $h(s) = s^3 - s^2 + s + 5$ d) $u(-2 \cdot 5)$ where $u(t) = 2t^3 + 5t - 2$.

3 Write each of these polynomials in nested form and hence evaluate:

a) $f(2)$ where $f(x) = x^3 - 3x^2 + 2x - 1$ b) $g(-3)$ where $g(x) = 2x^3 + 4x^2 - x + 5$

c) $h(-2)$ where $h(x) = 3x^3 + 2x^2 - x + 3$ d) $u(3)$ where $u(x) = x^4 + x^3 + x^2 + x + 1$.

4 Use synthetic division [remembering the zeros in parts c) to f)] to evaluate:

a) $v(2)$ where $v(t) = 5t^3 + 3t^2 - t + 11$ b) $w(-2)$ where $w(s) = 3s^4 - s^3 + s^2 + 2s - 1$

c) $f(2)$ where $f(y) = y^3 - y - 1$ d) $g(3)$ where $g(t) = 3t^3 + 2t^2 - 3$

e) $h(4)$ where $h(u) = u^4 - u^2 + u - 2$ f) $p(-2)$ where $p(t) = 3t^3 + 2t^2 - t$.

63 The Remainder Theorem

> **Reminder**

The remainder on dividing $f(x)$ by $(x - h)$ (until the remainder is just a number) is $f(h)$.

Example Find the remainder on dividing $2x^4 - 4x^2 + 3x - 2$ by $(x + 3)$.

Solution Let $2x^4 - 4x^2 + 3x - 2 = f(x)$

remainder is $f(-3)$
[Think of the number which makes the divisor zero.]

$$
\begin{array}{c|ccccc}
-3 & 2 & 0 & -4 & 3 & -2 \\
   &   & -6 & 18 & -42 & 117 \\
\hline
   & 2 & -6 & 14 & -39 & 115
\end{array}
$$

$\Rightarrow$ remainder $= 115$.

Example Find the value of k if $2x^3 + kx^2 - x - 2$ divided by $(x - 2)$ has remainder 4.

Solution Direct substitution is the obvious method.
By synthetic division, work from both ends of the table towards k.

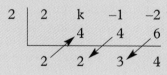

• middle = bottom – top
• divide on the down arrows

$\Rightarrow \quad k + 4 = 2 \quad \Rightarrow \quad k = -2.$

Exercise 63

1 Use the Remainder Theorem to find the remainder on dividing:

a) $x^3 + 5x^2 - 4x + 1$ by $x - 1$

b) $3x^3 + 4x^2 - 2x - 3$ by $x + 1$

c) $x^4 - 5x^2 + 4$ by $x - 2$

d) $x^5 - x^3 + 11$ by $x + 2$
e) $x^3 - 7x + 2$ by $x + 4$
f) $x^3 - x^2 - x + 5$ by $x - 5$
g) $x^4 - 13$ by $x - 3$
h) $x - x^3 - x^5$ by $x + 2$
i) $x^6 + x^5 + x^4 + x^3 + x^2 + x + 1$ by $x + 1$
j) $ax^3 + bx^2 + cx + d$ by $x - 1$.

2 Find the value of k given that $x^3 + kx^2 + 7x - 2$ has remainder 1 on division by $x - 3$.

3 Find the value of a given that $ax^4 - 3x^2 - 5$ has remainder 15 on division by $x + 2$.

4 Find the value of t given that $2x^3 + tx + 3$ has remainder 6 on division by $x + 1$.

5 Find the value of q given that $6x^3 - 2qx + 3$ has remainder 31 on division by $x - 2$.

> **Reminder**

The remainder on dividing $f(x)$ by $(ax + b)$ (until the remainder is just a number) is $f\left(-\dfrac{b}{a}\right)$.

Example   Find the remainder on dividing $3x^3 + 4x^2 + 7x + 5$ by $(2x + 1)$.

Solution   Let $f(x) = 3x^3 + 4x^2 + 7x + 5$, so remainder $= f\left(-\dfrac{1}{2}\right)$

$$
\begin{array}{r|rrrr}
-\frac{1}{2} & 3 & 4 & 7 & 5 \\
& & -\frac{3}{2} & -\frac{5}{4} & -\frac{23}{8} \\
\hline
& 3 & \frac{5}{2} & \frac{23}{4} & \frac{17}{8}
\end{array}
$$

Remainder $= \dfrac{17}{8}$.

6B Use the Remainder Theorem, but not your calculator, to find the exact value of the remainder on dividing:
a) $2x^3 + 3x^2 - 2x - 1$ by $2x - 1$
b) $3x^3 + x^2 - 6x - 5$ by $3x + 1$
c) $4x^3 + 4x^2 + 7$ by $2x + 1$
d) $5x^3 + 3x^2 + 8x + 1$ by $5x - 2$
e) $6x^4 + 3x^3 - 5x^2 + 3$ by $2x + 3$
f) $6x^3 - x^2 + 4x - 5$ by $3x - 2$.

64 The Division Algorithm

> **Reminder**

An Algorithm is a process or set of rules to be followed in calculations.

Example   Obtain the division algorithm for:

a) 21 divided by 4 (remainder r, $0 \leqslant r < 4$)
b) $x^3 + 5x^2 - 4x + 1$ divided by $(x - 1)$ $\Big\{$ divisors have degree 1,
c) $6x^3 + 7x^2 + 4x + 5$ divided by $(2x + 1)$.   remainders are numbers

Solution   a) By inspection $21 = 4 \times 5 + 1$. (divisor × quotient + remainder)

b)
$$
\begin{array}{r|rrrr}
1 & 1 & 5 & -4 & 1 \\
  &   & 1 & 6 & 2 \\
\hline
  & 1 & 6 & 2 & 3
\end{array}
$$

$\Rightarrow x^3 + 5x^2 - 4x + 1 = (x - 1)(x^2 + 6x + 2) + 3.$

(Note how the coefficients in the quotient appear in the bottom row of the synthetic division, followed by the remainder of course.)

c)
$$
\begin{array}{r|rrrr}
-\frac{1}{2} & 6 & 7 & 4 & 5 \\
  &   & -3 & -2 & -1 \\
\hline
  & 6 & 4 & 2 & 4
\end{array}
$$

$$\Rightarrow 6x^3 + 7x^2 + 4x + 5 = \left(x + \frac{1}{2}\right)(6x^2 + 4x + 2) + 4$$
$$= (2x + 1)(3x^2 + 2x + 1) + 4.$$

Note the extra step required here:
double the first bracket and halve the second.

Exercise 64

1 Obtain the division algorithm for
  a) $23 \div 4$ b) $111 \div 7$ c) $1000 \div 9$ d) $191 \div 32$.

2 Use synthetic division to obtain the division algorithm for
  a) $(x^3 + 2x^2 + 3x - 1) \div (x - 2)$ b) $(3x^3 + 4x^2 + 5x - 7) \div (x + 1)$
  c) $(x^3 + x^2 - 2x - 3) \div (x + 2)$ d) $(x^4 + x^3 - x^2 + x - 2) \div (x + 3)$
  e) $(x^3 - 5) \div (x + 1)$ f) $(x^4 - x^2 + 2) \div (x - 2)$
  g) $(2x^3 + x^2 + 3x - 3) \div (2x - 1)$ h) $(3x^3 + 5x^2 - 4x - 9) \div (3x + 2)$
  i) $(6x^4 - 3x^3 + 5x^2 + 2x - 3) \div (2x + 1)$ j) $(25x^4 - x^2 + 5) \div (5x + 1)$.

65 Factorising Polynomials

> **Reminder**

Example   Factorise $x^3 - 3x^2 - 4x + 12$.

Solution   The method starts off with finding a linear factor by trial and error, making use of the fact that dividing by a factor gives remainder zero. [Some text books elevate this notion to the level of 'The Factor Theorem'.]
You only need to try factors of the constant term.*

Let $f(x) = x^3 - 3x^2 - 4x + 12$

By direct substitution and inspection: *By synthetic division:*

$f(1) = 1 - 3 - 4 + 12 \neq 0$

± 1 do not give zero remainder

$f(-1) = -1 - 3 + 4 + 12 \neq 0$

$f(2) = 8 - 12 - 8 + 12 = 0$

2	1	-3	-4	12
		2	-2	-12
	1	-1	-6	0

$\Rightarrow f(x) = (x - 2)(x^2 - x - 6)$**

$\Rightarrow f(x) = (x - 2)(x + 2)(x - 3).$

$\Rightarrow f(x) = (x - 2)(x^2 - x - 6)$

$\Rightarrow f(x) = (x - 2)(x + 2)(x - 3).$

*This statement has to be expanded to include examples where the leading coefficient is not 1. The numbers to be tried might all turn out to be fractions, but the numerator still has to be a factor of the constant term and the denominator a factor of the leading coefficient.

**To obtain the quadratic factor by inspection:

to ensure x^3 when you expand the brackets again, start the second bracket with x^2

to ensure $-3x^2$, you already have $-2x^2$, $[-2 \times x^2]$, and so need a further $-x^2$, hence the second term must be $-x$

to ensure $-4x$, you already have $2x$, $[(-2) \times (-x)]$, and so need a further $-6x$, hence the last term must be -6.

As a check, notice that this also gives 12 for the constant term.

Note: The quadratic factor may not factorise. If so, do not just make a statement to that effect. Prove it by examining the discriminant.).

Exercise 65

1 Factorise each of these cubic polynomials into three linear factors:
   a) $x^3 - 2x^2 - x + 2$ b) $x^3 - x^2 - 4x + 4$
   c) $x^3 - 7x + 6$ d) $x^3 - 4x^2 + x + 6$
   e) $x^3 + 3x^2 - 10x - 24$ f) $6x^3 - x^2 - 4x - 1$
   g) $6x^3 - 17x^2 - 4x + 3$ h) $2x^3 + 5x^2 - 28x - 15$
   i) $2u^3 - 3u^2 - 39u + 20$ j) $30t^3 + 17t^2 - 3t - 2$.

2 Show that $(x - 1)^2$ is a factor of $x^3 + x^2 - 5x + 3$.

3 Show that $(x + 2)^2$ is a factor of $x^3 + 3x^2 - 4$.

4 Factorise fully:
   a) $x^3 + 3x^2 + x - 5$ b) $x^3 + 5x^2 + 9x + 6$.

5 Find the value of p if $x^3 - 2x^2 + px + 6$ is divisible by $(x + 2)$.

6 Find the value of k if $x^3 + kx^2 - x - 4$ is divisible by $(x + 4)$.

7 Find the values of a if $x^3 + 5x^2 + ax - 6a^2$ is divisible by $(x - 2)$.

8B Find the values of a and b if $(x - 3)$ and $(x + 5)$ are both factors of $x^3 + ax^2 + bx - 15$.

9B Find the values of p and q if $x^2 - 4$ is a factor of $f(x) = x^3 + px^2 + qx - 12$. Hence show that $f(x)$ is also divisible by $(x + 3)$.

10B Find the values of a and b for which $g(x) = 2x^3 + x^2 + ax + b$ is divisible by $(x - 2)$ and $(x + 3)$, and hence factorise $g(x)$ completely.

▸ Reminder

Example

Factorise $x^4 - 2x^3 + 4x^2 - 6x + 3$.

Solution

The method consists of finding a linear factor by trial and error. The other factor will then be cubic and can be factorised as above.

Let $x^4 - 2x^3 + 4x^2 - 6x + 3 = f(x)$:

1	1	−2	4	−6	3	
		1	−1	3	−3	
1	1	−1	3	−3	0	$\Rightarrow f(x) = (x - 1)(x^3 - x^2 + 3x - 3)$
		1	0	3		$= (x - 1)g(x)$.
	1	0	3	0		$\Rightarrow g(x) = (x-1)(x^2 + 3)$.

hence $x^4 - 2x^3 + 4x^2 - 6x + 3 = (x - 1)^2(x^2 + 3)$.

11B Factorise:

a) $x^4 - 5x^2 + 4$

b) $x^4 - 4x^3 + 3x^2 + 4x - 4$

c) $x^4 - 9x^2 - 4x + 12$

d) $x^4 + x^3 - 29x^2 - 9x + 180$

e) $36x^4 + 36x^3 + 5x^2 - 4x - 1$.

12B Factorise the polynomial in question 11(a) without using the remainder theorem.

13B Factorise $x^5 - x^4 - 5x^3 + 5x^2 + 4x - 4$ fully.

66 Solving Polynomial Equations

> **Reminder**

Example   Solve $x^3 - 5x^2 + 9x - 5 = 0$.

Solution

$$
\begin{array}{c|cccc}
1 & 1 & -5 & 9 & -5 \\
  &   & 1 & -4 & 5 \\
\hline
  & 1 & -4 & 5 & 0
\end{array}
$$

$\Rightarrow (x - 1)(x^2 - 4x + 5) = 0$.

For $x^2 - 4x + 5$, $\Delta = 16 - 20 < 0 \Rightarrow$ no real roots.

Hence this equation has only one real root, namely $x = 1$.

Exercise 66

1 Show that $(x - 1)$ is a factor of $f(x) = x^3 - 8x^2 - x + 8$, and hence solve $f(x) = 0$.

2 Solve

a) $x^3 + 2x^2 - x - 2 = 0$

b) $x^3 - 3x^2 - 4x + 12 = 0$

c) $x^3 + 2x^2 - 5x - 6 = 0$

d) $x^3 - 3x^2 - 10x + 24 = 0$

e) $6x^3 - 5x^2 - 2x + 1 = 0$

f) $6x^3 + 17x^2 - 15x - 36 = 0$

g) $x^4 - 6x^3 + 13x^2 - 12x + 4 = 0$

h) $x^4 + 2x^3 - 13x^2 - 14x + 24 = 0$

i) $x^3 - 6x^2 + 15x - 14 = 0$

j) $2x^3 - 3x^2 + 3x + 8 = 0$.

3 Show that $x = \frac{1}{3}$ is a root of the equation $6x^3 - 17x^2 - 31x + 12 = 0$, and hence find all the roots of the equation.

4 Find the value of a if $(x - 4)$ is a factor of $p(x) = 2x^3 - 5x^2 + ax - 20$, and hence show that $p(x) = 0$ has only one solution.

5 Find the equation of the tangent to the curve $y = x^3 - 2x + 1$ at the point $(-1, 2)$. Find also where this tangent intersects the curve again.

6 Find the equation of the tangent to the curve $y = x^3 - 3x^2 + 5$ at the point where $x = 3$. Find also where this tangent intersects the curve again.

67 Approximate Roots

> **Reminder**

Example   Show that the equation $x^3 - 2x^2 + 4x - 5 = 0$ has a root between 0 and 3 and find it correct to 3 decimal places.

Solution   Every polynomial has a continuous graph, so that if there is a change of sign in the value of the polynomial, there must be a root in between.

Let $x^3 - 2x^2 + 4x - 5 = f(x)$.

$\therefore f(0) = -5 < 0$

and $f(3) = 27 - 18 + 12 - 5 = 16 > 0$

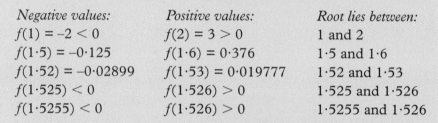

Hence there is a root between 0 and 3.

Negative values:	*Positive values:*	*Root lies between:*
$f(1) = -2 < 0$	$f(2) = 3 > 0$	1 and 2
$f(1{\cdot}5) = -0{\cdot}125$	$f(1{\cdot}6) = 0{\cdot}376$	1·5 and 1·6
$f(1{\cdot}52) = -0{\cdot}02899$	$f(1{\cdot}53) = 0{\cdot}019777$	1·52 and 1·53
$f(1{\cdot}525) < 0$	$f(1{\cdot}526) > 0$	1·525 and 1·526
$f(1{\cdot}5255) < 0$	$f(1{\cdot}526) > 0$	1·5255 and 1·526

Hence $x = 1{\cdot}526$ (to 3 decimal places)

Note. These values should be obtained from your calculator using the programming facility or the table function. Not all the values found have been shown, but provide the minimum to explain the solution.

It is left as an interesting exercise to the reader to prove that this is the only root of this equation. [Hint: consider where the function is increasing and decreasing.]

Exercise 67

1 Show that the equation $x^3 - x - 1 = 0$ has a root between 1 and 2, and find it correct to 1 decimal place.

2 Show that the equation $x^3 + x + 1 = 0$ has a root between -1 and 0, and find it correct to 1 decimal place.

3 Show that the equation $2x^3 - 3x + 2 = 0$ has a root between -2 and -1, and find it correct to 2 decimal places.

4 Show that the equation $3x^3 - 2x^2 - 4 = 0$ has a root between 1 and 2, and find it correct to 2 decimal places.

5 Find all three roots of the equation $2x^3 - 4x - 1 = 0$, each correct to 3 decimal places.

6 Find all three roots of the equation $x^3 - 4x^2 + 2x + 2 = 0$, each correct to 3 decimal places.

7 The line with equation $y = x + 1$ intersects the curve with equation $y = 2x^3 - 4x - 3$ between $x = 1$ and $x = 2$. Find the x-coordinate of this point correct to 2 decimal places.

8 The line with equation $y = 7x - 4$ intersects the curve with equation $y = x^3 + 4x - 3$ in three points. Find their x-coordinates correct to 2 decimal places.

68 Finding the Equation of a Cubic Function from its Graph

> **Reminder**

Example

Find the equation of the cubic curve shown:

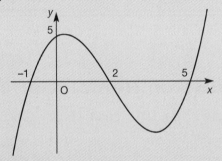

Solution

Roots at -1, 2 and 5 $\Rightarrow y = k(x + 1)(x - 2)(x - 5)$

$y = 5$ when $x = 0$ $\Rightarrow 5 = k(1)(-2)(-5)$ $\Rightarrow k = \dfrac{1}{2}$.

Hence $y = \dfrac{1}{2}(x + 1)(x - 2)(x - 5) = \dfrac{1}{2}(x + 1)(x^2 - 7x + 10)$

$= \dfrac{1}{2}(x^3 - 6x^2 + 3x + 10)$.

Exercise 68

1 Find the equation of each of these cubic curves:

a)

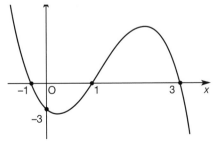

b)

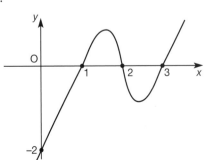

c)
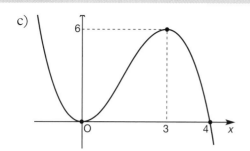

d)
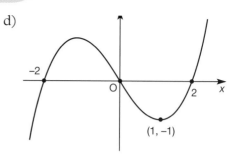

e)
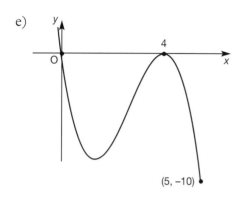

f)
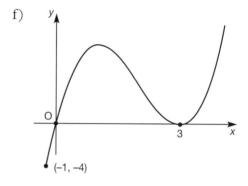

69 TOPIC TEST on Remainder Theorem

⏱ Allow 45 minutes for this test (Non-Calculator)

1 Given $f(x) = 2x^3 - 4x^2 + 3x + 5$, write down
  a) the degree of the polynominal $f(x)$
  b) the coefficient of x^2
  c) the value of (i) $f(0)$ (ii) $f(-1)$.

2 Find the remainder on dividing:
  a) $x^3 + x^2 - 2x - 1$ by $x - 2$
  b) $x^3 - x - 2$ by $x + 3$
  c) $x^{101} - 1$ by $x + 1$.

3 Is $(x - 4)$ a factor of $2x^3 - 3x^2 - 4x - 32$?

4 For what value of k is $(x+2)$ a factor of $2x^3 + 3x^2 + kx - 4$?

5 Prove that $(x - 3)$ is a factor of $f(x) = x^3 - 2x^2 - 5x + 6$ and hence factorise $f(x)$ completely.

6 a) Show that the equation of the tangent to the curve $y = x^3 - x^2$ at the point where $x = -1$ is $y = 5x + 3$.
  b) Find the coordinates of the point where this tangent intersects the curve again.

INTEGRATION

70 Integration as Anti-differentiation

The integral of ax^n is $\dfrac{ax^{n+1}}{n+1} + c$, n $\neq -1$

Example

Integrate with respect to x

a) $8x^3$

b) $\dfrac{1}{2\sqrt{x}}$

c) $\dfrac{(x+1)^2}{\sqrt{x}}$

Solution

Since integration is the inverse process to differentiation, the only real test of whether you have integrated an expression correctly is if your answer can be differentiated to give the original expression.

To differentiate, we multiply by the index and reduce the index by 1, so to undo this, we increase the index by 1 and divide by the new index.

a) $f'(x) = 8x^3 \Rightarrow f(x) = 8\left(\dfrac{x^{3+1}}{4}\right) + c = 2x^4 + c.$

(Check: $\dfrac{d}{dx}(2x^4 + c) = 8x^3$. The derivative of any constant c is zero. c is called the (arbitrary) constant of integration.)

b) $f'(x) = \dfrac{1}{2\sqrt{x}} = \dfrac{1}{2}x^{-\frac{1}{2}} \Rightarrow f(x) = \dfrac{1}{2}\dfrac{x^{\frac{1}{2}}}{\frac{1}{2}} + c = \sqrt{x} + c.$

(Note that $f'(x) \neq 2x^{-\frac{1}{2}}$; $2x^{-\frac{1}{2}} = \dfrac{2}{\sqrt{x}}$ *take care here*.)

c) $f'(x) = \dfrac{(x+1)^2}{\sqrt{x}} = \dfrac{x^2 + 2x + 1}{x^{\frac{1}{2}}} = x^{\frac{3}{2}} + 2x^{\frac{1}{2}} + x^{-\frac{1}{2}}$

[You must arrange $f'(x)$ as a string of terms of the form ax^p, i.e. an expression must be in the same form prior to integration as it needs to be for differentiation.]

$\Rightarrow f(x) = \dfrac{x^{\frac{5}{2}}}{\frac{5}{2}} + 2\dfrac{x^{\frac{3}{2}}}{\frac{3}{2}} + \dfrac{x^{\frac{1}{2}}}{\frac{1}{2}} + c = \dfrac{2}{5}x^{\frac{5}{2}} + \dfrac{4}{3}x^{\frac{3}{2}} + 2x^{\frac{1}{2}} + c.$

> **Reminder** continued

Example

Find the equation of the curve which passes through the point $(1, 2)$ and for which the gradient at the point (x, y) is given by $(x^2 + 3)$.

Solution

This example illustrates evaluating the constant of integration.

The derived function gives the value of the gradient at each point.

So $\dfrac{dy}{dx} = x^2 + 3 \quad \Rightarrow \quad y = \dfrac{x^3}{3} + 3x + c.$

This equation represents a family of cubic curves, which can be seen on your graphic calculator screen, by choosing $c = 0, \pm 1, \pm 2$ etc.

We wish to choose the particular curve which passes through $(1, 2)$.

Substituting $x = 1$ and $y = 2$ into this equation gives

$2 = \dfrac{1}{3} + 3 + c \quad \Rightarrow \quad c = -\dfrac{4}{3},$ hence $y = \dfrac{1}{3}x^3 + 3x - \dfrac{4}{3}$

or $3y = x^3 + 9x - 4.$

Exercise 70

1 Integrate with respect to x:

a) x^4 b) x^5 c) $5x^3$ d) $4x^{11}$

e) 13 f) $5x + 1$ g) $x^{\frac{1}{2}}$ h) $x^{\frac{2}{3}}$

i) $4x^{-5}$ j) $x^{-\frac{4}{3}}$ k) $3x^2 - 2$ l) $7x^2 + 2x$

m) $\dfrac{3}{x^4}$ n) $\dfrac{1}{x^3}$ o) $\dfrac{2}{x^2}$ p) $\dfrac{2}{x^{\frac{1}{3}}}$

q) $2 - \dfrac{5}{x^2}$ r) $\dfrac{1}{\sqrt{x}}$ s) $4 - \dfrac{3}{x^3}$ t) $\dfrac{4}{x^2} + \dfrac{x^2}{4}.$

2 Find $f(x)$ where $f'(x)$ is given by:

a) $3x + 1$ b) $2x^2 + 5x + 4$ c) $14 - 10x$ d) $(2x + 3)^2$

e) $x(x - 1)$ f) $\sqrt{x}(x + 1)$ g) $(x - 1)(x - 2)$ h) $x(2x + 5)$

i) $(x + 2)^2$ j) $\dfrac{x^5 - 3x^2}{x}$ k) $(3x - 4)^2$ l) $(x + 5)(x - 6)$

m) $\sqrt{x}(3x - 1)$ n) $(4 + x\sqrt{x})^2$ o) $x^{\frac{1}{3}}(x + 2x^{\frac{1}{2}})$ p) $\dfrac{(x + 1)^2}{x^4}$

q) $\dfrac{x - 3x^2}{\sqrt{x}}$ r) $\dfrac{\sqrt{x} + 2}{x^2}$ s) $x^{-\frac{1}{2}}(1 - x)^2$ t) $\dfrac{3 + 5x}{x\sqrt{x}}.$

3 Find $f(x)$ in each case given that:

a) $f'(x) = 5x^4$ and $f(0) = 1$ b) $f'(x) = 9x^2$ and $f(1) = 5$

c) $f'(x) = 2x + 3$ and $f(2) = 10$ d) $f'(x) = (x + 1)^2$ and $f(3) = 15$

e) $f'(x) = \sqrt{x}$ and $f(9) = 20$ f) $f'(x) = \dfrac{1}{\sqrt{x}}$ and $f(4) = 10$

g) $f'(x) = 3(x^2 - \dfrac{1}{x^2})$ and $f(1) = 3$ h) $f'(x) = x + \sqrt{x}$ and $f(4) = 8$.

4 Find the equation of the curve which has the given derived function and which passes through the given point:

a) $\dfrac{dy}{dx} = 3$ A(4, 0)   b) $\dfrac{dy}{dx} = 1 - x$ B(1, 1)

c) $\dfrac{dy}{dx} = 5x$ C(0, 0)   d) $\dfrac{dy}{dx} = 2x - 3$ D(2, 2)

e) $f'(x) = 3x^2 - 8x$ E(1, 2)   f) $f'(x) = 6x^2 - 4x + 3$ F(1, −3)

g) $\dfrac{df}{dx} = 2x(3x - 1)$ G(−1, 0)   h) $\dfrac{df}{dx} = 1 - \dfrac{1}{x^2}$ H(1, 4).

5 For a certain curve $y' = 3x^2 - 2x$. If $y = -7$ when $x = -2$, find y when $x = -1$.

6 For a certain curve $\dfrac{dy}{dx} = 5x^{\frac{2}{3}} + \dfrac{3}{x^{\frac{2}{3}}}$. If $y = 6$ when $x = 1$, find the value of y when $x = 8$.

7 For a certain curve $f'(x) = 3x^2 - 6x + 4$. If the curve passes through the point (2,5), show that it also passes through the point (3,13).

8 For a certain curve $\dfrac{df}{dx} = 6 - 2x$. If the maximum value of f is 0, find the equation of the curve.

9 For each given velocity-time relationship, establish the appropriate displacement-time relationship for the rectilinear motion, subject to the conditions given.
$\left[\text{Remember that } v = \dfrac{ds}{dt}.\right]$

a) $v = 3 + \dfrac{1}{t^2}$ $s = 2$ when $t = 1$ b) $v = 3t^2 - 4$ $s = 0$ when $t = 0$

c) $v = 5 - 4t$ $s = 6$ when $t = 0$ d) $v = 10(4t - 1)$ $s = 67$ when $t = 2$

e) $v = (t - 2)^2$ $s = 5$ when $t = 3$ f) $v = 6t^2 + 8t - 1$ $s = 10$ when $t = 1$

g) $v = 9(2 + 3t^2)^2$ $s = 0$ when $t = 0$ h) $v = 5t^2 - \dfrac{3}{t^2}$ $s = 6$ when $t = 3$

10 If the acceleration-time relationship for a particle moving in a straight line is $a = 6(t - 1)$, and $s = 0$ and $v = 0$ when $t = 0$, find the position of the particle and its velocity when $t = 2$.
$\left[\text{Remember that } a = \dfrac{dv}{dt}.\right]$

11 If the acceleration of a particle moving in a straight line is given by $a = 36t^2 - 30t$, find s in terms of t, given that $v = 2$ and $s = -5$ when $t = 0$.

12 The acceleration of a particle moving in a straight line is given by $a = 12\left(t^2 - \dfrac{1}{t^4}\right)$. If $s = 0$ and $v = 0$ when $t = 1$, find the displacement when $t = 2$.

71 Integral Notation & Definite Integrals

> **Reminder**

Example   Find $\int(2x^3 + 4x + 3)dx$.

Solution   This is the same as asking, if $y' = 2x^3 + 4x + 3$, find y.

So $\int(2x^3 + 4x + 3)dx = 2\frac{x^4}{4} + 4\frac{x^2}{2} + 3x + c = \frac{1}{2}x^4 + 2x^2 + 3x + c.$

This is an **indefinite** integral. It is a function of x and involves an arbitrary constant of integration.

Example   Evaluate $\displaystyle\int_1^4 \frac{1}{x\sqrt{x}}dx.$

Solution $\displaystyle\int_1^4 \frac{1}{x\sqrt{x}}dx = \int_1^4 \frac{1}{x^{\frac{3}{2}}} dx = \int_1^4 x^{-\frac{3}{2}} dx = \left[\frac{x^{-\frac{1}{2}}}{-\frac{1}{2}}\right]_1^4 = -2\left[\frac{1}{\sqrt{x}}\right]_1^4 = -2\left[\frac{1}{2} - 1\right] = 1.$

This is a **definite** integral. It is a number. x is a 'dummy' variable.

$\displaystyle\int_1^4 \frac{1}{t\sqrt{t}} dt$ has exactly the same value.

Exercise 71

Find the following integrals:

1 $\int(3x^2 + 4x + 5)\,dx$

2 $\int(x^5 + 3)\,dx$

3 $\int 2x^{\frac{-1}{2}}\,dx$

4 $\int(7x - 1)\,dx$

5 $\int(2x^3 - 11)\,dx$

6 $\int(3x^{\frac{1}{2}} - x^{\frac{-1}{2}})\,dx$

7 $\int\left(4x^{\frac{2}{3}} + x^{\frac{1}{4}}\right)dx$

8 $\int(x^2 - 1)^2\,dx$

9 $\int x(x - 1)(x + 1)\,dx$

10 $\int(2 - 3x)^2\,dx$

11 $\int\left(x^{\frac{1}{2}} + 1\right)\left(x^{\frac{1}{3}} - 1\right)dx$

12 $\int x^{\frac{1}{2}}(2x^2 + 3)\,dx$

13 $\int\left(\frac{2}{\sqrt{x}} + \frac{\sqrt{x}}{2}\right)dx$

14 $\int(\sqrt{x} - 1)^2\,dx$

15 $\int 3x\left(2x - \frac{5}{x}\right)dx$

16 $\int x^{\frac{1}{2}}(3x^2 + 1)\,dx$

17 $\int x^2(1 - x)^2\,dx$

18 $\int\left(\frac{x^2 + 3x}{x}\right)dx$

19 $\int\left(\frac{x + 3x^2}{\sqrt{x}}\right)dx$

20 $\int\left(\frac{x^{\frac{1}{2}} + x^{\frac{1}{3}}}{2x}\right)dx$

21 $\int\frac{(1 - x^2)^2}{x^2}\,dx$

Evaluate the following integrals:

22 $\int_0^3 5x\,dx$

23 $\int_1^2 9x^2\,dx$

24 $\int_{-1}^1 2x^3\,dx$

25 $\int_0^3 (5x + 8)\,dx$

26 $\int_0^1 \sqrt{x}\,dx$

27 $\int_4^9 \frac{1}{\sqrt{x}}\,dx$

28 $\int_3^6 (9 - x)\,dx$

29 $\int_0^2 (2x^2 + 3x - 1)\,dx$

30 $\int_{-2}^2 (3x^2 + 4x^3)\,dx$

31 $\int_0^4 (x - 2)^2\,dx$

32 $\int_0^1 r(r^2 - 2)\,dr$

33 $\int_0^1 (t^3 + 1)^2\,dt$

34 $\int_1^4 (\sqrt{y} - 1)^2\,dy$

35 $\int_{-1}^2 \left(z^2 - \frac{1}{z^2}\right)\,dz$

36 $\int_0^2 (1 - 2v)(2v + 3)\,dv$

37 $\int_0^1 x(x - 1)(x - 2)\,dx$

38 $\int_0^4 x(x - 4)\,dx$

39 $\int_0^{\frac{2\pi}{3}} du$

40 $\int_{\frac{-\pi}{2}}^{\frac{\pi}{2}} dx$

41 $\int_{-2}^{-1} w\,dw$

72 Area Under a Curve

> **Reminder**

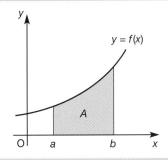

$$A = \int_a^b f(x)\,dx$$

Example   Calculate the area bounded by the curve with equation

$y = \frac{1}{6}(x + 2)(x - 3)^2$, the x-axis, $x = -1$ and $x = 1$.

Solution   We need a rough sketch of what this area looks like first.

$y = 0 \quad \Rightarrow \quad x = -2, 3, 3$

$x = 0 \quad \Rightarrow \quad y = 3.$

Hence curve has the appearance shown

We must also expand the brackets before
we can integrate.
So,

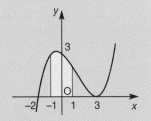

$y = \frac{1}{6}(x + 2)(x - 3)^2 = \frac{1}{6}(x + 2)(x^2 - 6x + 9) = \frac{1}{6}(x^3 - 4x^2 - 3x + 18).$

> ▸ **Reminder** continued

$$\text{Thus area} = \int_{-1}^{1} \frac{1}{6}\left(x^3 - 4x^2 - 3x + 18\right)dx = \frac{1}{6}\left[\frac{x^4}{4} - \frac{4x^3}{3} - \frac{3x^2}{2} + 18x\right]_{-1}^{1}$$

$$= \frac{1}{6}\left\{\left[\frac{1^4}{4} - \frac{4 \times 1^3}{3} - \frac{3 \times 1^2}{2} + 18 \times 1\right] - \left[\frac{(-1)^4}{4} - \frac{4(-1)^3}{3} - \frac{3(-1)^2}{2} + 18(-1)\right]\right\}$$

$$= \frac{1}{6}\left\{\frac{0}{4} - \frac{8}{3} - \frac{0}{2} + 36\right\} = \frac{108 - 8}{6 \times 3} = \frac{50}{9} \text{ units}^2.$$

Exercise 72

1 By sketching a curve and shading the area under it appropriately, illustrate the areas represented by:

a) $\int_{0}^{4} x\,dx$

b) $\int_{1}^{3} (x + 2)\,dx$

c) $\int_{-2}^{2} (2x + 5)\,dx$

d) $\int_{1}^{3} x^2\,dx$

e) $\int_{-3}^{3} x^2\,dx$

f) $\int_{0}^{2} x^3\,dx$

g) $\int_{0}^{\frac{\pi}{2}} \sin x\,dx$

h) $\int_{\frac{-\pi}{2}}^{\frac{\pi}{2}} \cos x\,dx.$

2 Write down the integral, but do not evaluate it, which represents each shaded area shown:

a)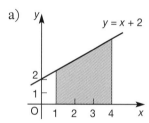

b)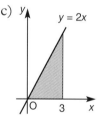

c)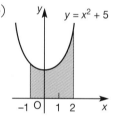

d)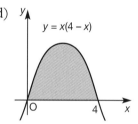

3 Find the area of each shaded region shown:

a)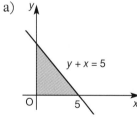

b)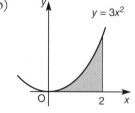

c)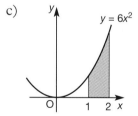

d)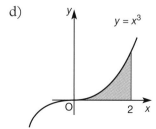

e)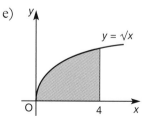

f)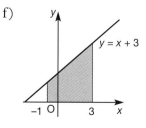

g)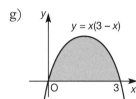

h)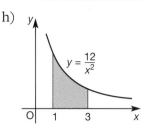

4 Find the area under each curve between the given ordinates:

a) $y = x^2$ from $x = 3$ to $x = 6$ b) $y = x^3$ from $x = 4$ to $x = 6$

c) $y = 5x$ from $x = 1$ to $x = 5$ d) $y = 3x^2 + 4$ from $x = 0$ to $x = 2$

e) $y = x^2 - 6x + 14$ from $x = 2$ to $x = 5$ f) $y = \sqrt{x}$ from $x = 0$ to $x = 9$

g) $y = \dfrac{12}{x^2}$ from $x = 3$ to $x = 4$ h) $y = \dfrac{x^2 + 2}{x^2}$ from $x = 1$ to $x = 2$

5 Calculate the area bounded by:

a) $y = 1 - x^2$ and the x-axis   b) $y = x(4 - x)$ and the x-axis

c) $y = x^2(3 - x)$ and the x-axis   d) $y = (x - 2)^2$, and the x and y-axes

e) $y = 2x^2$, $x = 1$, $x = 2$ and $y = 0$ f) $y = 3x^2$, $x = 4$ and $y = 0$

g) $y = 3x^2$, $x = -1$, $x = 3$ and $y = 0$ h) $y = 4 + x^2$, $x = -3$, $x = -1$ and $y = 0$.

6B Q is the point $(4, 64)$ and OPQR is a rectangle with P on the x-axis and R on the y-axis. Show that the curve $y = x^3$ divides this rectangle into two parts whose areas are in the ratio 3:1.

7B Show that the line $x + y = 5$ divides the area under $y = 5 + 4x - x^2$ in the first quadrant into two parts in the ratio 5:3.

73 Area below the x-axis

> **Reminder**

Example

Calculate the finite area between the parabola with equation

$y = x^2 - 4x$ and the x-axis.

Solution

A rough sketch is again required to start with.
[Familiarity with sketching parabolae will be assumed at this stage.]
Hence:

Since the area is completely

below the x-axis, $\int_0^4 (x^2 - 4x)\,dx$ is negative.

Hence the area is equal to $-\int_0^4 (x^2 - 4x)\,dx$.

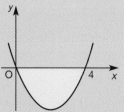

So area =

$-\int_0^4 (x^2 - 4x)\,dx = \int_0^4 (4x - x^2)\,dx = \left[2x^2 - \dfrac{x^3}{3}\right]_0^4 = \left[32 - \dfrac{64}{3}\right] - 0 = \dfrac{32}{3} \text{ units}^2.$

> **Reminder** continued

Example Calculate the total shaded area shown.

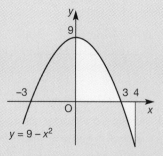

$y = 9 - x^2$

Solution The area must be calculated in two parts.

$$A_1 = \int_0^3 (9 - x^2)\,dx = \left[9x - \frac{x^3}{3}\right]_0^3$$
$$= [27 - 9] - 0 = 18.$$
$$A_2 = -\int_3^4 (9 - x^2)\,dx = \left[9x - \frac{x^3}{3}\right]_4^3$$
$$= [27 - 9] - \left[36 - \frac{64}{3}\right] = 18 - 36 + 21\tfrac{1}{3} = 3\tfrac{1}{3} \Rightarrow \text{total area} = 21\tfrac{1}{3}.$$

Note 1. Simply integrating from 0 to 4 gives $14\tfrac{2}{3}$ which is wrong.

2. The negative sign at the beginning of A_2 was dealt with differently this time. Instead of using $x^2 - 9$, the limits were interchanged.

Exercise 73

1 Calculate the area bounded by:
  a) $y = -2x$, $y = 0$ and $x = 3$
  b) $y = x^3$, $y = 0$ and $x = -2$ and $x = -1$
  c) $y = x^2 - 5x$, $y = 0$, $x = 1$ and $x = 4$
  d) $y = x(x + 4)$, $y = 0$, $x = -3$ and $x = -1$
  e) $y = x^2 - 3x$ and the x-axis
  f) $y = x^2 - 3x + 2$ and the x-axis
  g) $y = 3x(x + 2)$ and the x-axis
  h) $y = x^2 - 2x - 8$ and the x-axis.

2 Calculate the finite area between the x-axis and:
  a) $y = x^3 - 4x$
  b) $y = x(1 - x^2)$
  c) $y = x^2(x - 3)$
  d) $y = x^3(x - 1)$
  e) $y = x(x^2 - 9)$
  f) $y = x(x - 1)(x - 2)$
  g) $y = x^3 - x^2 - 6x$
  h) $y = x^3 - 6x^2 + 11x - 6$.

3 Calculate the total shaded area in each of the following diagrams:
  a)
  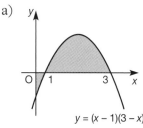

  $y = (x - 1)(3 - x)$

  b)
  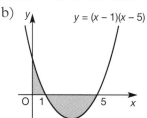

  $y = (x - 1)(x - 5)$

  c)
  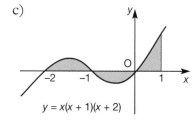

  $y = x(x + 1)(x + 2)$

4B Show that the area bounded by the x-axis and the parabola with equation
$y = 6x - x^2$ is divided into two parts in the ratio 20:7 by the ordinate $x = 4$.

5B Show that the area bounded by the x-axis and the parabola with equation
$y = 3 + 2x - x^2$ is divided into two parts in the ratio 5:27 by the y-axis.

6B Show that the y-axis divides the area bounded by the parabola with equation
$y = x^2 + x - 6$ and the x-axis into two parts in the ratio 81:44.

74 Area between two Curves

Reminder

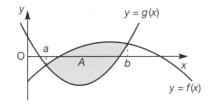

$$A = \int_a^b [f(x) - g(x)]\,dx$$

Example   Calculate the area between $y = (x - 4)^2$ and $y = x(4 - x)$.

Solution   It is useful to sketch these curves.
Their points of intersection may then be noted by inspection.
It is more usual to find the x-coordinates
of these points by solving the equation:
$g(x) = f(x)$

$\Rightarrow$ $(x - 4)^2 = x(4 - x)$

$\Rightarrow$ $x^2 - 8x + 16 = 4x - x^2$

$\Rightarrow$ $2x^2 - 12x + 16 = 0$

$\Rightarrow$ $x^2 - 6x + 8 = 0 = (x - 2)(x - 4)$

$\Rightarrow$ $x = 2, 4$ (these are the limits of the integration).

The shaded area can be thought of as the difference of these two
areas:

   minus   i.e. $\int_2^4 f(x)\,dx - \int_2^4 g(x)\,dx$

It is more usual to write $\int_2^4 [f(x) - g(x)]\,dx$,
i.e. the integral of the upper curve minus the lower curve.

> ### *Reminder* continued

It is a sloppy mathematical technique to omit the sketch, possibly subtract the curves the wrong way round and dispose of the resulting negative sign at the end. Show the examiner you know what you are talking about. There is more to mathematics than just getting the correct answer.

$$\text{Area} = \int_2^4 [(4x - x^2) - (x^2 - 8x + 16)]dx = \int_2^4 (12x - 2x^2 - 16)dx$$

$$= 2\int_2^4 (6x - x^2 - 8)\, dx = 2\left[3x^2 - \frac{x^3}{3} - 8x\right]_2^4$$

$$= 2\left[\left(48 - \frac{64}{3} - 32\right) - \left(12 - \frac{8}{3} - 16\right)\right] = 2\left[20 - \frac{56}{3}\right] = \frac{8}{3}\ \text{units}^2.$$

Example

Find the area enclosed between the curves $y = 4x - x^2$ and $y = x^2 - 2x$.

Solution

The point of this example is to illustrate that no special steps need to be taken when the area between two curves is partly above and partly below the x-axis.

for intersections,

$$4x - x^2 = x^2 - 2x$$

$$\Rightarrow\ 2x^2 - 6x = 0 = 2x(x - 3)$$

$$\Rightarrow\ x = 0, 3.$$

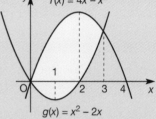

$$\text{Area} = \int_0^3 [f(x) - g(x)]dx = \int_0^3 [(4x - x^2) - (x^2 - 2x)]dx = \int_0^3 (6x - 2x^2)dx$$

$$= \left[3x^2 - \frac{2x^3}{3}\right]_0^3 = [27 - 18] - [0] = 9\ \text{units}^2.$$

Exercise 74

Calculate the area bounded by the curves given in each of questions 1 to 22:

1 $y = x, y = 2x, x = 3$

2 $y = x^2, y = x$

3 $y = x^2, y = 2x$

4 $y = x^2, y = x^3$

5 $y = x^2, y^2 = x$

6 $y = x^2, y = x^4$

7 $y = x^3, y = x$

8 $y = x^3, y = 4x$

9 $y^2 = x, y = x$

10 $y = x^2, y = 9$

11 $y = 2x^2 + 1, y = 9$

12 $y = x^2, y = x + 2$

13 $y = 4 - x, y = x(x - 4)$

14 $y = 6x - x^2, y = 2x$

15 $y = x^2 - 5x, y = x$

16 $y = 3x^2 + 5, y = 2x^3, x=1, x=2$

17 $y = 4x - x^2$, $y = x^2 - 6x$

18 $y = 9 - x^2$, $y = (x + 3)^2$

19 $y = (x + 4)^2$, $y = 24 + 2x - x^2$

20 $y = x^2 + 4$, $y = 2x^2$

21 $y = x^2 - 9$, $y = 9x^2 - x^4$

22 $y = 6x - 2 - x^2$, $y = x - 2$.

23B Calculate the area in the first quadrant bounded by the curve $y = x - x^3$.
Show that the line $4y = 3x$ divides the area into two parts in the ratio 1:15.

24B Calculate the finite area between $y + 4x + x^2 = 0$ and the x-axis.
Show that the curve $y = x^2$ divides this area into two parts in the ratio 1:3.

25B Calculate the finite area enclosed between $y = 6x^2 - x^3$ and the x-axis.
Show that this area is equal to the area enclosed between the curve and the line $y = 32$.

75 TOPIC TEST on Integration

⏱ **Allow 45 minutes for this test (Non-Calculator)**

1 Integrate
a) $x^{-\frac{1}{3}}$
b) $\dfrac{1}{2\sqrt{x}}$
c) $\dfrac{2x^3 - 3}{x^2}$

2 The gradient of a certain curve at the point (x, y) is given by $9x^2 + 8x - 1$, and the curve passes through the point $(-1, -7)$.
Find the equation of the curve.

3 Evaluate
a) $\displaystyle\int_1^2 x^{-2}\, dx$
b) $\displaystyle\int_{-1}^1 (2x + 1)^2 dx$

4 Calculate the area of the shaded region:

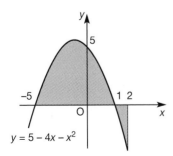

$y = 5 - 4x - x^2$

5 A blouse manufacturer requires shoulder pads, the shape of which can be described by the area between the curves with equations $2y = 11 - x^2$ and $y = 10 - x^2$.

Shoulder pad

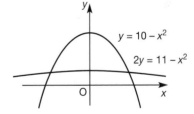

$y = 10 - x^2$

$2y = 11 - x^2$

She requires to know the area of cloth involved.
Find the coordinates of the points of intersection of these two curves, and hence find the area between them.

COMPOUND AND MULTIPLE ANGLES

76 Compound Angles

> **Reminder**

$$\sin(a + \beta) = \sin a \cos \beta + \cos a \sin \beta \qquad \cos(a + \beta) = \cos a \cos \beta - \sin a \sin \beta$$

$$\sin(a - \beta) = \sin a \cos \beta - \cos a \sin \beta \qquad \cos(a - \beta) = \cos a \cos \beta + \sin a \sin \beta$$

Example

If x and y are acute angles such that $\sin x = \dfrac{8}{17}$ and $\tan y = \dfrac{11}{60}$, find the exact value of $\cos (x - y)$.

Solution

The method is to construct right-angled triangles containing x and y using the given ratios, find the third side by Pythagoras' Theorem, in order to obtain the other trig ratios of x and y.

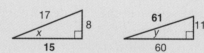

$\cos (x - y) = \cos x \cos y + \sin x \sin y.$

$$= \frac{15}{17} \times \frac{60}{61} + \frac{8}{17} \times \frac{11}{61} = \frac{900 + 88}{17 \times 61} = \frac{988}{1037}.$$

Exercise 76

1 Write down expressions for the following:

a) $\cos (a - y)$ b) $\sin (x - y)$ c) $\cos (\theta + \phi)$ d) $\sin (a + \beta)$

e) $\cos (A - B)$ f) $\cos (x + x)$ g) $\sin (A + A)$ h) $\cos (A - \theta)$

i) $\sin (2x + y)$ j) $\cos (\Sigma + \Delta)$ k) $\sin (3p - 2q)$ l) $\sin (\star + \bullet)$.

2 Simplify:

a) $\cos P \cos Q - \sin P \sin Q$ b) $\sin a \cos 2\beta - \cos a \sin 2\beta$

c) $\sin \theta \sin \phi + \cos \theta \cos \phi$ d) $\cos A \sin B + \cos B \sin A$

e) $\sin x \cos y - \cos x \sin y$ f) $\cos a \cos 2a + \sin a \sin 2a$

g) $\sin 25° \cos 10° - \cos 25° \sin 10°$ h) $\sin 80° \sin 85° - \cos 80° \cos 85°$

i) $\sin 33° \cos 57° + \cos 33° \sin 57°$ j) $\cos 200° \cos 160° - \sin 200° \sin 160°$

k) $\cos 45° \cos 15° - \sin 45° \sin 15°$ l) $\cos 16° \sin 29° + \sin 16° \cos 29°$

m) $\sin a° \cos (90 - a)° + \cos a° \sin (90 - a)°$ n) $\cos \beta \cos (\pi - \beta) - \sin \beta \sin (\pi - \beta)$

o) $\cos (x + y) \sin (y + z) - \sin (x + y) \cos (y + z)$

p) $\cos \left(\dfrac{\pi}{2} + a\right) \cos a + \sin \left(\dfrac{\pi}{2} + a\right) \sin a.$

3 Use the compound angle formulae to prove:

   a) $\sin (90° - A) = \cos A$ b) $\cos (90° - A) = \sin A$

   c) $\sin (90° + A) = \cos A$ d) $\sin (270° - A) = - \cos A.$

4 If A and B are acute angles such that $\sin A = \dfrac{3}{5}$ and $\sin B = \dfrac{7}{25}$, show that

   $\sin (A + B) = \dfrac{4}{5}.$

5 If x and y are acute angles such that $\tan x = \dfrac{12}{5}$ and $\tan y = \dfrac{4}{3}$, find the exact values of

   a) $\cos (x - y)$ b) $\cos (x + y).$

6 If K and L are acute angles such that $\sin K = \dfrac{5}{13}$ and $\cos L = \dfrac{3}{5}$, show that

   $\sin (K + L) = \dfrac{63}{65}.$

7 If P and Q are acute angles such that $\tan P = \dfrac{3}{4}$ and $\tan Q = \dfrac{7}{24}$, find the exact values of

   a) $\sin (P + Q)$ b) $\sin (P - Q).$

8 If a and β are acute angles such that $\cos a = \dfrac{1}{\sqrt 5}$ and $\sin \beta = \dfrac{3}{5}$, show that

   $\cos (a - \beta) = \dfrac{2}{5}\sqrt 5.$

9 If θ and ϕ are acute angles such that $\tan \theta = \dfrac{3}{4}$ and $\tan \phi = \dfrac{1}{7}$, show that $\cos (\theta + \phi) = \dfrac{1}{\sqrt 2}.$

10 If R and S are acute angles such that $\cos R = \dfrac{5}{13}$ and $\sin S = \dfrac{4}{5}$, find the exact value of $\tan (R + S).$

11 If X and Y are acute angles such that $\sin X = \dfrac{3}{5}$ and $\tan Y = \dfrac{1}{7}$, show that $X + Y = \dfrac{\pi}{4}.$

12 a) By expressing $15°$ as $(45° - 30°)$, show that $\sin 15° = \dfrac{\sqrt 3 - 1}{2\sqrt 2}.$

   b) By expressing $75°$ as $(45° + 30°)$, show that $\cos 75° = \dfrac{\sqrt 3 - 1}{2\sqrt 2}.$

13 In this figure, BC = 1 = CD.

   a) Calculate the lengths of AB and AD.

   b) Use the formula for $\sin (A + B)$ with $A = a°$ and $B = 30°$

      to show that $\sqrt 3 \sin a° + \cos a° = \dfrac{4}{\sqrt 7}.$

14 In this figure, SR = 3 = QR, and PS = 5.

   a) Write down the length of PR and the size of $Q\hat{S}R$.

   b) Use the formula for $\sin (A + B)$ to show that

      $\sin x° + \cos x° = \dfrac{4\sqrt 2}{5}.$

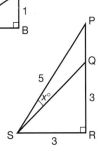

15 a and β are acute angles such that $\sin a = \dfrac{3}{5}$ and $\cos \beta = \dfrac{12}{13}$.
Evaluate exactly:

    a) $\sin(a + \beta)$ b) $\cos(a + \beta)$ c) $\tan(a + \beta)$ d) $\sin(a + a)$.

16 Angles A and B are both obtuse with $\sin A = \dfrac{4}{5}$ and $\sin B = \dfrac{7}{25}$.
Evaluate exactly:

    a) $\cos(A - B)$ b) $\sin(A + B)$ c) $\cos(A + A)$.

17 P is the point $(3, 4)$ and Q $(1, 3)$. Find the exact value of $\sin P\hat{O}Q$.

18 Prove the following :

    a) $\sin(a + \beta) + \sin(a - \beta) = 2 \sin a \cos \beta$

    b) $\cos(a - \beta) - \cos(a + \beta) = 2 \sin a \sin \beta$

    c) $\sin \theta + \sin\left(\theta + \dfrac{2\pi}{3}\right) + \sin\left(\theta + \dfrac{4\pi}{3}\right) = 0$

    d) $\cos \theta + \cos\left(\theta + \dfrac{2\pi}{3}\right) + \cos\left(\theta + \dfrac{4\pi}{3}\right) = 0$.

77 Multiple Angles

▶ Reminder

$$\sin 2a = 2\sin a \cos a \qquad \cos 2a = \cos^2 a - \sin^2 a \qquad \cos^2 a = \tfrac{1}{2}(1 + \cos 2a)$$
$$= 2\cos^2 a - 1$$
$$= 1 - 2\sin^2 a \qquad \sin^2 a = \tfrac{1}{2}(1 - \cos 2a)$$

Example

If A is an acute angle such that $\tan A = \dfrac{4}{3}$, find the exact value of $\tan 2A$.

Solution

Construct a right-angled triangle with sides 4 and 3 as appropriate.

The hypotenuse must be 5.

$$\sin 2A = 2 \sin A \cos A = 2 \times \frac{4}{5} \times \frac{3}{5} = \frac{24}{25}$$

$$\cos 2A = \cos^2 A - \sin^2 A = \left(\frac{3}{5}\right)^2 - \left(\frac{4}{5}\right)^2 = -\frac{7}{25}\star$$

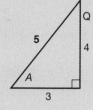

Hence $\tan 2A = \dfrac{\sin 2A}{\cos 2A} = \dfrac{\frac{24}{25}}{\frac{-7}{25}} = -\dfrac{24}{7}$.

$\star$ The negative sign is to be expected here, because $2A$ must be obtuse:

A acute and $\tan A > 1 \Rightarrow 45° < A < 90° \Rightarrow 90° < 2A < 180°$.

Exercise 77

1 Write down expressions for:

a) $\sin 2z$ b) $\cos 4Y$ c) $\sin 6Q$ d) $\cos 3A$

e) $\sin x$ f) $\cos \frac{x}{3}$ g) $\sin \frac{y}{2}$ h) $\cos x$.

2 Simplify:

a) $\cos^2 4A - \sin^2 4A$ b) $2\sin \left(\frac{x}{2}\right) \cos \left(\frac{x}{2}\right)$ c) $2 \cos 5x \sin 5x$

d) $\sin^2 \left(\frac{x}{2}\right) - \cos^2 \left(\frac{x}{2}\right)$ e) $2 \cos^2 15° - 1$ f) $\cos^2 75° - \sin^2 75°$

g) $2 \sin 15° \cos 15°$ h) $\cos^2 \frac{\pi}{12} - \sin^2 \frac{\pi}{12}$ i) $1 - 2 \sin^2 \left(\frac{\theta}{2}\right)$

j) $4 \cos^2 \left(\frac{A}{2}\right) - 2$ k) $\sin^2 x - \cos^2 x$ l) $\cos^2 22\frac{1}{2}° + \sin^2 22\frac{1}{2}°$.

3 If A is an acute angle such that $\sin A = \frac{3}{5}$, find the exact values of:

a) $\sin 2A$ b) $\cos 2A$ c) $\tan 2A$.

4 If B is an acute angle such that $\tan B = \frac{1}{2}$, find the exact values of:

a) $\sin 2B$ b) $\cos 2B$ c) $\tan 2B$.

5 If C is an acute angle such that $\tan C = 3$, find the exact values of:

a) $\sin 2C$ b) $\cos 2C$ c) $\sin 4C$.

6 If D is an acute angle such that $\sin D = \frac{2}{\sqrt{5}}$, find the exact values of:

a) $\sin 2D$ b) $\cos 2D$ c) $\tan 2D$.

7 Express:

a) $\cos 2x + 3 \cos x + 2$ as a quadratic expression in $\cos x$.

b) $1 + \sin x - \cos 2x$ as a quadratic expression in $\sin x$.

c) $\cos 2x - 4 \sin x + 3$ as a quadratic expression in $\sin x$.

d) $3 \sin^2 x + 5 \cos^2 x - 1$ in terms of $\cos 2x$.

e) $4 - 2 \sin^2 x + 6 \cos^2 x$ in terms of $\cos 2x$.

8B Prove the following :

a) $\cos 15° = \frac{1}{2}\sqrt{(2 + \sqrt{3})}$

b) $\sin 15° = \frac{1}{2}\sqrt{(2 - \sqrt{3})}$

c) θ is acute and $\cos \theta = 0.62 \quad \Rightarrow \quad \cos \frac{\theta}{2} = 0.9$

d) $\sin a = \frac{1}{3}$ and $\cos a$ is negative $\quad \Rightarrow \quad \tan 2a = \frac{-4\sqrt{2}}{7}$.

9B If A is an acute angle such that $\cos 2A = \frac{1}{4}$, show that $\cos A = \frac{\sqrt{5}}{2\sqrt{2}}$ and $\sin A = \frac{\sqrt{3}}{2\sqrt{2}}$.

10B Use $\tan \theta = \dfrac{\sin \theta}{\cos \theta}$ to prove the following:

a) $\dfrac{2 \tan x}{1 + \tan^2 x} = \sin 2x$

b) $\dfrac{1 - \tan^2 x}{1 + \tan^2 x} = \cos 2x$

c) $\dfrac{2 \tan x}{1 - \tan^2 x} = \tan 2x$

d) $\tan x + \tan 3x = \dfrac{\sin 4x}{\cos x \cos 3x}$

e) $\tan x - \tan y = \dfrac{\sin (x - y)}{\cos x \cos y}$.

11B Express $3A$ as $2A + A$ to prove the following:

a) $\sin 3A = 3 \sin A - 4 \sin^3 A$

b) $\cos 3A = 4 \cos^3 A - 3 \cos A$.

12B The two equal sides of an isosceles triangle have length x and the two equal angles measure y radians.

Prove that the area of the triangle is given by $\dfrac{1}{2} x^2 \sin 2y$.

13B Find the coordinates of the points of intersection of the graphs of $f(x) = \cos 2x$ and $g(x) = \sin x$, for $0 \leqslant x \leqslant 2\pi$.

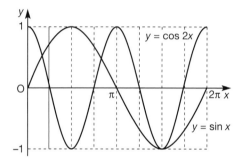

14B Find the coordinates of the points A and B, the points of intersection of the graphs of $f(x) = \cos 2x°$ and $g(x) = 1 - \cos x°$.

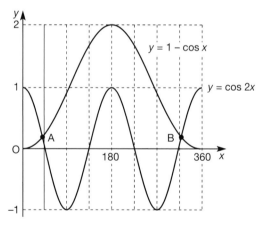

15B Sketch the graphs of $f(x) = \sin 2x°$ and $g(x) = 1 - \cos x°$ for $0 \leqslant x \leqslant 360$ in order to illustrate that there is only one solution of the equation $f(x) = g(x)$ for $0 < x < 360$. Find (numerically) this solution, correct to the nearest degree.

[Hint: consider the equation $f(x) - g(x) = 0$.]

78 Equations involving Multiple Angles

Reminder

Example   Solve $3 \cos 2x° + \cos x° + 1 = 0$ for $0 \leq x \leq 360$.

Solution   Choose the correct replacement for $\cos 2x°$. (Because there is a $\cos x°$ term in the equation, $2 \cos^2 x° - 1$ is the appropriate substitution.)

$3 \cos 2x° + \cos x° + 1 = 0$
$\Rightarrow 3(2 \cos^2 x° - 1) + \cos x° + 1 = 0$
$\Rightarrow 6 \cos^2 x° + \cos x° - 2 = 0$ ** recognise that this is quadratic
$\Rightarrow (2 \cos x° - 1)(3 \cos x° + 2) = 0$
$\Rightarrow \cos x° = \dfrac{1}{2}, -\dfrac{2}{3}$.
$\Rightarrow x = 60, 300, 131·8, 228·2 \Rightarrow x = 60, 131·8, 228·2, 300.$

Example   Solve $\sin 2x - 2 \sin x = 0$ for $0 \leqslant x \leqslant 2\pi$.

Solution

$\sin 2x - 2 \sin x = 0$	**OR** $\sin 2x = 2 \sin x$
$\Rightarrow 2\sin x \cos x - 2 \sin x = 0$	$\Rightarrow 2 \sin x \cos x = 2 \sin x$
$\Rightarrow 2 \sin x (\cos x - 1) = 0$	we can only divide both sides
$\Rightarrow \sin x = 0$ or $\cos x = 1$	by $2 \sin x$ if $2 \sin x \neq 0$, so
$\Rightarrow x = 0, \pi, 2\pi$ or $x = 0, 2\pi$	$\sin x = 0$ or $\cos x = 1$ (which
$\Rightarrow x = 0, \pi, 2\pi.$	gives the same solutions).

Note: the second method carries a health warning. You are very likely to omit the solutions for $\sin x = 0$.

Exercise 78

Solve equations $1 - 16$ for $0 \leqslant x \leqslant 360$, giving exact solutions for equations $1 - 11$.

 1 $\sin 2x° + \sin x° = 0$ **2** $\sin 2x° - \cos x° = 0$

 3 $\cos 2x° - \cos x° = 0$ **4** $\cos 2x° - \sin x° = 0$

 5 $\cos 2x° - 3 \cos x° + 2 = 0$ **6** $\cos 2x° - 3 \sin x° - 1 = 0$

 7 $\cos 2x° - 4 \sin x° + 5 = 0$ **8** $\cos 2x° - \sin x° - 1 = 0$

 9 $\cos 2x° + 5 \cos x° - 2 = 0$ **10** $\cos 2x° + 3 \cos x° + 2 = 0$

11 $\cos 2x° + \cos x° = 0$ **12** $5 \cos 2x° - \cos x° + 2 = 0$

13 $3 \sin 2x° + 5 \cos x° = 0$ **14** $6 \cos 2x° - 5 \cos x° + 4 = 0$

15 $4 \cos 2x° - 2 \sin x° - 1 = 0$ **16** $5 \cos 2x° + 7 \sin x° + 7 = 0$

Solve equations 17 – 20 exactly for $0 \leqslant \theta \leqslant 2\pi$.

17 $\sin 2\theta - \sin \theta = 0$

18 $\sin 2\theta + \cos \theta = 0$

19 $\cos 2\theta + \cos \theta = 0$

20 $\cos 2\theta + \sin \theta = 0$

Solve equations 21 – 26 exactly for $0 \leqslant x \leqslant 360$. [This is revision; see section 44]
[You do not need the multiple angle formulae for these equations.]

21 $\cos 2x° = -\dfrac{\sqrt{3}}{2}$

22 $\tan 2x = -\dfrac{1}{\sqrt{3}}$

23 $\sin \dfrac{x}{2} = \dfrac{1}{2}$

24 $\sin \dfrac{3x}{2} = -\dfrac{1}{\sqrt{2}}$

25 $\cos 3x = \dfrac{1}{\sqrt{2}}$

26 $\tan 4x = -1$.

Solve equations 27 – 30 for $0 \leqslant A \leqslant 360$.

27 $3 \sin 2A° = 2 \sin A°$

28 $3 \cos 2A° = 2 + \cos A°$

29B $6 \cos A° + 5 \sin \dfrac{A°}{2} = 3$

30B $10 \sin^2 2A° - \sin 4A° = 2 - \cos^2 2A°$.

[If stuck, consult the answers for a hint.]

79 TOPIC TEST on Compound and Multiple Angles

🕐 Allow 45 minutes for this test

1 Simplify
a) $\cos^2 5u + \sin^2 5u$
b) $\dfrac{\sin 3v}{\cos 3v}$
c) $1 - \cos^2 2w$
d) $\cos^2 3r - \sin^2 3r$
e) $1 - 2 \sin^2 4s$
f) $2 \cos^2 2t - 1$
g) $\cos 3P \cos 2Q - \sin 3P \sin 2Q$
h) $\sin 2x \cos 3y + \cos 2x \sin 3y$
i) $\dfrac{1}{2}(1 + \cos 2x)$.

2 Given that $\tan a = \dfrac{8}{15}$ and $\cos \beta = \dfrac{24}{25}$ where a and β are acute angles, find the *EXACT* value of $\sin (a - \beta)$.

3 Given that $\sin x = \dfrac{5}{13}$, find the *EXACT* values of
a) $\cos x$
b) $\cos 2x$
c) $\sin 2x$.

4 Solve $\sin 2x = 2 \cos x$ for $0 < x < 2\pi$.

5 Solve $3 \cos 2x° + \cos x° + 2 = 0$ for $0 \leqslant x \leqslant 360$.

Calculator required 🖩 *for question 5.*

THE CIRCLE

80 The Circle Centre the Origin, Radius R

> **Reminder**

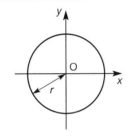

$$x^2 + y^2 = r^2$$

Example

a) Find the equation of the circle with centre at the origin and passing through the point P $(-1, 4)$.

b) Find the equation of the tangent to the circle at P.

c) Show that the chord with equation $3y = 5x - 17$ subtends a right angle at the centre of the circle.

Solution

a) $r^2 = OP^2 = (-1)^2 + 4^2 = 17$
   ∴ the equation of the circle is
   $x^2 + y^2 = 17$.

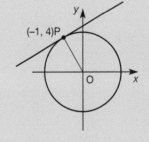

b) $m_{OP} = \dfrac{4 - 0}{-1 - 0} = -4$

   $\Rightarrow m_{tgt} = \dfrac{1}{4}$

   $\Rightarrow$ tangent is $y - 4 = \dfrac{1}{4}(x + 1)$

   i.e. $4y - 16 = x + 1$ or $4y = x + 17$.

c) The method is to make x or y the subject of the linear equation and substitute into the circle equation:

   $3y = 5x - 17 \Rightarrow y = \dfrac{5x - 17}{3}$

   Substituting gives $x^2 + \left(\dfrac{5x - 17}{3}\right)^2 = 17$.

   Now multiply through by 9

   to give $9x^2 + (5x - 17)^2 = 9 \times 17$
   $\Rightarrow 9x^2 + 25x^2 - 170x + 17^2 = 9 \times 17$
   $\Rightarrow 34x^2 - 170x + 17(17 - 9) = 0$.

115

> **▶ Reminder** continued

Now divide through by (17×2)

$\Rightarrow x^2 - 5x + 4 = 0$

$\Rightarrow (x - 4)(x - 1) = 0 \quad \Rightarrow \quad x = 1, 4$

$\Rightarrow \quad y = -4, 1$ (from the linear equation).

So the ends of the chord are K $(1, -4)$ and L $(4, 1)$,

$\Rightarrow m_{OK} = \frac{-4}{1} = -4 \quad$ and $\quad m_{OL} = \frac{1}{4}$

$\Rightarrow m_{OK} \times m_{OL} = -4 \times \frac{1}{4} = -1$

$\Rightarrow$ OK and OL are perpendicular

i.e. the chord (KL) subtends a right angle at O the centre of the circle.

Exercise 80

1 Write down the equation of the circle with centre at the origin and radius
   a) 1   b) 2   c) 7.

2 Write down the equation of the circle with centre at the origin and passing through the point
   a) $(3, 4)$ b) $(1, 1)$ c) $(-2, 3)$.

3 Write down the length of the radius of the circle with equation
   a) $x^2 + y^2 = 16$ b) $x^2 + y^2 = 9$ c) $x^2 + y^2 = 25$.

4 Find the length of the diameter of the circle with equation $x^2 + y^2 = 36$.

5 Find the length of the circumference of the circle with equation $x^2 + y^2 = 100$.

6 Find the area of the circle with equation $x^2 + y^2 = 81$.

7 Find the equation of the circle with centre at the origin and with radius twice that of the circle with equation   a) $x^2 + y^2 = 4$ b) $x^2 + y^2 = 8$.

8 Find
   a) the length of OB
   b) the equation of the circle, (and for revision)
   c) the size of $A\hat{O}B$ in radians
   d) the length of the arc AB
   e) the area of the sector AOB.

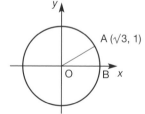

9 a) Make a sketch of the circle with equation $x^2 + y^2 = 9$
   b) Shade vertically the region defined by $x^2 + y^2 < 9$
   c) Shade horizontally the region defined by $x^2 + y^2 > 9$.

10 Does the point A $(3, 6)$ lie inside, outside, or on the circle with equation $x^2 + y^2 = 50$?

11 a) Sketch the lines with equations $x = 5$, $x = -5$, $y = 7$, $y = -7$.
   b) These four lines define a rectangle. Find the equation of the circle which passes through the vertices of this rectangle.

12 a) Sketch the lines with equations $x = \pm 2$, $y = \pm 2$.
   b) These four lines are tangents to a circle. Find the equation of the circle.

13 Find two possible values of t if the point $(6, t)$ lies on the circle with equation $x^2 + y^2 = 100$.

14 Find two possible values of k if the point $(k, 12)$ lies on the circle with equation $x^2 + y^2 = 169$.

15 AB is a diameter of the circle with equation $x^2 + y^2 = 625$.
   Write down the coordinates of B if A is the point
   a) $(15, 20)$ b) $(24, 7)$ c) $(-20, 15)$ d) $(-7, -24)$.

16 a) Show that the point A $(4, 1)$ lies on the circle with equation $x^2 + y^2 = 17$.
   b) Find (i)   the gradient of the radius OA
             (ii) the gradient of the tangent at A
             (iii) the equation of the tangent at A.

17 Find the equation of the tangent at
   a) $(3, 7)$ to the circle with equation $x^2 + y^2 = 58$
   b) $(-2, 3)$ to the circle with equation $x^2 + y^2 = 13$
   c) $(4, -2)$ to the circle with equation $x^2 + y^2 = 20$.

18 [Revision] Show that the line with equation $y = 2x + 5$ is a tangent to the circle with equation $x^2 + y^2 = 5$, stating the coordinates of the point of intersection.
   [Reminder : substitute the linear equation into the circle equation.]

19 Find the coordinates of the points of intersection of the line with equation $y = 7x - 25$ and the circle with equation $x^2 + y^2 = 25$, and hence find the length of the chord.

20 Show that the line with equation $y = x + 5$ does not intersect the circle with equation $x^2 + y^2 = 10$.

21 a) Find the equation of the tangent to the circle with equation $9x^2 + 9y^2 = 25$ at the point A $\left(-1, \dfrac{4}{3}\right)$.
   b) Show that the line with equation $12x + 9y = 25$ is also a tangent to the circle in part (a), stating the coordinates of the point of contact.

22 Show that the chord with equation $2x + y = 5$, of the circle with equation $x^2 + y^2 = 10$ subtends a right angle at the centre of the circle.

81 The Circle centre (*a*, *b*), radius *r*

> **Reminder**

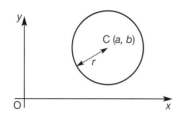

$$(x - a)^2 + (y - b)^2 = r^2$$

Example

a) Find the equation of the circle with centre P $(-7, -2)$ and passing through A $(-2, -5)$.

b) AB is a diameter of this circle. Find the equation of the tangent at B.

c) Show that this circle touches externally the circle with centre Q and equation $(x - 8)^2 + (y - 7)^2 = 136$, stating the coordinates of their common point.

d) Find the equation of the circle which has PQ as diameter.

Solution

a) $(x + 7)^2 + (y + 2)^2 = r^2 = (-7 + 2)^2 + (-2 + 5)^2$.
$\Rightarrow (x + 7)^2 + (y + 2)^2 = 34$.

b) From A to P is 5 left and 3 up, so P to B is the same

$\Rightarrow$ B is $(-12, 1)$

$$m_{BP} = m_{AP} = \frac{-2 + 5}{-7 + 2} = -\frac{3}{5}$$

$$\therefore m_{tgt} = \frac{5}{3}.$$

Tangent has equation $y - 1 = \frac{5}{3}(x + 12)$

$\Rightarrow 3y - 3 = 5x + 60 \Rightarrow 3y = 5x + 63$.

c) From the given equation the centre Q is $(8, 7)$ and $r_Q = \sqrt{136}$, $r_P = \sqrt{34}$ (from part (a)), $r_Q = \sqrt{136} = \sqrt{(4 \times 34)} = 2\sqrt{34}$.

The sum of the radii $= r_P + r_Q = 3\sqrt{34}$.

The distance between the centres of the circles $=$ PQ and
$PQ^2 = [8 - (-7)]^2 + [7 - (-2)]^2 = 225 + 81 = 306 = 9 \times 34$
$\Rightarrow$ PQ $= \sqrt{(9 \times 34)} = 3\sqrt{34} = r_P + r_Q$.

(i.e. the circles touch externally)

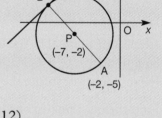

$r_Q = 2\sqrt{34} = 2 \times r_P$
$\Rightarrow$ the common point C is one third of the way along PQ.

▶ **Reminder** continued

From P to Q is 15 along and 9 up, so from P to C is 5 along and 3 up, i.e. C is (−2, 1).

d) The midpoint of PQ is M $\left(\frac{1}{2}, \frac{5}{2}\right)$

$$\Rightarrow r^2 = QM^2 = \left(8 - \frac{1}{2}\right)^2 + \left(7 - \frac{5}{2}\right)^2 = \frac{225}{4} + \frac{81}{4} = \frac{306}{4} = \frac{153}{2}.$$

So the circle has equation $\left(x - \frac{1}{2}\right)^2 + \left(y - \frac{5}{2}\right)^2 = \frac{153}{2}.$

Exercise 81

1 Write down the equation of the circle with centre:
   a) (1, 2) and radius 4   b) (2, −4) and radius 5   c) (−2, −3) and radius 7.

2 Write down the centre and radius of the circle with equation:
   a) $(x - 1)^2 + (y - 3)^2 = 4$ b) $(x + 2)^2 + (y + 5)^2 = 16$ c) $(x - 4)^2 + (y + 3)^2 = 8$.

3 Find the equation of the circle with centre:
   a) (3, 4) and passing through (7, 8)
   b) (1, −1) and passing through (2, −3)
   c) (−2, 4) and passing through (0, 6).

4 Find the equation of the circle with ends of a diameter at
   a) A (2, 5) and B (8, 3)
   b) P (0, 3) and Q (6, −1)
   c) S (−3, 4) and T (−7, −2).

5 a) Sketch the lines with equations $x = -1$, $x = 3$, $y = 2$, $y = 8$.
   b) These four lines define a rectangle. Find the equation of the circle which passes through the vertices of this rectangle.

6 a) Sketch the lines with equations $x = 2$, $x = 6$, $y = 1$, $y = 5$.
   b) These four lines are tangents to a circle. Find the equation of the circle.

7 Show that the point A (7, 5) lies on the circle with equation $(x - 3)^2 + (y + 2)^2 = 65$, and find the coordinates of the other extremity of the diameter through A.

8 Find two possible values for:
   a) k, if $(k, 2)$ lies on the circle $(x - 3)^2 + (y - 4)^2 = 20$
   b) m, if $(3, m)$ lies on the circle $(x + 5)^2 + (y - 2)^2 = 100$
   c) t, if $(t, 5)$ lies on the circle $(x - 1)^2 + (y - 2)^2 = 10$.

9 Show that each of the circles with equations $(x + 1)^2 + (y - 2)^2 = 25$ and $(x - 2)^2 + (y - 6)^2 = 25$ passes through the centre of the other.

10 Draw a quick sketch and hence find the equation of the circle which has centre:
a) $(1, 4)$ and touches the x-axis
b) $(2, 3)$ and touches the y-axis
c) on the line with equation $x + y = 10$ and touches both axes
d) $(3, 4)$ and touches the line with equation $y = -1$.

11 Draw a quick sketch and hence find the equation of the circle which passes through:
a) $(0, 2)$ and $(0, 8)$ and touches the x-axis
b) $(2, 0)$ and $(18, 0)$ and touches the y-axis
c) $(0, 0)$ and $(0, 10)$ and touches the line with equation $y = -8$ (two answers)
d) $(2, 0)$ and touches the y-axis and the line with equation $y = -1$ (two answers).

12 The circle with centre Q has equation $(x - 5)^2 + (y - 8)^2 = 9$.
PQR is a diameter of this circle parallel to the y-axis.
The circles with centres P and R touch the circle with centre
Q at R and P respectively.
Find the equations of the larger circles.

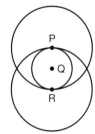

13 In this sketch of a road roller, the diameter of the front
wheel is half that of the rear wheel.
The distance AB is 35 units.
The equation of the rear wheel is
$(x - 12)^2 + (y - 13)^2 = 100$.
Find the equation of AB and the equation of the
front wheel.

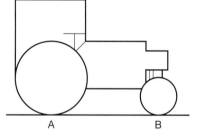

14 a) Show that the point A $(1, 2)$ lies on the circle with equation $(x + 3)^2 + (y + 2)^2 = 32$.
b) Find (i) the gradient of the radius through A
(ii) the gradient of the tangent at A
(iii) the equation of the tangent at A.

15 Find the equation of the tangent at the point:
a) A $(1, 2)$, to the circle with equation $(x - 3)^2 + (y + 4)^2 = 40$
b) P $(3, -2)$, to the circle with equation $(x + 5)^2 + (y - 2)^2 = 80$
c) L $(-7, 3)$, to the circle with equation $(x - 3)^2 + (y + 1)^2 = 116$
d) R $(-2, -9)$, to the circle with equation $(x + 1)^2 + (y + 7)^2 = 5$.

16 Two circles have equations $(x + 2)^2 + (y + 3)^2 = 13$ and $(x - 7)^2 + (y - 3)^2 = 52$.
a) Calculate as a surd in its simplest form, the distance between their centres.
b) Show that this distance is equal to the sum of their radii, and hence state how these
circles are positioned relative to one another.

17 Prove that the line with equation $x + y = 11$ is a tangent to the circle with equation
$(x + 2)^2 + (y - 3)^2 = 50$.

18 Show that the line with equation $y = 3x - 24$ is a diameter of the circle with equation $(x - 7)^2 + (y + 3)^2 = 90$ and find the coordinates of its extremities.

19 Find the coordinates of the points of intersection of the line with equation $5x + y = 20$, and the circle with equation $(x - 1)^2 + (y - 2)^2 = 13$.

20 Show that the line with equation $5y = 2x - 26$ is a diameter of the circle with equation $(x - 3)^2 + (y + 4)^2 = 29$, and find the equation of the diameter which is perpendicular to the diameter given.

21B Show that the chord with equation $7y = x + 12$, of the circle with equation $(x + 2)^2 + (y - 5)^2 = 25$ subtends a right angle at the centre of the circle.

22B Three rollers in a printing machine can be represented by three circles with collinear centres, as shown.
The equations of the outer circles are $(x - 1)^2 + (y - 3)^2 = 225$ and $(x - 29)^2 + (y - 24)^2 = 100$.
Find the equation of the middle circle.

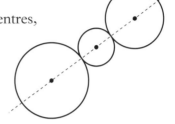

82 Finding the Centre and Radius from First Principles

> **Reminder**

Example By completing the square on x and y, investigate the locus which has equation $x^2 + y^2 - 12x - 6y + 36 = 0$.

Solution
$x^2 + y^2 - 12x - 6y + 36 = 0$
$\Rightarrow x^2 - 12x + 36 + y^2 - 6y + 9 = 36 + 9 - 36$
$\Rightarrow (x - 6)^2 + (y - 3)^2 = 9$
$\Rightarrow$ centre $(6, 3)$ and radius 3.

So the x-axis is a tangent to the circle at $(6, 0)$.

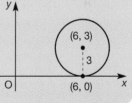

Exercise 82

By completing the square on both x and y, find the centre and radius of each circle whose equation is given below, and make a rough sketch in each case, noting any particular points of interest, e.g. the circle passes through the origin, the centre lies on an axis, an axis is a tangent etc.

1 $x^2 + y^2 - 4x - 6y - 12 = 0$

2 $x^2 + y^2 + 6x + 4y + 12 = 0$

3 $x^2 + y^2 - 6x - 6y = 0$

4 $x^2 + y^2 - 6x + 2y + 9 = 0$

5 $x^2 + y^2 + 2x - 2y + 1 = 0$

6 $x^2 + y^2 - 8x = 0$

7 $x^2 + y^2 + 6y = 0$ 8 $x^2 + y^2 + 8x - 6y = 0$

9 $x^2 + y^2 - 2ay = 0$ 10 $x^2 + y^2 - 2ax - 2ay + a^2 = 0.$

83 The General Equation of the Circle

> **Reminder**

The equation $x^2 + y^2 + 2gx + 2fy + c = 0$ represents a circle with centre $(-g, -f)$ and radius $\sqrt{g^2 + f^2 - c}$ provided $g^2 + f^2 - c > 0.$

Example   Calculate the length of the tangent(s) from the point P $(10, -10)$ to the circle with equation $x^2 + y^2 + 20x - 10y + 76 = 0.$

Solution   Centre is $(-10, 5)$,

Radius $= \sqrt{(100 + 25 - 76)} = \sqrt{49} = 7.$

$PT^2 = PC^2 - CT^2$
$= [(10+10)^2+(5+10)^2]-[7]^2$
$= 400 + 225 - 49$
$= 576$

$\Rightarrow PT = 24.$

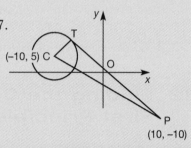

Exercise 83

1 State whether or not each of the following equations represents a circle, and find the coordinates of the centre and the length of the radius of those which are circles.
   a) $x^2 + y^2 + 6x + 8y - 11 = 0$ b) $x^2 + 2xy + y^2 - 4x + 6y + 3 = 0$
   c) $x^2 + y^2 = 9$ d) $x^2 + y^2 + 2x - 2y + 3 = 0$
   e) $x + y = 3$ f) $y = 3x^2 + 4x + 5$
   g) $x^2 - y^2 = 9$ h) $x^2 + y^2 - 10x + 8y = 0.$

2 Find the coordinates of the centre and the length of the radius of the circle with equation:
   a) $x^2 + y^2 - 2x - 4y - 4 = 0$ b) $x^2 + y^2 + 6x - 8y - 24 = 0$
   c) $x^2 + y^2 + 6x - 10y - 2 = 0$ d) $4x^2 + 4y^2 - 4x + 4y + 1 = 0$
   e) $x^2 + y^2 + 4x - 2y + 1 = 0$ f) $x^2 + y^2 + 10x - 14y + 65 = 0$
   g) $x^2 + y^2 + 2ax + 2ay + a^2 = 0$ h) $x^2 + y^2 - 2ax - 4ay - 4a^2 = 0.$

3 Determine whether each of the points A $(1, 2)$ B $(3, 4)$ C $(5, 6)$ lies inside, on, or outside the circle with equation $x^2 + y^2 - 4x - 4y + 3 = 0.$

4 Show that the point P $(5, 7)$ lies on the circle with equation $x^2 + y^2 - 6x - 10y + 26 = 0$, and find the coordinates of the point Q which is diametrically opposite to P.

5 Find two possible values of t if the point $(5, t)$ lies on the circle with equation $x^2 + y^2 - 4x - 6y = 0$.

6 Find two possible values of k if the point $(k, 4)$ lies on the circle with equation $x^2 + y^2 - 4x + 2y - 29 = 0$.

7 Two circles have equations $x^2 + y^2 + 2x - 6y - 31 = 0$, and $x^2 + y^2 - 8x - 14y + 24 = 0$. Show that each passes through the centre of the other.

8 Two circles have equations $x^2 + y^2 + 4x + 6y + 8 = 0$, and $x^2 + y^2 - 12x - 2y - 8 = 0$. Show that these circles touch externally.

9 Two circles have equations $x^2 + y^2 - 4x - 10y + 16 = 0$, and $x^2 + y^2 + 8x - 2y - 100 = 0$. Prove that the smaller circle touches the larger one internally.

10 Find the equation of the tangent at:
   a) $(2, 5)$ to the circle with equation $x^2 + y^2 + 6x - 8y - 1 = 0$
   b) $(-3, 6)$ to the circle with equation $x^2 + y^2 - 8x + 10y - 129 = 0$
   c) $(-2, 5)$ to the circle with equation $x^2 + y^2 - 14x + 6y - 87 = 0$.

11 Show that the line with equation $y = x + 7$ is a tangent to the circle with equation $x^2 + y^2 - 4x + 2y - 45 = 0$, stating the coordinates of the point of contact.

12 a) Show that the chord, with equation $y = 2x - 1$ of the circle with equation $x^2 + y^2 - 2x - 12y + 27 = 0$ subtends a right angle at the centre of the circle.
   b) Calculate the length of the chord.

13 Prove that the line with equation $y = x$ does not intersect the circle with equation $x^2 + y^2 - 10x + 2y + 10 = 0$.

14 a) Find the equation of the tangent to the circle with equation $x^2 + y^2 + 8x - 10y + 36 = 0$ at the point A $(-5, 7)$.
   b) Show that the line with equation $y = 2x + 8$ is also a tangent to the circle in part (a), stating the coordinates of the point of contact.

15 a) Show that the points A $(7, 3)$ and B $(-2, 2)$ lie on the circle with equation $x^2 + y^2 - 6x + 4y - 28 = 0$.
   b) Find the coordinates of C and D which are diametrically opposite A and B.
   c) Prove analytically that ABCD is a rectangle.

16 Show that the line with equation $9y = 4x + 47$ is a diameter of the circle with equation $x^2 + y^2 + 10x - 6y - 63 = 0$, and find the equation of the diameter which is perpendicular to the one given.

17 Show that the line with equation $2y = x - 3$ is a diameter of the circle with equation $x^2 + y^2 - 2x + 2y - 43 = 0$, and find the coordinates of its extremities.

18 A circle has equation $x^2 + y^2 - 48x - 30y + 176 = 0$. Calculate the length of the chord of this circle which is part of the
   a) x-axis   b) y-axis.

19 a) Sketch the tangents from the point A $(7, 1)$ to the circle with equation
$x^2 + y^2 = 25$.

b) State the radius of the circle and calculate the length of OA. (O is the origin.)

c) Hence calculate the length of the tangents from A.

20B Calculate the length of the tangents from the point B $(8, 3)$ to the circle with
equation $x^2 + y^2 + 4x + 14y + 49 = 0$.

21B a) Find the equation of the tangent at the point C $(-1, 2)$ to the circle with equation
$x^2 + y^2 = 5$.

b) Show that this tangent is also a tangent to the circle with equation
$x^2 + y^2 - 28x - 4y + 155 = 0$, and calculate the length of this common tangent.

22B Find the equations of the tangents with gradient 2 to the circle with equation
$x^2 + y^2 - 4x - 6y - 7 = 0$, stating the coordinates of the points of contact.

▶ Reminder

Example

Find the equation of the circle passing through the points K $(-1, -3)$
L $(7, 1)$ and M $(8, -6)$ and note anything particular about the circle.

Solution

a) *The geometric method*
(i.e. find where the perpendicular bisectors of two of the sides
meet)
Midpoint of KL is $(3, -1)$,

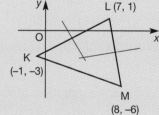

$$m_{KL} = \frac{1 + 3}{7 + 1} = \frac{1}{2} \Rightarrow m_{\perp} = -2,$$

So perpendicular bisector of KL
has equation

$$y + 1 = -2(x - 3) \Rightarrow y = 5 - 2x \quad ......(1)$$

Midpoint of LM is $\left(\frac{15}{2}, -\frac{5}{2}\right)$

$$m_{LM} = \frac{1 + 6}{7 - 8} = -7 \Rightarrow m_{\perp} = \frac{1}{7},$$

So perpendicular bisector of KL has equation $y + \frac{5}{2} = \frac{1}{7}(x - \frac{15}{2})$

i.e. $7y + \frac{35}{2} = x - \frac{15}{2} \Rightarrow 7y = x - 25 \quad ....(2)$

Solving equations (1) and (2) gives $7(5 - 2x) = x - 25$

$\Rightarrow 60 = 15x \Rightarrow x = 4 \Rightarrow y = -3 \Rightarrow$ centre $(4, -3)$
$\Rightarrow$ (radius)$^2 = (7 - 4)^2 + (1 + 3)^2 = 25$
$\Rightarrow (x - 4)^2 + (y + 3)^2 = 25$ or $x^2 + y^2 - 8x + 6y = 0$

(which passes through the origin).

Reminder continued

b) *algebraic method*

(i.e. substitute the coordinates of the three points into the general equation of the circle and solve the system of three equations in three unknowns)

$(-1, -3) \Rightarrow 1 + 9 - 2g - 6f + c = 0$ ....(1)
$(7, 1) \quad \Rightarrow 49 + 1 + 14g + 2f + c = 0$ ......(2)
$(8, -6) \quad \Rightarrow 64 + 36 + 16g - 12f + c = 0$ .....(3)

$(2) - (1) \Rightarrow 40 + 16g + 8f = 0 \Rightarrow 5 + 2g + f = 0$ ....(4)
$(3) - (2) \Rightarrow 50 + 2g - 14f = 0 \Rightarrow 50 + 2g - 14f = 0$ ....(5)
$(5) - (4) \Rightarrow 45 - 15f = 0 \Rightarrow f = 3$

Hence from (4), $g = -4$ and from (1), $c = -[10 + 8 - 18] = 0$

Hence $x^2 + y^2 - 8x + 6y = 0$ (which passes through the origin).

23B a) (i) Sketch the triangle with vertices A $(-6, -1)$ B $(8, 5)$ and C $(8, -1)$.
(ii) Note that triangle ABC is right-angled at C, so the centre of the circle passing through A, B and C is the midpoint of AB. Hence find the equation of the circle through ABC.
b) Similarly find the equation of the circle through O $(0, 0)$ P $(0, 8)$ and Q $(6, 0)$.
c) Similarly find the equation of the circle through K $(1, 1)$, L $(5, 7)$ and M $(8, 5)$.

24B a) (i) Sketch triangle ABC with vertices A $(7, 13)$ B $(3, 5)$ and C $(15, 5)$.
(ii) Write down the equation of the perpendicular bisector of BC.
(iii) Find the equation of the perpendicular bisector of AB.
(iv) Find the coordinates of D, the point of intersection of these two bisectors.
(v) Note that D is equidistant from A, B and C, so must be the circumcentre. Hence find the equation of the circumcircle of triangle ABC.
b) Similarly, find the equation of the circle passing through K $(5, 5)$ L $(2, 2)$ and M $(6, 2)$.

25B By finding the point of intersection of the perpendicular bisectors of two chords, find the equation of the circle passing through the points:
a) S $(-4, -1)$ T $(4, 3)$ U $(5, -4)$ b) F $(-3, 1)$ G $(2, 6)$ H $(5, 5)$.

26B Use the general equation of the circle to obtain three equations to find the equation of the circle passing through the points:
a) A $(-3, -3)$ B $(-1, 1)$ C $(6, -6)$ b) D $(4, 2)$ E $(6, -2)$ F $(-3, -5)$.

84 TOPIC TEST on The Circle

⏱ Allow 45 minutes for this test (Non-Calculator)

1 Write down the equation of the circle with centre
   a) the origin, passing through A(4, 5)
   b) A(4, 5), passing through the origin
   c) B(7, −1) and touching the x-axis.

2 Find the equation of the circle which has points P(3, −2) and Q(9, 8) as the ends of a diameter.

3 Find the equation of the tangent to the circle $x^2 + y^2 − 8x − 6y + 12 = 0$ at the point (7, 1) on its circumference.

4 Show that the circles
   $(x + 2)^2 + (y + 4)^2 = 20$ and $(x − 4)^2 + (y + 1)^2 = 5$ touch each other.

5 Is the line with equation $2x − y − 25 = 0$ a tangent to the circle with equation $x^2 + y^2 − 12x + 6y + 25 = 0$?

6 The diagram shows a small snow plough. The equation of the circumference of the front wheel is $x^2 + y^2 − 12x − 4y + 36 = 0$. The radius of the rear wheel is twice that of the front wheel.

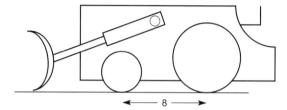

The distance between the points where the wheels touch the ground is 8 units. Find the equation of the circumference of the rear wheel.

PRACTICE UNIT TESTS

85 Practice Unit Test on Unit 2

(Calculator may be used)

marks

1 Show that $(x - 1)$ is a factor of $f(x) = x^3 - 2x^2 - 5x + 6$, and hence express $f(x)$ in its fully factorised form. (4)

2 Use the discriminant to determine the nature of the roots of the equation $x^2 - 10x + 25 = 0$. (2)

3 Find $\int \dfrac{3}{x^4}\, dx$. (3)

4 Calculate the area of the shaded region shown in the diagram. (5)

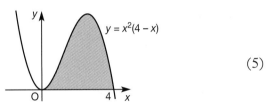

$y = x^2(4 - x)$

5 Write down, but do not evaluate, an integral to represent the shaded area enclosed between the line with equation $y = x + 3$ and the parabola with equation $y = x^2 - 3x + 3$. (3)

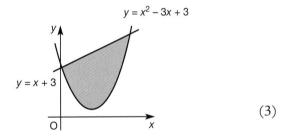

$y = x^2 - 3x + 3$

$y = x + 3$

6 Solve $2 \cos 2x + 1 = 0$ for $0 \leqslant x \leqslant \pi$. (3)

7 The acute angles $a°$ and $b°$ are contained in right-angled triangles, as shown.

   a) Write down the values of $\cos a°$ and $\sin b°$. (2)
   b) By expanding $\cos (a + b)°$, show that the exact value of $\cos (a + b)°$ is $0·6$. (2)

8 a) Express $\sin x° \cos 25° - \cos x° \sin 25°$ in the form $\sin (A - B)°$. (1)
   b) Hence solve $\sin x° \cos 25° - \cos x° \sin 25° = \dfrac{2}{3}$ for $0 \leqslant x \leqslant 180$. (4)

9 a) Write down the equation of the circle with centre $(3, -4)$ and radius 2 units. (2)
   b) Find the coordinates of the centre and the length of the radius of the circle with equation $x^2 + y^2 - 6x + 8y - 11 = 0$. (3)

10 Show that the straight line with equation $y = 11 - 2x$ is a tangent to the circle with equation $x^2 + y^2 - 6x + 4 = 0$. (5)

11 The point P $(1, -3)$ lies on a circle with centre $(5, -1)$ as shown in the diagram. Find the equation of the tangent at P.

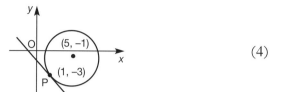

(4)

86 Revision (Non-calculator) Tests on Unit 2

TEST 1

🕐 Allow 45 minutes for this test

1 Factorise fully : $6x^3 - x^2 - 11x + 6$.

2 Is the line $y = 2x$ a tangent to the circle with equation $x^2 + y^2 - 8x - 6y + 20 = 0$?

3 Solve: $\cos 2\theta + \cos \theta + 1 = 0$ for $0 \le \theta \le 2\pi$.

4 This is the logo for the next Tiddley-Winks World Cup.

a) Relative to suitable axes, the equation of the head is $x^2 + y^2 - 8x - 10y + 16 = 0$, and that of the rim of the hat is $x - 2y + 11 = 0$. Find the coordinates of A and B, the points of intersection of the head and the hat.

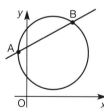

b) If C, the bottom of the nose, is diametrically opposite A, find the coordinates of C.

5 Find the exact value of $\cos(\alpha + \beta)$ in this diagram.

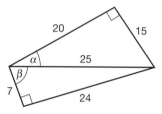

6 The large field in the diagram (between the railway and the river) is susceptible to flooding. In order to introduce effective flood prevention measures, the farmer needs to know the area of the field.

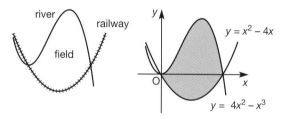

Relative to suitable axes, the river course can be represented by $y = 4x^2 - x^3$ and the railway line by $y = x^2 - 4x$. Calculate the area of the field, represented by the shaded region in the second diagram.

TEST 2

⏱ Allow 45 minutes for this test

1 Find the two values of k for which the equation $kx^2 + (k-2)x + k = 0$ has equal roots.

2 a) Given that x is an acute angle such that $\tan x = \frac{3}{2}$, find the exact value of
    (i) $\sin 2x$
    (ii) $\cos 2x$.
   b) Hence prove that
      $$\sin\left(2x + \frac{\pi}{3}\right) = \frac{12 - 5\sqrt{3}}{26}.$$

3 Prove that the circles with equations $x^2 + y^2 - 18x - 20y + 81 = 0$ and $x^2 + y^2 + 6x - 2y - 15 = 0$ touch each other externally.

4 a) Use differentiation to show that the equation of the tangent at $(-2, 2)$ on the curve with equation $y = x^3 + 2x^2 - 3x - 4$ is $y = x + 4$.
   b) Find where this tangent meets the curve again.
   c) Calculate the finite area enclosed between the curve and the tangent.

VECTORS

87 Components and Addition

[Sections 87–92 deal with plane vectors (i.e. vectors in two dimensions)]

> ▶ **Reminder**

This vector has components $\begin{pmatrix} 4 \\ 3 \end{pmatrix}$.

4 is the x-component
3 is the y-component

$\left[\text{Do not confuse with a gradient of } \dfrac{3}{4}. \right]$

Notation: Vectors can be labelled by a single letter, which is printed in bold type (e.g. **u**) or is written in manuscript with an underline (straight or wavy) (e.g. <u>u</u> or <u>u</u>).

Alternatively a directed line segment can be used, e.g. $\overrightarrow{AB}$

Example Sketch the vectors $\overrightarrow{AB} + \overrightarrow{CD}$ and
u + **v** and state the components of
all six vectors.

Solution To add the vectors, lay them nose to tail and follow the arrows.

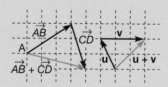

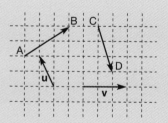

$$\overrightarrow{AB} = \begin{pmatrix} 3 \\ 2 \end{pmatrix} \qquad \overrightarrow{CD} = \begin{pmatrix} 1 \\ -3 \end{pmatrix} \qquad \overrightarrow{AB} + \overrightarrow{CD} = \begin{pmatrix} 4 \\ -1 \end{pmatrix}$$

$$\mathbf{u} = \begin{pmatrix} -1 \\ 2 \end{pmatrix} \qquad \mathbf{v} = \begin{pmatrix} 3 \\ 0 \end{pmatrix} \qquad \mathbf{u} + \mathbf{v} = \begin{pmatrix} 2 \\ 2 \end{pmatrix}$$

Note: to find the sum in component terms, add the x-components
and add the y-components.

Exercise 87

1 In this diagram, it can be seen that

$\vec{AB} = \begin{pmatrix} 3 \\ 4 \end{pmatrix}$. Write down the components of every

other vector in the diagram.

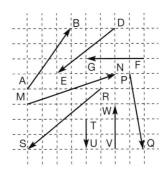

2 On squared paper, draw and label (as in question 1) representatives of the vectors:

$$\vec{AB} = \begin{pmatrix} -3 \\ 1 \end{pmatrix} \quad \vec{CD} = \begin{pmatrix} 4 \\ 7 \end{pmatrix} \quad \vec{EF} = \begin{pmatrix} -4 \\ -5 \end{pmatrix} \quad \vec{QR} = \begin{pmatrix} 3 \\ -4 \end{pmatrix} \quad \vec{KL} = \begin{pmatrix} -7 \\ 0 \end{pmatrix} \quad \vec{PT} = \begin{pmatrix} 0 \\ 5 \end{pmatrix}.$$

3 The vectors **p, q, r, s, t** are defined in the diagram below.

Make additional sketches on squared paper illustrating each of the following:

a) **p + q**　　　　　　　b) **q + r**　　　　　　　c) **r + s**

d) **s + t**　　　　　　　e) **p + r + q**　　　　　　f) **q + r + s**.

4 a) Draw and label carefully, representatives of the following vectors:

(i) $\mathbf{u} = \begin{pmatrix} 1 \\ -2 \end{pmatrix}$　　　　(ii) $\mathbf{v} = \begin{pmatrix} -4 \\ 0 \end{pmatrix}$　　　　(iii) $\mathbf{w} = \begin{pmatrix} 2 \\ 5 \end{pmatrix}$

(iv) **u + v**　　　　　　(v) **v + w**　　　　　　(vi) **u + v + w**

b) Write down the components of your answers to parts (iv) (v) and (vi).

5 In the given diagram, find a single vector equal
to each of the following:-

a) $\vec{CD} + \vec{DA}$　　　　b) $\vec{DA} + \vec{AC}$

c) $\vec{AB} + \vec{BC}$　　　　d) $\vec{AC} + \vec{CD}$.

6 $\vec{XY}$ is a directed line segment which can be found in the given diagram.

Find the correct replacement for $\vec{XY}$ in each of these vector equations:

a) $\vec{AD} + \vec{DE} = \vec{XY}$　　　　b) $\vec{ED} + \vec{DC} = \vec{XY}$

c) $\vec{EA} + \vec{AD} = \vec{XY}$　　　　d) $\vec{AB} + \vec{XY} = \vec{AC}$

e) $\vec{BE} + \vec{XY} = \vec{BC}$　　　　f) $\vec{BE} + \vec{XY} = \vec{BD}$.

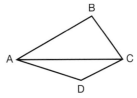

88 Subtraction of Vectors

> **Reminder**

Example Simplify $\vec{KL} - \vec{ML}$.

Solution $\vec{KL} - \vec{ML} = \vec{KL} + \vec{LM} = \vec{KM}$

Note:
(i) this depends on the fact that $(-\vec{AB}) = \vec{BA}$
(ii) this simplification can be made without reference to a sketch.

Example $\mathbf{r} = \begin{pmatrix} 4 \\ 3 \end{pmatrix}$ $\mathbf{s} = \begin{pmatrix} 2 \\ -1 \end{pmatrix}$. Illustrate $\mathbf{r} - \mathbf{s}$ on squared paper stating its components.

Solution Find $\mathbf{r} + (-\mathbf{s})$:
$(-\mathbf{s})$ is the same line segment as $\mathbf{s}$, but with the arrow reversed.

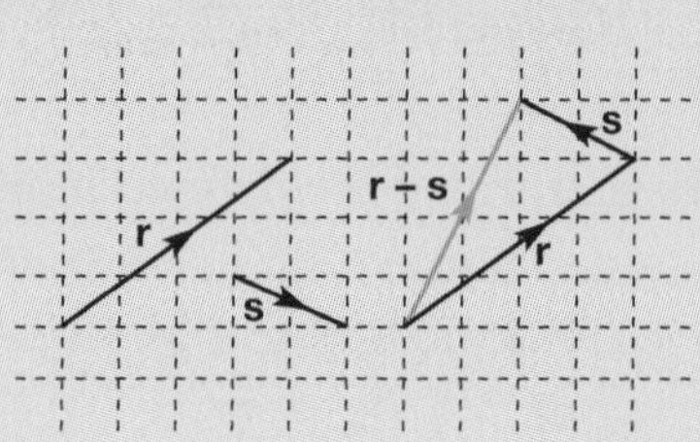

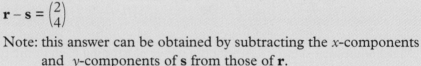

$\mathbf{r} - \mathbf{s} = \begin{pmatrix} 2 \\ 4 \end{pmatrix}$

Note: this answer can be obtained by subtracting the x-components and y-components of $\mathbf{s}$ from those of $\mathbf{r}$.

Exercise 88

1 Express each difference as a sum and simplify (as above).
  a) $\vec{AB} - \vec{CB}$ b) $\vec{BC} - \vec{AC}$ c) $\vec{CB} - \vec{AB}$ d) $\vec{CA} - \vec{BA}$
  e) $\vec{AC} - \vec{BC}$ f) $\vec{BA} - \vec{CA}$ g) $\vec{BC} - \vec{BA}$ h) $\vec{AC} - \vec{AB}$.

2 a) Draw representatives of $\mathbf{u} = \begin{pmatrix} 2 \\ 1 \end{pmatrix}$, $\mathbf{v} = \begin{pmatrix} 1 \\ -1 \end{pmatrix}$, and $\mathbf{w} = \begin{pmatrix} 2 \\ 3 \end{pmatrix}$.
  b) Hence draw representatives of $-\mathbf{u}, -\mathbf{v}, -\mathbf{w}$.
  c) Hence draw representatives of
      (i) $\mathbf{u} + (-\mathbf{v})$ (ii) $\mathbf{v} - \mathbf{w}$ (iii) $\mathbf{w} - \mathbf{u}$ (iv) $(-\mathbf{u}) + (-\mathbf{v})$.

3 Given that $\mathbf{x} = \begin{pmatrix} 1 \\ 2 \end{pmatrix}$, $\mathbf{y} = \begin{pmatrix} -3 \\ 4 \end{pmatrix}$, and $\mathbf{z} = \begin{pmatrix} 2 \\ -1 \end{pmatrix}$, write down the components of
  a) $\mathbf{x} + \mathbf{y}$ b) $\mathbf{y} + \mathbf{z}$ c) $-\mathbf{x}$ d) $-\mathbf{y}$
  e) $\mathbf{z} - \mathbf{x}$ f) $\mathbf{x} - \mathbf{y}$ g) $\mathbf{x} + \mathbf{y} + \mathbf{z}$ h) $-\mathbf{y} - \mathbf{z}$.

4 $\mathbf{x}$ is a vector which is represented in the given diagram.
Solve each vector equation for $\mathbf{x}$.
  a) $\mathbf{a} + \mathbf{x} + \mathbf{b} = 0$ b) $\mathbf{a} + \mathbf{d} + \mathbf{x} = \mathbf{c}$
  c) $\mathbf{b} + \mathbf{c} - \mathbf{e} = \mathbf{x}$ d) $\mathbf{c} - \mathbf{x} - \mathbf{d} = \mathbf{a}$

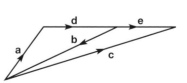

89 Scalar Multiplication

> **Reminder**

Example Illustrate **u** and 3**u** where $\mathbf{u} = \begin{pmatrix} 2 \\ -1 \end{pmatrix}$.

Solution 3**u** has the same direction and sense as **u** but has three times the magnitude.

The components of 3**u** are 3 times the components of **u**. ie $\begin{pmatrix} 6 \\ -3 \end{pmatrix}$

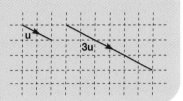

Exercise 89

1 Draw a representative of $\mathbf{u} = \begin{pmatrix} 4 \\ 2 \end{pmatrix}$ on squared paper, and hence representatives of
   a) 2**u**   b) 3**u**   c) $\frac{1}{2}\mathbf{u}$ d) –2**u**   e) $-\frac{3}{2}\mathbf{u}$.

2 A to H are consecutive points on a number line as shown:

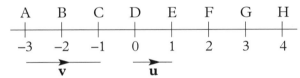

a) If $\overrightarrow{DE} = \mathbf{u}$, find three representatives of each of 2**u**, 3**u**, 4**u**, and –**u**.

b) If $\overrightarrow{AC} = \mathbf{v}$, find a directed line segment equal to each of 2**v**, 3**v**, $\frac{1}{2}\mathbf{v}$, –2**v**, and $-\frac{1}{2}\mathbf{v}$.

c) If $\overrightarrow{GD} = \mathbf{w}$, name a directed line segment equal to each of 2**w**, –**w**, –2**w**, $\frac{1}{3}\mathbf{w}$ and $-\frac{1}{3}\mathbf{w}$.

3 For $\mathbf{a} = \begin{pmatrix} 2 \\ -1 \end{pmatrix}$, $\mathbf{b} = \begin{pmatrix} 5 \\ 0 \end{pmatrix}$, and $\mathbf{c} = \begin{pmatrix} -3 \\ -4 \end{pmatrix}$, find the components of each of:
   a) **a** + **b** + **c**   b) **c** – **b**   c) **a** + **b** – **c**   d) **b** – **a**   e) **c** – **a** + **b**
   f) 2**a** + 3**b**   g) 4**c** – 3**b**   h) 2**b** – 5**a**   i) **a** – 2**b** + **c**   j) 3**c** – 2**a** – 2**b**.

90 Position Vectors and Midpoints

> **Reminder**

The position vector of a point is the vector which starts at the origin and ends at the point.

The components of the position vector are the same numbers as the coordinates of the point.

It is common practice to use **p** for the position vector of P, without further explanation.

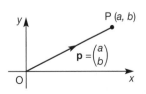

⟩ **Reminder** continued

Example

Calculate the area of triangle ABC where A B and C have position vectors

$$\mathbf{a} = \begin{pmatrix} 2 \\ 1 \end{pmatrix}, \mathbf{b} = \begin{pmatrix} 7 \\ 1 \end{pmatrix}, \text{ and } \mathbf{c} = \begin{pmatrix} 2 \\ 5 \end{pmatrix}.$$

Solution

The components of the position vectors provide the coordinates of the points.

Area of triangle ABC

$$= \frac{1}{2} \times \text{base} \times \text{height}$$

$$= \frac{1}{2}(5)(4) = 10 \text{ units}^2.$$

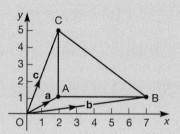

Exercise 90

1 On a single coordinate diagram, plot the points P, Q and R which have position vectors:

$\mathbf{p} = \begin{pmatrix} 5 \\ 3 \end{pmatrix}, \mathbf{q} = \begin{pmatrix} -2 \\ 1 \end{pmatrix}$ and $\mathbf{r} = \begin{pmatrix} 6 \\ -5 \end{pmatrix}$, and hence write down the components of:

a) $\overrightarrow{PQ}$
b) $\overrightarrow{QR}$
c) $\overrightarrow{PR}$
d) $\overrightarrow{PQ} + \overrightarrow{PR}$
e) $\overrightarrow{QR} + 2\overrightarrow{RP}$
f) $\overrightarrow{OP} + \frac{1}{2}\left(\overrightarrow{OQ} + \overrightarrow{OR}\right)$
g) $3\overrightarrow{OP} - 2\overrightarrow{QR}$.

2 a) Plot the points A (1, 3) and B (6, 9) and write down the components of their position vectors **a** and **b**, the components of **b** − **a**, and those of $\overrightarrow{AB}$.

b) Repeat part (a) when A is (−7, 2) and B is (5, −3).

c) Repeat part (a) when A is (−2, −2) and B is (1, 3).

d) Make a generalisation from these three special cases and prove it. [Check the answers and memorise this result.]

3 For A (3, 6) and B (4, 2), $\overrightarrow{AB} = \mathbf{b} - \mathbf{a} = \begin{pmatrix} 4 \\ 2 \end{pmatrix} - \begin{pmatrix} 3 \\ 6 \end{pmatrix} = \begin{pmatrix} 1 \\ -4 \end{pmatrix}.$

Similarly find the components of:

a) $\overrightarrow{CD}$ where C is (2, 3) and D is (5, 6)

b) $\overrightarrow{EF}$ where E is (4, 11) and F is (5, −1)

c) $\overrightarrow{HG}$ where G is (−1, 3) and H is (2, −5)

d) $\overrightarrow{LK}$ where K is (2, 7) and L is (−7, 3)

e) $\overrightarrow{MN}$ where M is (−3, 5) and N is (−2, −3).

4 A is the point (4, 3) and $\mathbf{u} = \begin{pmatrix} 18 \\ 12 \end{pmatrix}$. Write down the coordinates of B, C, D, E, F and G given that they have position vectors defined by:

$\mathbf{b} = \mathbf{a} + \frac{1}{2}\mathbf{u}$ $\mathbf{c} = \mathbf{a} - \frac{1}{2}\mathbf{u}$ $\mathbf{d} = \mathbf{a} + \frac{2}{3}\mathbf{u}$

$\mathbf{e} = \mathbf{a} - \frac{2}{3}\mathbf{u}$ $\mathbf{f} = \mathbf{a} + \frac{5}{6}\mathbf{u}$ $\mathbf{g} = 2\mathbf{a} - \frac{1}{6}\mathbf{u}$.

5 a) Plot the points A (2, 5), B (8, 9) and M where M is the midpoint of AB.
   Find the components of $\overrightarrow{AB}$, $\overrightarrow{AM}$, $\overrightarrow{OM}$ and $\frac{1}{2}(\mathbf{a} + \mathbf{b})$.

b) Repeat part (*a*) for A (−2, 5) and B (0, 9).

c) Repeat part (*a*) for A (2, 2) and B (6, 8).

d) Make a conjecture based on these three special cases and prove it.
   [Check the answers and memorise this result.]

e) Hence WRITE DOWN the components of the position vector of the midpoint of:
   (i) (−1, 3) and (5, 7)   (ii) (−4, −8) and (−2, 12)   (iii) (5, −2) and (−3, 0).

f) Hence also WRITE DOWN the coordinates of the midpoint of the line joining:
   (i) (6, 8) and (10, 12)   (ii) (−1, −3) and (7, 5)   (iii) (−3, 5) and (−1, 11).
   [Remember that you covered midpoints in section 2]

91 The Length of a Vector

> **Reminder**

$$\Rightarrow u = |\mathbf{u}| = \sqrt{a^2 + b^2}$$

It is acceptable to use a plain *u* for $|\mathbf{u}|$, provided you are fastidious about always using the underscore when you refer to a vector.

Example   Find the length of the vector $\mathbf{u} = \begin{pmatrix} 2 \\ -3 \end{pmatrix}$.

Solution   Sketch the vector and use the Theorem of Pythagoras.

Length $= \sqrt{(2)^2 + (-3)^2} = \sqrt{13}$.

Without the sketch, square the components, add them, and take the square root.

Exercise 91

1 Calculate the lengths of these vectors (leaving irrational answers as surds in their simplest form):

$$\mathbf{a} = \begin{pmatrix} -5 \\ 12 \end{pmatrix} \qquad \mathbf{b} = \begin{pmatrix} 3 \\ -4 \end{pmatrix} \qquad \mathbf{c} = \begin{pmatrix} 8 \\ -15 \end{pmatrix} \qquad \mathbf{d} = \begin{pmatrix} -6 \\ -8 \end{pmatrix} \qquad \mathbf{e} = \begin{pmatrix} 24 \\ 7 \end{pmatrix} \qquad \mathbf{f} = \begin{pmatrix} 2 \\ 2 \end{pmatrix}$$

$$\mathbf{g} = \begin{pmatrix} 3 \\ -5 \end{pmatrix} \qquad \mathbf{r} = \begin{pmatrix} 7 \\ 8 \end{pmatrix} \qquad \mathbf{s} = \begin{pmatrix} -4 \\ 11 \end{pmatrix} \qquad \mathbf{t} = \begin{pmatrix} 20 \\ 21 \end{pmatrix} \qquad \mathbf{u} = \begin{pmatrix} -3 \\ -7 \end{pmatrix} \qquad \mathbf{v} = \begin{pmatrix} a \\ b \end{pmatrix}.$$

92 Using Vectors

▶ Reminder

Example ABCD is a square with vertices A (1, 2), B (2, 2), C (2, 3) and D (1, 3). PQRS is a quadrilateral defined by $\mathbf{p} = 2\mathbf{a}$, $\mathbf{q} = 2\mathbf{b}$, $\mathbf{r} = 2\mathbf{c}$ and $\mathbf{s} = 2\mathbf{d}$. Compare the areas of PQRS and ABCD.

Solution

P (2, 4)
Q (4, 4)
R (4, 6)
S (2, 6)

ABCD has area 1
PQRS has area 4

PQRS has 4 times the area of ABCD.
[Recall areas of similar figures.]

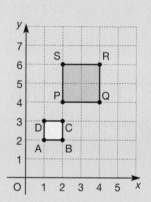

Exercise 92

1 ABCDEF is a regular hexagon with centre O.

$\overrightarrow{AB} = \mathbf{u}$, $\overrightarrow{BC} = \mathbf{v}$, $\overrightarrow{CD} = \mathbf{w}$.

Express in terms of **u**, **v**, and **w**:

$\overrightarrow{DE}$, $\overrightarrow{EF}$, $\overrightarrow{FA}$, $\overrightarrow{OC}$, $\overrightarrow{OD}$, $\overrightarrow{OE}$, $\overrightarrow{AC}$, $\overrightarrow{AD}$ and $\overrightarrow{AE}$.

Show also that $\mathbf{v} = \mathbf{u} + \mathbf{w}$.

2 ABDC is a kite with diagonals meeting at M such that AD = 3AM, as shown.

$\overrightarrow{AB} = \mathbf{u}$, $\overrightarrow{AC} = \mathbf{v}$.

Express in terms of **u** and **v**:

$\overrightarrow{BC}$, $\overrightarrow{BM}$, $\overrightarrow{AM}$, $\overrightarrow{AD}$, $\overrightarrow{BD}$ and $\overrightarrow{DC}$.

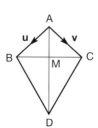

3 ABCD, EFGH is a cuboid with $\vec{AB} = \mathbf{x}$, $\vec{AD} = \mathbf{y}$ and $\vec{AE} = \mathbf{z}$.
Express in terms of $\mathbf{x}$, $\mathbf{y}$, and $\mathbf{z}$:

$\vec{AF}$, $\vec{BC}$, $\vec{FH}$, $\vec{AC}$, $\vec{EC}$, $\vec{BH}$, $\vec{FD}$ and $\vec{AG}$.

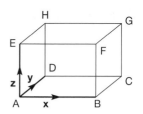

4 In triangle EAB, C and D are the midpoints of
EA and EB respectively.

Let $\vec{EA} = 2\mathbf{u}$ and $\vec{EB} = 2\mathbf{v}$.

Express in terms of $\mathbf{u}$ and $\mathbf{v}$:
$\vec{EC}$ $\vec{ED}$ $\vec{CD}$ and $\vec{AB}$.

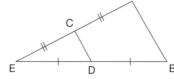

Hence make two statements about CD and AB.

5B a) Vectors provide a convenient way of finding the coordinates of a point P dividing
the line AB in the ratio 2:1. This means that P lies two thirds of the way along AB
from A to B.

If A is (2, 5) and B is (5, 11), find the components of $\vec{AB}$, $\vec{AP}$ and $\vec{OP}$ and hence
write down the coordinates of P.

b) Repeat part (a) for A (−1, 3) and B (5, 0).
c) Repeat part (a) for A (−3, 7) and B (6, −2).

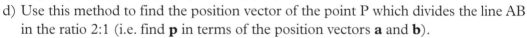

d) Use this method to find the position vector of the point P which divides the line AB
in the ratio 2:1 (i.e. find $\mathbf{p}$ in terms of the position vectors $\mathbf{a}$ and $\mathbf{b}$).
e) Extend this method of part (d) to find the position vector of Q which divides the
line AB in the ratio 3:1.

6B a) BD is a median of triangle ABC.
G divides BD in the ratio 2:1.
Let $\vec{AB} = 2\mathbf{v}$ and $\vec{AD} = \mathbf{u}$.
Express $\vec{BD}$ $\vec{BG}$ and $\vec{AG}$ in terms of $\mathbf{u}$ and $\mathbf{v}$.

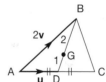

b) AE is another median of triangle ABC.
H divides AE in the ratio 2:1.
Express $\vec{BC}$ $\vec{BE}$ $\vec{AE}$ and $\vec{AH}$ in terms of $\mathbf{u}$ and $\mathbf{v}$.

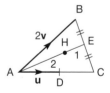

c) CF is the third median of triangle ABC.
K divides CF in the ratio 2:1.
Express $\vec{AC}$, $\vec{AF}$, $\vec{CF}$, $\vec{CK}$ and $\vec{AK}$ in terms of $\mathbf{u}$ and $\mathbf{v}$.

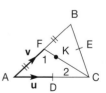

d) Hence make a statement about G, H and K.

93 Position vectors; i, j, k; length; equations; unit vectors.

> **Reminder**

If P is (a, b, c), then $\mathbf{p} = a\mathbf{i} + b\mathbf{j} + c\mathbf{k}$ and $p = |\mathbf{p}| = \sqrt{a^2 + b^2 + c^2}$.

The unit vector in the direction OP is $\dfrac{1}{\sqrt{a^2 + b^2 + c^2}}(a\mathbf{i} + b\mathbf{j} + c\mathbf{k})$.

Example   Given that $\mathbf{p} = 2\mathbf{i} - 3\mathbf{j} + 4\mathbf{k}$ and $\mathbf{q} = 3\mathbf{i} + 5\mathbf{j} - \mathbf{k}$, find the unit vector in the PQ direction.

Solution $\overrightarrow{PQ} = \mathbf{q} - \mathbf{p} = \begin{pmatrix} 3 \\ 5 \\ -1 \end{pmatrix} - \begin{pmatrix} 2 \\ -3 \\ 4 \end{pmatrix} = \begin{pmatrix} 1 \\ 8 \\ -5 \end{pmatrix}$

$\Rightarrow PQ = |\overrightarrow{PQ}| = \sqrt{1^2 + 8^2 + (-5)^2} = \sqrt{90} = 3\sqrt{10}$

$\Rightarrow \mathbf{u}_{PQ} = \dfrac{1}{3\sqrt{10}}\mathbf{i} + \dfrac{8}{3\sqrt{10}}\mathbf{j} - \dfrac{5}{3\sqrt{10}}\mathbf{k}$.

Exercise 93

1 Three points P, Q and R have coordinates $(3, -2, 2)$, $(4, 1, -1)$ and $(-2, 3, 4)$.
   a) Write down the column vectors which represent $\overrightarrow{OP}, \overrightarrow{OQ}, \overrightarrow{OR}, \overrightarrow{PQ}, \overrightarrow{RP}$ and $\overrightarrow{QR}$.
   b) Express each of these column vectors in terms of $\mathbf{i}, \mathbf{j}$ and $\mathbf{k}$.
   c) Find the length of each of these six vectors.

2 OABC, DEFG is a cuboid measuring 6 units × 3 units × 2 units as shown. Write down the components of:

   a) $\overrightarrow{OA}$ b) $\overrightarrow{OB}$ c) $\overrightarrow{OC}$

   d) $\overrightarrow{OF}$ e) $\overrightarrow{OG}$ f) $\overrightarrow{OE}$

   g) $\overrightarrow{GA}$ h) $\overrightarrow{FC}$ i) $\overrightarrow{DH}$ where
   H is the midpoint of CB.

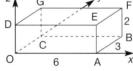

3 If $\mathbf{u} = \mathbf{i} - 2\mathbf{j} + 3\mathbf{k}$, $\mathbf{v} = 4\mathbf{i} - \mathbf{k}$, and $\mathbf{w} = 3\mathbf{i} + \mathbf{j} - 3\mathbf{k}$,
   a) express in component form:

   $\mathbf{a} = \mathbf{u} + \mathbf{v} + \mathbf{w}$ $\mathbf{b} = \mathbf{u} - 2\mathbf{v} + 3\mathbf{w}$ $\mathbf{c} = 3\mathbf{u} + 4\mathbf{v} - 5\mathbf{w}$ $\mathbf{d} = 2(\mathbf{u} - \mathbf{v}) - 3\mathbf{w}$

   b) calculate the lengths of $\mathbf{u}, \mathbf{v}, \mathbf{w}, \mathbf{a}, \mathbf{b}, \mathbf{c}$ and $\mathbf{d}$.

4 If $\mathbf{p} = \mathbf{i} - 2\mathbf{j} + 2\mathbf{k}$, and $\mathbf{q} = 3\mathbf{i} + 2\mathbf{j} - 6\mathbf{k}$, calculate:
   a) $|\mathbf{p}|$ b) $|\mathbf{q}|$ c) $|\mathbf{p} + \mathbf{q}|$ d) $|\mathbf{p} - \mathbf{q}|$.

5 If $\mathbf{a} = \begin{pmatrix} 3 \\ -2 \\ 1 \end{pmatrix}$, $\mathbf{b} = \begin{pmatrix} 3 \\ 0 \\ -1 \end{pmatrix}$, and $\mathbf{c} = \begin{pmatrix} -2 \\ 3 \\ 1 \end{pmatrix}$, solve these equations for $\mathbf{x}$:

  a) $\mathbf{a} + \mathbf{x} = \mathbf{b}$ b) $\mathbf{b} - \mathbf{x} = \mathbf{c}$ c) $5\mathbf{x} + \mathbf{a} = \mathbf{c}$.

6 Find a unit vector parallel to:

  a) $\begin{pmatrix} 2 \\ -3 \\ 6 \end{pmatrix}$ b) $\begin{pmatrix} 8 \\ 4 \\ -1 \end{pmatrix}$ c) $\begin{pmatrix} -3 \\ 0 \\ 4 \end{pmatrix}$ d) $\begin{pmatrix} 4 \\ 12 \\ -3 \end{pmatrix}$

  e) $\begin{pmatrix} 2 \\ 3 \\ -1 \end{pmatrix}$ f) $\begin{pmatrix} 13 \\ -12 \\ 5 \end{pmatrix}$ g) $\begin{pmatrix} 7 \\ 4 \\ -3 \end{pmatrix}$ h) $\begin{pmatrix} 1 \\ -1 \\ 1 \end{pmatrix}$.

94 The distance formula and the converse of the Theorem of Pythagoras

> **Reminder**

$A(x_a, y_a, z_a)$, $B(x_b, y_b, z_b)$ $\Rightarrow$ $AB = \sqrt{(x_a - x_b)^2 + (y_a - y_b)^2 + (z_a - z_b)^2}$.

Example   Triangle ABC has vertices A (2, 3, 5), B (3, 1, 9) and C (9, 2, 8).
            Prove that triangle ABC is right-angled.

Solution $AC^2 = (9 - 2)^2 + (2 - 3)^2 + (8 - 5)^2 = 49 + 1 + 9 = 59$
            $AB^2 = (3 - 2)^2 + (1 - 3)^2 + (9 - 5)^2 = 1 + 4 + 16 = 21$
            $BC^2 = (9 - 3)^2 + (2 - 1)^2 + (8 - 9)^2 = 36 + 1 + 1 = 38$
            $\Rightarrow AB^2 + BC^2 = 21 + 38 = 59 = AC^2$
            $\Rightarrow$ triangle ABC is right-angled at B (by the converse of
            Pythagoras' Theorem).

Exercise 94

1 Calculate the distance between the following pairs of points:
  a) A (4, 5, –6) and B (3, 7, –8)   b) C (4, –3, –2) and D (6, 0, –8)
  c) E (5, –6, –6) and F (8, –2, 6)   d) G (–5, 9, 5) and H (4, –3, –3)
  e) K (6, 1, 16) and L (2, –3, 9).

2 Show that the points L (11, –1, 6), M (–1, –7, 10) and N (17, 3, 18) are the vertices of an isosceles triangle.

3 The SIDES of a triangle are represented by the vectors $\mathbf{a} = 2\mathbf{i} - \mathbf{j} - 3\mathbf{k}$, $\mathbf{b} = \mathbf{i} - 4\mathbf{j} + 2\mathbf{k}$, and $\mathbf{c} = -3\mathbf{i} + 5\mathbf{j} + \mathbf{k}$. Prove that the triangle is right-angled.

4 Show that OPQR is a parallelogram, where O is the point (0, 0, 0), P (3, 2, 1), Q (4, 3, 2), and R (1, 1, 1).

5 Show that the points P $(4, -4, 5)$, Q $(3, -5, 5)$, and R $(3, -4, 4)$ are the vertices of an equilateral triangle.

6 Prove that X $(-1, 6, 4)$, Y $(1, 8, 5)$, and Z $(-3, 7, 6)$ are three vertices of a square, and find the coordinates of the fourth vertex.

7 Prove that triangle KLM is right-angled, where K is $(7, -5, 3)$, L $(9, -6, 0)$ and M $(10, -10, 2)$.

8 A is the point $(1, 2, 3)$ and B $(4, 1, 5)$.
  a) Prove that triangle OAB is isosceles.
  b) If C is the point $(5, -4, 1)$, prove that triangle ABC is right-angled.

95 Collinearity

> **Reminder**

Points are **collinear** if they lie on the same straight line.
Only points can be collinear, not lines or vectors.

Example

Show that the points K $(-5, 6, 3)$ L $(-1, 0, 1)$ and M $(5, -9, -2)$ are collinear, and find the ratio in which L divides KM.

Solution

$$\vec{KL} = \begin{pmatrix} 4 \\ -6 \\ -2 \end{pmatrix} = 2\begin{pmatrix} 3 \\ -3 \\ -1 \end{pmatrix} \text{ and } \vec{LM} = \begin{pmatrix} 6 \\ -9 \\ -3 \end{pmatrix} = 3\begin{pmatrix} 3 \\ -3 \\ -1 \end{pmatrix}$$

<u>either</u>

$$\vec{KL} = \tfrac{2}{3}\vec{LM}$$

<u>or</u>

$\vec{KL}$ and $\vec{LM}$ are both parallel to $\begin{pmatrix} 3 \\ -3 \\ -1 \end{pmatrix}$

So KL is parallel to LM, with the point L in common.

Hence K L and M are collinear.   Clearly KL:LM = 2:3.

Note that $\vec{AB} = k\vec{CD}$ implies that the lines AB and CD are parallel, **not** that A, B, C, and D are collinear. To score full marks in the exam it is essential to communicate adequately and mention both **parallel** and the **common point**.

Exercise 95

1 P is the point $(3, 0, 7)$, Q $(7, 2, 3)$ and R $(15, 6, -5)$.

Find the components of $\vec{PQ}$ and $\vec{QR}$, and hence show that P, Q, and R are collinear, stating the value of the ratio PQ:QR.

2 A is the point $(3, 6, 5)$, B $(7, 8, 1)$ and C $(15, 12, -7)$. Show that A, B and C are collinear and find the ratio AB:BC.

3 P is the point (4, –4, 6), Q (5, –6, 5), and R (2, 0, 8). Show that P, Q and R are collinear and find the ratio RP:RQ.

4 Prove that the points A (1, 2, 3), B (3, 3, 2), and C (7, 5, 0) are collinear, and find the ratio AB:BC.

96 Three-dimensional diagrams

> **Reminder**

Example

OABC, DEFG is a parallelopiped with O (0, 0, 0), A (5, 1, 2), D (2, 7, 2), and C (1, 3, 6).

Find the coordinates of M, the point of the intersection of DF and GE.

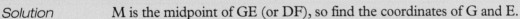

Solution

M is the midpoint of GE (or DF), so find the coordinates of G and E.

$$\overrightarrow{OE} = \overrightarrow{OA} + \overrightarrow{AE} = \overrightarrow{OA} + \overrightarrow{OD} = \begin{pmatrix} 5 \\ 1 \\ 2 \end{pmatrix} + \begin{pmatrix} 2 \\ 7 \\ 2 \end{pmatrix} = \begin{pmatrix} 7 \\ 8 \\ 4 \end{pmatrix} = \mathbf{e}.$$

$$\overrightarrow{OG} = \overrightarrow{OD} + \overrightarrow{DG} = \overrightarrow{OD} + \overrightarrow{OC} = \begin{pmatrix} 2 \\ 7 \\ 2 \end{pmatrix} + \begin{pmatrix} 1 \\ 3 \\ 6 \end{pmatrix} = \begin{pmatrix} 3 \\ 10 \\ 8 \end{pmatrix} = \mathbf{g}.$$

$$\mathbf{m} = \frac{1}{2}(\mathbf{g} + \mathbf{e}) = \frac{1}{2}\left[\begin{pmatrix} 3 \\ 10 \\ 8 \end{pmatrix} + \begin{pmatrix} 7 \\ 8 \\ 4 \end{pmatrix} \right] = \begin{pmatrix} 5 \\ 9 \\ 6 \end{pmatrix} \quad \therefore \ \text{M is (5, 9, 6)}.$$

Exercise 96

1 OADB, CEFG is a parallelopiped,

with $\overrightarrow{OA} = \mathbf{i} + 2\mathbf{j} + 3\mathbf{k}$

$\overrightarrow{OB} = 3\mathbf{i} + \mathbf{j}$

$\overrightarrow{OC} = 5\mathbf{i} + 7\mathbf{j}$.

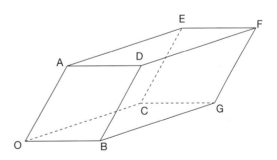

Find the components of:

a) $\overrightarrow{OG}$ b) $\overrightarrow{OF}$

c) $\overrightarrow{CF}$ d) $\overrightarrow{ED}$

e) $\overrightarrow{GE}$ f) $\overrightarrow{BE}$

g) $\overrightarrow{AG}$ h) $\overrightarrow{OH}$, where H is the midpoint of BC.

2 ABCD,EFGH is a cuboid with

$$\overrightarrow{AD} = \begin{pmatrix} 6 \\ -6 \\ 6 \end{pmatrix} \quad \overrightarrow{AB} = \begin{pmatrix} 3 \\ 3 \\ 0 \end{pmatrix} \quad \overrightarrow{AE} = \begin{pmatrix} 6 \\ -6 \\ -12 \end{pmatrix}$$

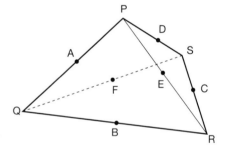

K is the midpoint of CG.
L is the midpoint of FG.
M is the point of trisection of KL nearer to L.

Find the components of   a) $\overrightarrow{AK}$ b) $\overrightarrow{AL}$ c) $\overrightarrow{AM}$.

3 V,ABCD is a right-pyramid with a rectangular base.

$$\overrightarrow{AV} = \begin{pmatrix} 18 \\ 14 \\ 2 \end{pmatrix}, \quad \overrightarrow{AD} = \begin{pmatrix} -4 \\ 16 \\ 8 \end{pmatrix}, \quad \overrightarrow{AB} = \begin{pmatrix} 8 \\ -4 \\ 12 \end{pmatrix}$$

X is the centre of the base.
M is the midpoint of VC.
N is the midpoint of VB.
L lies three quarters of the way up XV.

Find the components of   a) $\overrightarrow{AM}$ b) $\overrightarrow{DN}$ c) $\overrightarrow{CL}$.

4 PQRS is a tetrahedron with vertices P (5, 3, −1), Q (−1, 3, 1), R (−3, 5, 3) and S (1, −1, 5).

A is the midpoint of PQ.
B is the midpoint of QR.
C is the midpoint of RS.
D is the midpoint of SP.
E is the midpoint of PR.
F is the midpoint of QS.

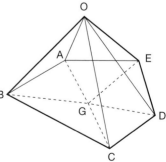

Find the coordinates of   a) W, the midpoint of EF,
b) X, the midpoint of AC,
c) Y, the midpoint of BD.

5 Show that if PQRS is any tetrahedron with midpoints labelled as in question 4, then W, X, and Y coincide.

6 O, ABCDE is a pentagonal pyramid.
AC and BD intersect in G.
In each of the following equations,
$\overrightarrow{XY}$ represents a vector somewhere in this diagram.

Solve each equation for $\overrightarrow{XY}$:

a) $\overrightarrow{AG} + \overrightarrow{GD} + \overrightarrow{XY} = \overrightarrow{AO}$
b) $\overrightarrow{BC} + \overrightarrow{XY} + \overrightarrow{GE} = \overrightarrow{BA} + \overrightarrow{AO} + \overrightarrow{OE}$
c) $\overrightarrow{GB} - \overrightarrow{GA} = \overrightarrow{AC} + \overrightarrow{CD} + \overrightarrow{XY}$.

7 Similarly to question 6, solve each equation for $\overrightarrow{XY}$:

a) $\overrightarrow{EF} + \overrightarrow{XY} + \overrightarrow{GD} = \overrightarrow{EK} + \overrightarrow{KD}$

b) $\overrightarrow{AC} + \overrightarrow{KF} = \overrightarrow{AF} - \overrightarrow{XY}$

c) $\overrightarrow{HD} - \overrightarrow{CD} + \overrightarrow{CE} = \overrightarrow{XY} + \overrightarrow{KF} - \overrightarrow{EF}$

d) $\overrightarrow{GE} - \overrightarrow{DB} + \overrightarrow{XY} = \overrightarrow{CE} - \overrightarrow{CA} - \overrightarrow{AB}$.

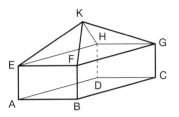

97 The Section Formula

(Division of a line in a given ratio)

> ### Reminder

If P divides AB in the ratio $m:n$,

then $\mathbf{p} = \dfrac{m\mathbf{b} + n\mathbf{a}}{m + n}$.

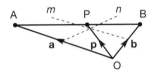

Example Find the coordinates of the point P which divides AB in the ratio 3:2, where A is $(7, 2, -1)$ and B is $(-3, 7, 14)$.

Solution *Method 1* (as described in Exercise 92, question 5)

The advantage of this method is that you can think it out from first principles each time, and so don't have to use the section formula. The disadvantage is that many users of this method omit the last step and think that the components of $\overrightarrow{AP}$ are the coordinates of P.

$$\overrightarrow{AB} = \mathbf{b} - \mathbf{a} = \begin{pmatrix} -3 \\ 7 \\ 14 \end{pmatrix} - \begin{pmatrix} 7 \\ 2 \\ -1 \end{pmatrix} = \begin{pmatrix} -10 \\ 5 \\ 15 \end{pmatrix}$$

$$\overrightarrow{AP} = \tfrac{3}{5}\,\overrightarrow{AB} = \tfrac{3}{5}\begin{pmatrix} -10 \\ 5 \\ 15 \end{pmatrix} = \begin{pmatrix} -6 \\ 3 \\ 9 \end{pmatrix}$$

$$\overrightarrow{OP} = \overrightarrow{OA} + \overrightarrow{AP} = \begin{pmatrix} 7 \\ 2 \\ -1 \end{pmatrix} + \begin{pmatrix} -6 \\ 3 \\ 9 \end{pmatrix} = \begin{pmatrix} 1 \\ 5 \\ 8 \end{pmatrix} \Rightarrow \text{P is } (1, 5, 8).$$

Method 2 (using the section formula, which is preferable in literal examples)

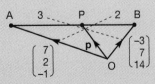

$$\mathbf{p} = \frac{1}{3 + 2}\,[3\begin{pmatrix} -3 \\ 7 \\ 14 \end{pmatrix} + 2\begin{pmatrix} 7 \\ 2 \\ -1 \end{pmatrix}] = \tfrac{1}{5}\begin{pmatrix} 5 \\ 25 \\ 40 \end{pmatrix} = \begin{pmatrix} 1 \\ 5 \\ 8 \end{pmatrix} \Rightarrow \text{P is } (1, 5, 8).$$

Exercise 97

1   This sketch illustrates a point Z dividing a line XY in the ratio 3:1.

Draw similar sketches to illustrate:
a) P dividing AB in the ratio 2:1.
b) Q dividing CD in the ratio 1:3.
c) R dividing EF in the ratio 1:1.
d) S dividing GH in the ratio 2:3.

2   Plot the points K (−2, 0), L (4, 0) and M (6, 0).
In what ratio does
a) L divide OM
b) L divide KM
c) O divide KL?

3   Draw a straight line PT divided into four equal parts by the points Q, R and S.
Write down the value of each of these ratios:
a) PQ:QS
b) PR:RT
c) PQ:PT
d) PR:PT.

4   Find the coordinates of P which divides the line AB where:
a) A is (5, 1) and B (11, 4), in the ratio 2:1
b) A is (−1, 2) and B (6, −5), in the ratio 4:3
c) A is (2, 2) and B (7, 12), in the ratio 3:2
d) A is (4, 4) and B (−1, −1), in the ratio 2:3
e) A is (1, 10) and B (6, 0), in the ratio 3:2
f) A is (1, 1) and B (−5, 7), in the ratio 2:1.

5   Find the coordinates of P which divides the line AB where:
a) A is (7, 8, 9) and B (10, 14, 21), in the ratio 2:1
b) A is (2, 5, 5) and B (6, 13, 17), in the ratio 1:3
c) A is (2, 1, 3) and B (7, 11, 8), in the ratio 3:2
d) A is (3, −1, 2) and B (7, 3, 10), in the ratio 3:1
e) A is (4, −3, 2) and B (−6, 2, 7), in the ratio 3:2
f) A is (4, 9, 10) and B (1, 3, 1), in the ratio 1:2.

6B   Express in terms of **a** and **b** (the position vectors of the points A and B) the position
vector of:
a) C which divides AB in the ratio 4:3
b) D which divides AB in the ratio 1:2
c) E which divides AB in the ratio 7:4.

7B   PQRS is a parallelogram with vertices P (2, −3, 5), Q (6, −1, −1), R (5, 6, −1), and
S (1, 4, 5). T is the midpoint of PQ and V divides ST in the ratio 2:1.
Prove that P, V and R are collinear and find the ratio PV:VR.

8B   Triangle ABC has vertices A (4, 7) B (1, 4) and C (7, 1). P divides AB in the ratio 1:2.
Q divides CA in the ratio 1:2. R lies on BC produced such that $3\vec{BR} = 4\vec{BC}$.
a) Find the coordinates of P, Q and R.
b) Show that P, Q and R are collinear and calculate the ratio PQ:QR.

9B Triangle ABC has vertices A $(2, 3, -4)$, B $(6, 7, -5)$ and C $(4, -1, 6)$.
D is the midpoint of AC, and G divides BD in the ratio 2:1.
E is the midpoint of AB, and H divides CE in the ratio 2:1.
F is the midpoint of BC, and K divides AF in the ratio 2:1.
a) Find the coordinates of G, H and K.
b) Hence make two statements about the medians of this triangle.
c) Show that the coordinates of G satisfy the formula $\mathbf{g} = \frac{1}{3}(\mathbf{a} + \mathbf{b} + \mathbf{c})$.

10B The vertices A, B, C of triangle ABC have position vectors $\mathbf{a}, \mathbf{b}, \mathbf{c}$ respectively.
a) D is the midpoint of AC. Express $\mathbf{d}$ in terms of $\mathbf{a}$ and $\mathbf{c}$.
b) G divides BD in the ratio 2:1. Express $\mathbf{g}$ in terms of $\mathbf{b}$ and $\mathbf{d}$.
c) Hence express $\mathbf{g}$ in terms of $\mathbf{a}, \mathbf{b}$ and $\mathbf{c}$.
d) G is called the *centroid* of the triangle. What have you just proved about G ?

11B ABCD is a tetrahedron with vertices A $(1, 1, 1)$, B $(2, -2, 3)$, C $(3, 4, 2)$ and D $(6, 9, -2)$.
a) Use the result of question 10 to write down the coordinates of D', the centroid of triangle ABC.
b) G divides DD′ in the ratio 3:1. Use the section formula to find the coordinates of G.
c) Similarly H, J, K divide BB′, CC′, AA′ in the ratio 3:1. Find the coordinates of H, J, K.
d) Verify that the coordinates of G satisfy the equation $\mathbf{g} = \frac{1}{4}(\mathbf{a} + \mathbf{b} + \mathbf{c} + \mathbf{d})$.

12B The vertices of tetrahedron ABCD have position vectors $\mathbf{a}, \mathbf{b}, \mathbf{c}, \mathbf{d}$ respectively.
a) Let H be the centroid of triangle ABC. Express $\mathbf{h}$ in terms of $\mathbf{a}, \mathbf{b}$ and $\mathbf{c}$.
b) Let G divide DH in the ratio 3:1. Express $\mathbf{g}$ in terms of $\mathbf{d}$ and $\mathbf{h}$.
c) Hence express $\mathbf{g}$ in terms of $\mathbf{a}, \mathbf{b}, \mathbf{c}$ and $\mathbf{d}$.
d) From the symmetry of your answer to part (c), deduce the relationship between DH and the other three corresponding lines.

(The remaining questions are best tackled *without* using the section formula.)
13 The points P $(1, 4, 2)$, Q $(4, -2, -4)$ and R $(5, x, y)$ are collinear.
a) Write down the value of the ratio PQ:QR.
b) Write down the values of x and y.

14 The points A $(2, -1, 11)$, B $(4, -5, 9)$ and C $(5, p, q)$ are collinear.
a) Write down the value of the ratio AB:BC.
b) Write down the values of p and q.

15 The following points are collinear:
P $(-1, 3, 2)$, Q $(0, 2, 4)$, R $(a, 1, 6)$, S $(2, b, 8)$, T $(3, -1, c)$ and V $(8, -6, 20)$.
a) Find the ratio in which PV is divided by i) Q ii) R iii) S iv) T.
b) Find the values of i) a ii) b iii) c.

16 Show that the points K $(-2, 5, 1)$, L $(-5, 17, 7)$ and M $(-6, 21, 9)$ are collinear and find the ratio KL:LM.

17 Show that the points P $(3, 5, 5)$, Q $(2, 0, 3)$ and R $(4, 10, 7)$ are collinear and find the coordinates of S such that $\overrightarrow{PS} = 3\overrightarrow{PQ}$.

98 The Scalar Product

$\mathbf{a}.\mathbf{b} = |\mathbf{a}||\mathbf{b}|\cos\theta$ or $\mathbf{a}.\mathbf{b} = ab\cos\theta$, which is a number (i.e. a scalar).

[You may write b for $|\mathbf{b}|$ provided that you are careful about underlining your vectors every time.]

It is often useful to think of $\mathbf{a}.\mathbf{b}$ as the length of one vector times the projection of the other vector upon it.

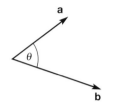

Example

ABCD is a rectangle, with AD = 5 and AB = 11. M is the midpoint of BC.

Evaluate

a) $\overrightarrow{AC}.\overrightarrow{AD}$ b) $\overrightarrow{AM}.\overrightarrow{MB}$.

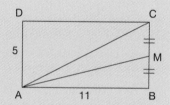

Solution

a) $\overrightarrow{AC}.\overrightarrow{AD} = AC \times AD \times \cos D\hat{A}C = \sqrt{146} \times 5 \times \dfrac{5}{\sqrt{146}} = 25.$

Notice that instead of working out $\sqrt{146}$, we could have just written AC in both cases, since they cancel.
Alternatively, the projection of AC on AD is AD, i.e. 5, so the scalar product is AD × (the projection of AC) = 5 × 5 = 25.

b) $\overrightarrow{AM}.\overrightarrow{MB} = -\overrightarrow{MA}.\overrightarrow{MB} = -MA \times MB \times \cos A\hat{M}B$

$$= -MA \times \frac{5}{2} \times \frac{\frac{5}{2}}{AM} = -\frac{25}{4}.$$

Notice that before applying the formula for the scalar product, the vectors were arranged to be both 'coming out' of M.
Alternatively, they could have both been 'going in' to M, but not 'one out' and 'one in'.
Alternatively, the projection of MA on MB is MB, i.e. $\frac{5}{2}$, so the

scalar product ($\overrightarrow{MA}.\overrightarrow{MB}$) is
MB × (the projection of MA) = $\dfrac{5}{2} \times \dfrac{5}{2} = \dfrac{25}{4}.$

Hence $\overrightarrow{AM}.\overrightarrow{MB} = -\dfrac{25}{4}$

Notice also that the answer is just a number in both cases.

Exercise 98

1 Evaluate **a.b** in each of these cases:

a)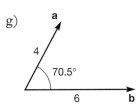

b)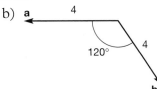

c)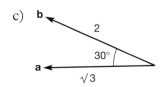

d)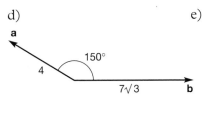

e)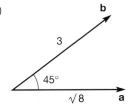

f)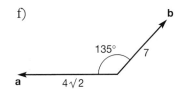

g)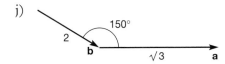

h)

i)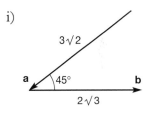

j)

2 OABC is a square of side 1 unit.
Evaluate:

a) $\overrightarrow{OA}.\overrightarrow{OB}$

b) $\overrightarrow{CB}.\overrightarrow{BO}$.

3 Triangle ABC is an equilateral triangle
with sides of length 3 units.
Evaluate:

a) $\overrightarrow{AB}.\overrightarrow{AC}$

b) $\overrightarrow{BA}.\overrightarrow{CB}$.

4 ABCD is a rectangle with AB = 8 and AD = 6 units.
Evaluate:
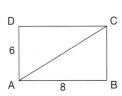
a) $\overrightarrow{AB}.\overrightarrow{AC}$

b) $\overrightarrow{DA}.\overrightarrow{AC}$.

c) $\overrightarrow{AB}.\overrightarrow{AD}$.

5 ABCDEF is a regular hexagon inscribed
in a circle with centre G and radius a units.
Evaluate:

a) $\overrightarrow{GB}.\overrightarrow{GD}$

b) $\overrightarrow{BA}.\overrightarrow{AF}$

c) $\overrightarrow{FE}.\overrightarrow{FC}$

d) $\overrightarrow{GE}.\overrightarrow{AD}$.

(Notice that question 1 part (*h*) and question 4 part (*c*) illustrate the fact that if two vectors are perpendicular, then their scalar product is zero. The converse is also true and provides us, for the next exercise, with a means of proving that two vectors are perpendicular.)

6 ABCD is a rectangle whose diagonals intersect at O.
AD = 5 units, AB = 12 units.
M is the midpoint of BC. N is the midpoint of AB.
Evaluate:

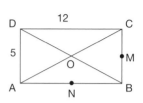

a) $\vec{AM}.\vec{CM}$ b) $\vec{NB}.\vec{DO}$ c) $\vec{AD}.\vec{NM}$.

7 Expand each of the following, using the distributive law:

a) $\mathbf{a}.(\mathbf{b} - \mathbf{c})$ b) $(\mathbf{p} - \mathbf{q}).\mathbf{r}$ c) $(\mathbf{u} + \mathbf{v}).(\mathbf{u} - \mathbf{v})$

d) $(\mathbf{u} + \mathbf{v}).(\mathbf{u} + \mathbf{v})$ e) $(\mathbf{r} - 2\mathbf{s}).(2\mathbf{r} - \mathbf{s})$ f) $(\mathbf{a} + \mathbf{b}).(\mathbf{c} - \mathbf{w})$.

8 Given that $|\mathbf{p}| = 3$, $|\mathbf{q}| = 4$ and the angle between **p** and **q** is 120°, evaluate

a) $\mathbf{p}.(\mathbf{p} + \mathbf{q})$ b) $(\mathbf{p} + \mathbf{q}).\mathbf{q}$.

9 If $\mathbf{p} = 3\mathbf{a} + 4\mathbf{b}$, where **a** and **b** are unit vectors (i.e. each of length 1) at 60° to each other, evaluate

a) $\mathbf{a}.\mathbf{a}$ b) $\mathbf{b}.\mathbf{b}$ c) $\mathbf{p}.\mathbf{p}$.

10 Prove that for any vector **p** in the plane of A, B and C $\mathbf{p}.\vec{AB} + \mathbf{p}.\vec{BC} + \mathbf{p}.\vec{CA} = 0$.

11 PQRS is a rhombus with $\vec{PQ} = \mathbf{a}$ and $\vec{PS} = \mathbf{b}$.

a) Express $\vec{PR}$ and $\vec{QS}$ in terms of **a** and **b**.

b) Simplify $\vec{PR}.\vec{QS}$.

c) What does this prove about the diagonals of a rhombus?

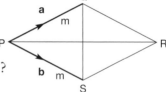

12 Draw a counter-example to show that $\mathbf{a}.\mathbf{b} = \mathbf{a}.\mathbf{c} \not\Rightarrow \mathbf{b} = \mathbf{c}$.

13 Evaluate: a) $\mathbf{i}.\mathbf{i}$ b) $\mathbf{i}.\mathbf{j}$ c) $\mathbf{j}.\mathbf{k}$.

99 The Scalar Product in Components

> **Reminder**

$\mathbf{a} = a_x\mathbf{i} + a_y\mathbf{j} + a_z\mathbf{k}, \mathbf{b} = b_x\mathbf{i} + b_y\mathbf{j} + b_z\mathbf{k} \Rightarrow \mathbf{a}.\mathbf{b} = a_xb_x + a_yb_y + a_zb_z.$

Example   Evaluate $\vec{OA}.\vec{BC}$ where A is (2, –1, 4) B (6, 7, –3) and C (0, –1, –2).

Solution $\vec{OA} = \begin{pmatrix} 2 \\ -1 \\ 4 \end{pmatrix}$, $\vec{BC} = \mathbf{c} - \mathbf{b} = \begin{pmatrix} 0 \\ -1 \\ -2 \end{pmatrix} - \begin{pmatrix} 6 \\ 7 \\ -3 \end{pmatrix} = \begin{pmatrix} -6 \\ -8 \\ 1 \end{pmatrix}$.

Hence $\vec{OA}.\vec{BC} = \begin{pmatrix} 2 \\ -1 \\ 4 \end{pmatrix} \cdot \begin{pmatrix} -6 \\ -8 \\ 1 \end{pmatrix} = 2 \times (-6) + (-1) \times (-8) + 4 \times 1 = 0$

(which in fact also shows that OA ⊥ BC).

Exercise 99

1 If $\mathbf{a} = \begin{pmatrix} 1 \\ 2 \\ 3 \end{pmatrix}$ $\mathbf{b} = \begin{pmatrix} -2 \\ 3 \\ 1 \end{pmatrix}$ $\mathbf{c} = \begin{pmatrix} 0 \\ -2 \\ -1 \end{pmatrix}$, evaluate: a) $\mathbf{a}.\mathbf{b}$ b) $\mathbf{b}.\mathbf{c}$ c) $\mathbf{c}.\mathbf{a}$.

2 If $\mathbf{u} = \begin{pmatrix} 3 \\ -2 \\ 4 \end{pmatrix}$ $\mathbf{v} = \begin{pmatrix} -1 \\ 2 \\ -3 \end{pmatrix}$ $\mathbf{w} = \begin{pmatrix} 2 \\ -1 \\ 0 \end{pmatrix}$, evaluate:

   a) $\mathbf{u}.\mathbf{v}$ b) $\mathbf{v}.\mathbf{w}$ c) $\mathbf{w}.\mathbf{u}$ d) $\mathbf{u}.(\mathbf{v} - \mathbf{w})$
   e) $\mathbf{v}.(\mathbf{u} - \mathbf{w})$ f) $(\mathbf{u} - \mathbf{v}).\mathbf{w}$ g) $2\mathbf{u}.(3\mathbf{v} - 2\mathbf{w})$.

3 Find the value of x if the vectors $\begin{pmatrix} -2 \\ -5 \\ 1 \end{pmatrix}$ and $\begin{pmatrix} x \\ -2 \\ 6 \end{pmatrix}$ are perpendicular.

4 Find the value of k if the vectors $\begin{pmatrix} k \\ -1 \\ 1 \end{pmatrix}$ and $\begin{pmatrix} 2 \\ -3 \\ -1 \end{pmatrix}$ are perpendicular.

5 A is the point (3, 2, 1), B (4, 5, −2) and C (4, 2, 3). Evaluate $\vec{AB}.\vec{OC}$.

6 A is the point (1, 2, 3), B (6, 5, 4), C (−1, −2, 6) and D (5, −4, 3). Evaluate $\vec{AB}.\vec{CD}$.

7 P is the point (2, 4, 3), Q (3, 0, 3), R (0, 2, 1) and S (−1, 6, 1).
   a) Show that PQRS is a parallelogram.
   b) Use the scalar product of two appropriate vectors to show that PQRS is in fact a rhombus.

8 Show that AD is perpendicular BC, where A is the point (7, −1, 3), B (7, 8, 7) C (1, 4, 9), and D (1, 13, 13).

9 Show that triangle LMN is right-angled and isosceles, where L is the point (3, 8, −6) M (6, 8, −7) and N (5, 8, −5).

10 $\mathbf{a} = \begin{pmatrix} 2 \\ -2 \\ 2 \end{pmatrix}$ $\mathbf{b} = \begin{pmatrix} 1 \\ 2 \\ 1 \end{pmatrix}$ $\mathbf{c} = \begin{pmatrix} 1 \\ 4 \\ x \end{pmatrix}$ Find the value of x if $\mathbf{a}.(\mathbf{b} + \mathbf{c}) = \mathbf{a}.\mathbf{a}$.

11 A is the point (21, 0, −21), B (3, 6, 9) and C (15, 6, −9). Point D divides AB in the ratio 2:1 and E divides BC in the ratio 2:1. Show that OB is perpendicular to DE.

12 The points A, B, C, D have coordinates (−3, 2, −2), (13, −6, 2), (−2, 5, 17), (7, 8, −7). P divides AB in the ratio 1:3 and Q divides CD in the ratio 2:1. Show that PQ is at right angles to both AB and CD.

13 K is the point (4, −2, 2) and L (7, 4, 11). P divides KL in the ratio 2:1. M is the point (8, −4, 9) and N (12, 4, 7). Q is the midpoint of MN. Prove that PQ is perpendicular to both KL and MN.

14 Triangle ABC has vertices A (1, −2, 4), B (7, 1, 4) and C (6, −2, 2). D divides AB in the ratio 2:1. Show that CD is an altitude of triangle ABC.

100 The Angle Between Two Vectors

> **Reminder**

Recall $\mathbf{a.b} = |\mathbf{a}||\mathbf{b}|\cos\theta$ and

$\mathbf{a} = a_x\mathbf{i} + a_y\mathbf{j} + a_z\mathbf{k}, \mathbf{b} = b_x\mathbf{i} + b_y\mathbf{j} + b_z\mathbf{k} \Rightarrow \mathbf{a.b} = a_xb_x + a_yb_y + a_zb_z$

i.e. $|\mathbf{a}||\mathbf{b}|\cos\theta = a_xb_x + a_yb_y + a_zb_z$ which allows us to calculate θ.

(Do not use this as a formula, but as a method).

Example   Calculate the angle between $\mathbf{u} = \begin{pmatrix} 2 \\ -1 \\ 2 \end{pmatrix}$ and $\mathbf{v} = \begin{pmatrix} 7 \\ 4 \\ -4 \end{pmatrix}$.

Solution $u = \sqrt{4 + 1 + 4} = 3$ $v = \sqrt{49 + 16 + 16} = 9$ $\mathbf{u.v} = 14 - 4 - 8 = 2$

$\therefore \cos\theta = \dfrac{\mathbf{u.v}}{uv} = \dfrac{2}{3 \times 9} = \dfrac{2}{27} \Rightarrow \theta = 85.75°.$

Exercise 100

1 Find the exact value of the cosine of the angle between each of the following pairs of vectors:

a) $\begin{pmatrix} 2 \\ -3 \\ 4 \end{pmatrix}, \begin{pmatrix} 4 \\ -2 \\ -3 \end{pmatrix}$ b) $\begin{pmatrix} -3 \\ 1 \\ 5 \end{pmatrix}, \begin{pmatrix} -1 \\ -5 \\ 3 \end{pmatrix}$ c) $\begin{pmatrix} -2 \\ 3 \\ 7 \end{pmatrix}, \begin{pmatrix} 12 \\ -8 \\ 28 \end{pmatrix}$ d) $\begin{pmatrix} -3 \\ 4 \\ -12 \end{pmatrix}, \begin{pmatrix} 8 \\ -9 \\ 12 \end{pmatrix}$

e) $\begin{pmatrix} 0 \\ 3 \\ 3 \end{pmatrix}, \begin{pmatrix} 3 \\ 0 \\ 3 \end{pmatrix}$ f) $\begin{pmatrix} 1 \\ 2 \\ -3 \end{pmatrix}, \begin{pmatrix} -1 \\ 3 \\ 2 \end{pmatrix}$ g) $\begin{pmatrix} 2 \\ -1 \\ 2 \end{pmatrix}, \begin{pmatrix} 6 \\ -2 \\ 3 \end{pmatrix}$.

2 Find the angle between each of these pairs of vectors:

a) $\begin{pmatrix} 2 \\ -2 \\ 6 \end{pmatrix}, \begin{pmatrix} 5 \\ 9 \\ 13 \end{pmatrix}$ b) $\begin{pmatrix} -6 \\ 8 \\ 24 \end{pmatrix}, \begin{pmatrix} 8 \\ -12 \\ 9 \end{pmatrix}$.

3 P is the point $(5, -3, 4)$ and Q $(-21, 29, -20)$. Find the size of $P\hat{O}Q$.

4 A is the point $(7, -1, 2)$ and B $(2, -3, -5)$.
Calculate
a) $\cos A\hat{O}B$ b) $\cos O\hat{A}B$ c) $\cos A\hat{B}O$.

5B Calculate the sizes of the angles of triangle ABC given that the vertices are A $(1, 2, 1)$, B $(2, 1, 2)$, C $(0, 1, 2)$.

6B A cuboid measuring 3 cm × 4 cm × 5 cm is placed centrally on top of another cuboid measuring 5 cm × 10 cm × 2 cm as shown.

Taking coordinate axes as shown,
a) State the coordinates of A, B and C.
b) Calculate the lengths of AB and BC.
c) Calculate the size of $A\hat{B}C$.

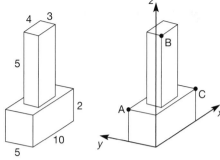

7B The wheel house of a Rhine barge is in the shape of half of a 2m cube placed centrally on the deck of the barge. There is a radio beacon attached at the forward starboard corner of the wheel house, as shown.

The top of the beacon is 4m above the deck and secured by a wire to the deck at a point 8m in front of the wheel house. Another wire to the near rear corner, and a strut to the opposite diagonal corner of the wheel house are used also to secure the beacon.
Coordinate axes are taken as shown.
a) Write down the coordinates of P, R, S and T.
b) Calculate the angle between the wire RP and the strut RS.

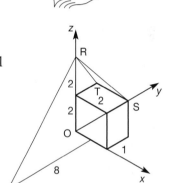

8B A small marquee is in the shape of a cuboid surmounted by a pyramid.
The cuboid and the pyramid have equal heights.

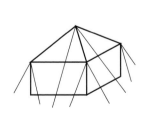

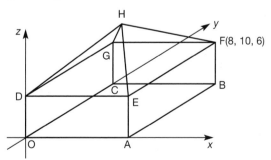

If axes are taken as shown, F has coordinates (8,10,6).
a) Write down the coordinates of B, D and H.
b) Calculate the size of $D\hat{H}B$.

9B The pyramid OPQR has vertices O(0,0,0) P(12,0,0) Q(0,6,0) and R(3,6,9) as shown.

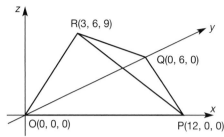

a) Find the coordinates of:
    (i) M and N, the midpoints of OP and OQ respectively
    (ii) S, which divides NR in the ratio 1:2
    (iii) T, which divides MR in the ratio 1:2.

b) Calculate the size of angle *TOS*.

10B This diagram shows a crystal of potash alum, which is in the shape of two congruent right square pyramids.
B has coordinates (6,6,0) and D(3,3,9).

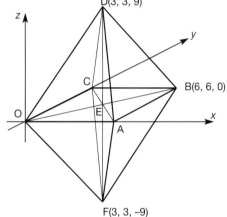

Find the coordinates of
(i) M, the midpoint of AB
(ii) G, which divides MD in the ratio 1:2
(iii) N, the midpoint of BC
(iv) H, which divides NF in the ratio 1:2.

Impurity ions are introduced at O, G, and H.
(v) Calculate the size of angle *GOH*.

11B PQRS is a quadrilateral with vertices
P(−2,−1,−4), Q(1,5,−7), R(7,8,5) and S(7,2,17).
a) Find the coordinates of T which lies on PR such that PT:TR = 5:4.
b) Show that Q, T, and S are collinear, and find the ratio in which T divides QS.
c) Calculate the size of the acute angle between the diagonals of the quadrilateral PQRS.

12B The points P (3, 5, 4), Q (7, 9, 8), R (5, −3, 6) and S (−1, 1, 2) lie on a spider's web. K, L, M, N are the midpoints of PS, PQ, QR, RS respectively.
a) Find the coordinates of K, L, M and N and prove that KLMN is a parallelogram.
b) Calculate the size of the acute angle between the diagonals of KLMN.

101 TOPIC TEST on Vectors

⏱ Allow 45 minutes for this test (Calculator required)

1 Show that the points P(7, −2, 11) Q(9, 0,7) and R(12, 3, 1) are collinear, and find the ratio PQ : QR.

2 K is the point (5, −1, 4) and L is (10, 4, −1). Find the coordinates of the point M which divides KL in the ratio 3: 2.

3 The vectors **p** and **q** are inclined at 60° to each other, with $|\mathbf{p}| = 3$ and $|\mathbf{q}| = 8$. Evaluate **p** . (**p** + **q**).

4 Evaluate **u.v** where **u** = **i** + 2**j** − **k**, and **v** = 2**i** + 3**j** + 7**k**.

5 Triangle RST has vertices R(2, −1, 7) S(10,3,5) and T (12, 0, 7).
Show that the triangle is right-angled.

6 Calculate the angle between the vectors
$$\mathbf{r} = \begin{pmatrix} 6 \\ 6 \\ -7 \end{pmatrix} \text{ and } \mathbf{s} = \begin{pmatrix} 4 \\ -7 \\ -4 \end{pmatrix}.$$

7 This diagram shows the crystal structure of a particular compound consisting of α ions and β ions. The α ions (denoted by •) are at the points O, B, E, G, M, K, and Q. The β ions (denoted by ⊗) are at the points H and

R, which lie at the centres of the cuboids OABC,DEFG & OAQP,LKNM respectively.

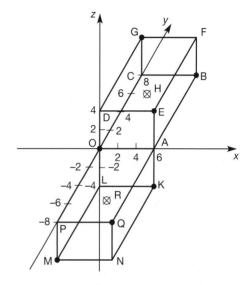

a) Calculate the size of the angle between OH and OR.

b) If an impurity molecule is introduced at the point S (3, 0.8, 0.4) in order to alter the tensile strength of the material, show that it is in line with the two β ions, and find the ratio in which it divides the line joining them.

UNIT 3 CALCULUS

FURTHER DIFFERENTIATION AND INTEGRATION

102 The Chain Rule

> **Reminder**

$\dfrac{dy}{dx} = \dfrac{dy}{du} \times \dfrac{du}{dx}$, where y is a function of a function of x, i.e. $y = f[u(x)]$.

Example Differentiate

a) $(x^2 + 3x + 2)^{\frac{3}{2}}$ b) $\dfrac{1}{1-x}$.

Solution a) $\dfrac{d(x^2 + 3x + 2)^{\frac{3}{2}}}{dx} = \dfrac{d(x^2 + 3x + 2)^{\frac{3}{2}}}{d(x^2 + 3x + 2)} \times \dfrac{d(x^2 + 3x + 2)}{dx}$ ....(★)

$= \dfrac{3}{2}(x^2 + 3x + 2)^{\frac{1}{2}} \times (2x + 3)$

$= \dfrac{3}{2}(2x + 3)(x^2 + 3x + 2)^{\frac{1}{2}}$.

It is not usual to write down the right hand side of equation (★). This is only included here by way of explanation; $u = (x^2 + 3x + 2)$.

b) $\dfrac{d}{dx}\left(\dfrac{1}{1-x}\right) = \dfrac{d}{dx}(1 - x)^{-1} = (-1)(1 - x)^{-2}(-1) = \dfrac{1}{(1 - x)^2}$

Notice the (-1) following the 'to the power -2'. This is the derivative of the bracket $(1 - x)$.

In general the rule boils down to 'the index × the bracket to the power (the index minus 1) × the derivative of the bracket.'

Exercise 102

For the function given in each of questions 1 to 4 find the derived function by a) applying the chain rule, b) first expanding the brackets and differentiating, and then confirm that both answers are equivalent.

1 $f(x) = (x + 1)^2$

2 $y(x) = (x^2 + 2)^2$

3 $g(t) = (3t - 2)^2$

4 $h(v) = (\sqrt{v} + 1)^2$

Differentiate:

5B $(x^3 + 11)^7$ **6B** $(x^2 - 2)^3$ **7B** $(x - 1)^5$

8B $(1 - x)^5$ **9B** $(4x^2 + x - 2)^3$ **10B** $\left(3x^2 + 5x - \dfrac{1}{x}\right)^4$

11B $\dfrac{1}{3 - y}$ **12B** $\dfrac{2}{5 + t^2}$ **13B** $\dfrac{1}{3u^2 + 4u - 7}$

14B $\dfrac{2}{z^9 - 7}$ **15B** $\dfrac{4}{7 + x^3}$ **16B** $\dfrac{1}{\sqrt{(3 - 2x)}}$

17B $\sqrt{(x - 1)}$ **18B** $\dfrac{1}{\sqrt{(x - 1)}}$ **19B** $(x^2 + 3)^{\frac{3}{2}}$

20B $(2v - 1)^{\frac{-1}{3}}$ **21B** $\sqrt[3]{(3x + 2)}$ **22B** $\sqrt{(x + 5)(x - 2)}$

23B $\dfrac{1}{1 + x} + \dfrac{1}{1 - x}$ **24B** $(x + 1)^2 + \dfrac{1}{(x + 1)^2}$ **25B** $\sqrt{(2x + 5)} + \dfrac{1}{\sqrt{(2x + 5)}}$

103 Trigonometric Differentiation

> **Reminder**

$\dfrac{d}{dx} (\sin x) = \cos x, \quad \dfrac{d}{dx} (\cos x) = -\sin x,$ provided x is measured in radians.

Example   Given $f(x) = x^2 + 2 \sin x + 3 \cos x$, find $f'\left(\dfrac{3\pi}{4}\right)$.

Solution $f'(x) = 2x + 2 \cos x - 3 \sin x$

$\Rightarrow f'\left(\dfrac{3\pi}{4}\right) = 2\left(\dfrac{3\pi}{4}\right) + 2 \cos\left(\dfrac{3\pi}{4}\right) - 3\sin\left(\dfrac{3\pi}{4}\right) = \dfrac{3\pi}{2} + 2\left(-\dfrac{1}{\sqrt{2}}\right) - 3\left(\dfrac{1}{\sqrt{2}}\right)$

$= \dfrac{3\pi}{2} - \dfrac{5}{\sqrt{2}} = \dfrac{1}{2} (3\pi - 5\sqrt{2}).$

Exercise 103

1 Differentiate:

a) $\sin x$ b) $\cos x$ c) $1 - \sin x$

d) $x + \cos x$ e) $4 \sin x$ f) $3 + 2 \cos x$

g) $2 - 3 \sin x$ h) $5 \cos x$ i) $x + \sin x$

j) $x^2 - \cos x$ k) $x^3 - 2 \sin x$ l) $2 \sin \dfrac{x}{2} \cos \dfrac{x}{2}.$

2 a) Given $f(x) = \sin x$, find   (i) $f'(0)$ (ii) $f'\left(\frac{\pi}{2}\right)$ (iii) $f'\left(-\frac{\pi}{2}\right)$

b) Given $f(x) = \cos x$, find   (i) $f'(0)$ (ii) $f'\left(\frac{3\pi}{2}\right)$ (iii) $f'\left(\frac{\pi}{4}\right)$

c) Given $f(x) = \sin x + \cos x$, find   (i) $f'(0)$ (ii) $f'\left(\frac{3\pi}{4}\right)$ (iii) $f'\left(\frac{\pi}{3}\right)$

d) Given $f(x) = \sin x - \cos x$, find   (i) $f'\left(\frac{\pi}{6}\right)$ (ii) $f'\left(\frac{\pi}{3}\right)$ (iii) $f'\left(\frac{3\pi}{2}\right)$

e) Given $f(x) = \cos x - \sin x$, find   (i) $f'\left(\frac{5\pi}{6}\right)$ (ii) $f'\left(\frac{2\pi}{3}\right)$ (iii) $f'\left(\frac{4\pi}{3}\right)$

f) Given $f(x) = x^2 + \cos x$, find   (i) $f'(0)$ (ii) $f'\left(\frac{5\pi}{4}\right)$ (iii) $f'\left(-\frac{\pi}{3}\right)$.

3 Find the gradient of the tangent to the curve with equation $y = 3 \cos x + 4 \sin x$ at the point where x is

a) 0 b) $\frac{\pi}{4}$ c) $\frac{\pi}{2}$ d) π e) a where $\tan a = \frac{3}{4}$.

4 Find the equation of the tangent to the curve with equation $y = 4 \cos x - 3 \sin x$ at the point where it crosses the y-axis.

5 Show that the functions $f(x) = x - \sin x$ and $g(x) = x - \cos x$ are never decreasing.

6 Simplify then differentiate:

a) $\cos^2 \frac{x}{2} - \sin^2 \frac{x}{2}$ b) $\cos^2 \frac{x}{2} + \sin^2 \frac{x}{2}$

c) $2 \sin \frac{x}{2} \sin\left(\frac{\pi}{2} - \frac{x}{2}\right)$ d) $2 \sin^2 \frac{x}{2} - 1$.

7 For the curve with equation $y = f(x) = \sqrt{3} \cos x + \sin x$, find:

a) $f(0), f(2\pi)$

b) the roots of $f(x) = 0$

c) the stationary values of f and their nature and hence sketch the curve.

104 The Chain Rule with Trigonometric Functions

> **Reminder**

Example   Differentiate a) $(x^3 + 3 \sin x)^4$ b) $\cos (1 + x^2)$.

Solution   a) $y = (x^3 + 3 \sin x)^4$ (an algebraic function of a trig function of x)

$\Rightarrow y' = 4(x^3 + 3 \sin x)^3(3x^2 + 3 \cos x)$

$= 12(x^2 + \cos x)(x^3 + 3 \sin x)^3$.

b) $y = \cos (1 + x^2)$ (a trig function of an algebraic function of x)

$\Rightarrow y' = -\sin (1 + x^2) (2x) = -2x \sin (1 + x^2)$.

Note: Although it may appear in the formula list on your exam paper, it is not advisable to learn the rule that the derivative of 'sin ax' is 'a cos ax'. It is far better to deal with the sine first and the function of x second, i.e. cos $(ax) \times a$. This can and

FURTHER DIFFERENTIATION AND INTEGRATION

> **Reminder** continued

should, of course, be tidied up to give $a \cos ax$. The principle, however, is important if you intend to pursue the study of Mathematics beyond Higher, or even if you are asked to deal with a function of a function of a function of x, e.g. $\sin^2 3x$. In this case:
$y = \sin^2 3x = (\sin 3x)^2 \Rightarrow y' = 2 (\sin 3x) (\cos 3x) (3) = 3 \sin 6x.$

Exercise 104

1B Differentiate:

a) $(x + 2)^6$

b) $(2x - 3)^5$

c) $(7 + x)^4$

d) $(2 - x)^3$

e) $(3x + 4)^2$

f) $(6 - x)^{-7}$

g) $(3 - 4x)^{-4}$

h) $(x^2 + 3)^4$

i) $(x^3 - 2)^5$

j) $(x^4 + 7)^3$

k) $(4 - x^5)^6$

l) $(3x - 2)^{\frac{3}{2}}$.

2B Differentiate:

a) $(x + \sin x)^4$

b) $(2 - \cos x)^{\frac{1}{2}}$

c) $(3 \sin x - 2 \cos x)^{\frac{3}{2}}$

d) $(5 \sin x - 1)^{-2}$

e) $(\cos x)^{\frac{-3}{4}}$

f) $(\sin x)^{\frac{2}{3}}$

g) $\sin^2 x$

h) $\cos^2 x$

i) $(1 + 3 \cos x)^{\frac{1}{2}}$

j) $(2x - 3 \sin x)^{\frac{4}{3}}$

k) $(x - \cos x)^{\frac{1}{5}}$

l) $7(x - 5 \sin x)^7$

m) $\cos^2 x - \sin^2 x$

n) $\cos^2 x + \sin^2 x$

o) $(1 + \cos x)(1 - \cos x)$.

3B Differentiate:

a) $\sin 4x$

b) $\cos 5x$

c) $\sin \frac{1}{2}x$

d) $\cos \frac{3}{2}x$

e) $\sin (3x + 5)$

f) $\cos (4x - 5)$

g) $\sin (2x - 7)$

h) $\cos (8 - 3x)$

i) $2 \sin 3x$

j) $3 \cos 2x$

k) $\sin^2 3x$

l) $\cos^3 2x$

m) $\sin^3 (2x^2)$

n) $(x + \sin 2x)^2$

o) $(\cos 3x - x^2)^{\frac{1}{2}}$.

4B Differentiate:

a) $(2x + 3)^{\frac{1}{2}}$

b) $(x - 1)^{\frac{1}{3}}$.

c) $(x^2 + x - 1)^{\frac{1}{2}}$

d) $(3x^2 + 4x - 2)^{\frac{3}{4}}$

e) $(5 - 7x)^{\frac{1}{4}}$

f) $(x^3 - 5)^{\frac{-2}{3}}$

g) $\dfrac{1}{3x - 2}$

h) $\dfrac{2}{3x^2 + 4}$

i) $\dfrac{11}{(5x - 10)^2}$

j) $\sqrt{(x^2 + 9)}$

k) $\sqrt{(x^3 + 7x - 2)}$

l) $\dfrac{1}{\sqrt{(1 - x)}}$

m) $(x - 1)^{\frac{3}{2}} - 3 (x - 1)^{\frac{1}{2}}$.

105 Trigonometric Integration

> **Reminder**

$$\int \sin x\, dx = -\cos x + c, \quad \int \cos x\, dx = \sin x + c.$$

Example   Evaluate $\int_0^{\frac{\pi}{4}}(1 + 2\sin x)dx.$

Solution $\int_0^{\frac{\pi}{4}}(1 + 2\sin x)dx = [x - 2\cos x]_0^{\frac{\pi}{4}} = \left[\frac{\pi}{4} - 2\cos\left(\frac{\pi}{4}\right)\right] - [0 - 2\cos 0]$

$$= \left[\frac{\pi}{4} - 2\frac{1}{\sqrt{2}}\right] + (2 \times 1) = 2 + \frac{\pi}{4} - \sqrt{2}.$$

Exercise 105

1 Integrate:

a) $\cos x$ b) $\sin x$ c) $1 + \cos x$ d) $x - \sin x$

e) $5 \sin x$ f) $3 + 2 \cos x$ g) $2 - 3 \sin x$ h) $7 \cos x$

i) $x + \cos x$ j) $x^2 + 2 \sin x$ k) $x^3 - 3 \cos x$ l) $\cos^2 \frac{x}{2} - \sin^2 \frac{x}{2}$.

2 Evaluate:

a) $\int_0^{\frac{\pi}{2}} \sin x\, dx$

b) $\int_0^{\frac{\pi}{4}} \cos x\, dx$

c) $\int_0^{\frac{\pi}{3}} (\sin x + \cos x)\, dx$

d) $\int_0^{\frac{\pi}{2}}(\sin x - \cos x)\, dx$

e) $\int_0^{\pi}(\cos x - \sin x)\, dx$

f) $\int_0^{\frac{\pi}{4}} (1 + \cos x)\, dx$

g) $\int_0^{\frac{\pi}{3}} (2 + 3 \sin x)\, dx$

h) $\int_0^{\frac{\pi}{6}} (3 - 2 \cos x)\, dx$

i) $\int_{-\pi}^{\pi} (x^2 + 2 \sin x)\, dx.$

3 Sketch the curve $y = \sin x$ for $0 \leqslant x \leqslant 2\pi$. Calculate the area under the curve from
   a) $x = 0$ to $x = \frac{\pi}{2}$ b) $x = 0$ to $x = \pi$.

4 Sketch the curve $y = \cos x$ for $0 \leqslant x \leqslant 2\pi$. Calculate the area under the curve from
   a) $x = 0$ to $x = \frac{\pi}{2}$ b) $x = \frac{\pi}{2}$ to $x = \pi$.

5 Calculate the area beneath the curve with equation $y = 1 + \cos x$ between $x = \frac{\pi}{6}$ and $x = \frac{\pi}{3}$.

6 Calculate the area enclosed by the curves with equations $y = 1 - \cos x$ and $y = \sin x$ for $0 \leqslant x \leqslant \frac{\pi}{2}$.

106 Three Special Integrals

> **Reminder**

$\int (ax + b)^n \, dx = \dfrac{(ax + b)^{n+1}}{(n + 1)a} + c.$

$\int \sin(ax + b)\,dx = -\dfrac{1}{a}\cos(ax + b) + c.$

$\int \cos(ax + b)\,dx = \dfrac{1}{a}\sin(ax + b) + c.$

These rules are only valid when a linear function $(ax + b)$ is involved.

Example Evaluate $\int_2^3 \sqrt{10 - 3x} \, dx.$

Solution $\displaystyle\int_2^3 \sqrt{10 - 3x} \, dx = \int_2^3 (10 - 3x)^{\frac{1}{2}} \, dx = \left[\dfrac{(10 - 3x)^{\frac{3}{2}}}{\frac{3}{2}(-3)} \right]_2^3 = -\dfrac{2}{9}\left[1^{\frac{3}{2}} - 4^{\frac{3}{2}}\right]$

$= -\dfrac{2}{9}[1 - 8] = \dfrac{14}{9}.$

Exercise 106

1B Integrate:

a) $(2x + 5)^3$ b) $(3x - 4)^4$ c) $(5x + 2)^5$ d) $(1 - 3x)^2$

e) $(2x + 3)^8$ f) $(3x - 2)^5$ g) $(x + 5)^3$ h) $(7 - x)^4$

i) $(3x + 4)^7$ j) $(2x - 3)^{\frac{2}{5}}$ k) $(8 + x)^{\frac{1}{3}}$ l) $(9 - 3x)^{\frac{3}{4}}$

m) $(3x + 7)^{\frac{5}{3}}$ n) $(1 - 2x)^{\frac{7}{4}}$ o) $(11 - x)^{\frac{2}{3}}$ p) $\dfrac{3}{\sqrt{(2x + 5)}}.$

2B Evaluate:

a) $\int_2^3 (3x - 8)^3 dx$ b) $\int_1^2 (5 - 3x)^4 dx$ c) $\int_{-1}^1 (x - 1)^3 dx$

d) $\int_{-2}^2 (4 - x)^2 dx$ e) $\int_0^5 \sqrt{(9 - x)}\, dx$ f) $\int_{-1}^4 (4 + 3x)^{\frac{3}{2}}\, dx.$

3B Integrate:

a) $\cos 3x$ b) $\sin 5x$ c) $\cos(2x - 1)$

d) $\sin(3x + 2)$ e) $x - \sin 3x$ f) $x^2 + 2\cos 3x$

g) $\sin(3 - x)$ h) $\cos(5 + x)$ i) $\cos \frac{1}{2}x$

j) $\sin \dfrac{2x + 1}{3}$ k) $\frac{1}{2}\cos(4x + 3)$ l) $\frac{2}{3}\sin(3x - 4)$

m) $3x^2 + \cos(3x + 2)$ n) $4x^3 - \sin(2x - 3)$ o) $6x - 3\cos 2x$

p) $5x^2 - 8\sin \frac{1}{2}x.$

4B Evaluate:

a) $\int_0^{\frac{\pi}{3}} \cos 3x \, dx$

b) $\int_0^{\frac{\pi}{2}} \sin 2x \, dx$

c) $\int_{-\frac{\pi}{2}}^{\frac{\pi}{2}} \cos \left(x + \frac{\pi}{4}\right) dx$

d) $\int_{-\frac{\pi}{3}}^{\frac{\pi}{6}} \cos \frac{3x}{2} \, dx$

e) $\int_0^{2\pi} \sin \left(3x - \frac{\pi}{2}\right) dx$

f) $\int_{-\frac{\pi}{4}}^{\frac{5\pi}{6}} \sin 3x \, dx$

g) $\int_0^{\frac{\pi}{2}} (\sin 2x - \cos 2x) \, dx$

h) $\int_0^{\frac{\pi}{12}} (\sin 6x + \cos 4x) \, dx$

i) $\int_{-\frac{\pi}{6}}^{\frac{\pi}{6}} (3 \cos 2x + 2 \cos 3x) \, dx.$

5B Integrate:

a) $\sin x \cos x$

b) $\cos^2 x$

c) $\sin^2 x$

d) $\sin^2 x - \cos^2 x.$

6B Calculate the area between:

a) $y = \cos 2x$, $x = 0$, and $y = 0$

b) $y = \sin 2x$, $x = 0$, and $x = \frac{\pi}{2}$

c) $y = \cos 2x$, $y = \sin 2x$, and $x = 0.$

107 TOPIC TEST on Further Differentiation and Integration

⏱ Allow 45 minutes for this test (Non-Calculator)

1 Differentiate: a) $x + \cos x$
    b) $\sin\sqrt{x}$

2 Integrate: a) $\sin(2x + 3)$
    b) $\cos(3x - 2)$

3 Differentiate: a) $(x^2 + 1)^{10}$
    b) $\dfrac{1}{x^2 - 5}$

4 Integrate: a) $\sqrt{2x + 7}$
    b) $\dfrac{1}{(1 - x)^2}$

5 Differentiate: a) $[x^2 + 2 \sin x]^3$
    b) $\sin^3 x$

6 A baker's oven is semi-cylindrical in shape, as shown in the diagram.

The baker wishes to have trays made for the oven by bending rectangular sheets of tin into U-shapes, and fitting them with rectangular ends. It is intended that the U-shape should fit snugly into the oven as shown.

He wishes to have trays of various depths, and so wishes to know the largest width of tin sheet that needs to be bought.

a) With axes as shown, the front of the oven can be represented by the semi-circle with equation:
$x^2 + y^2 = 32$.

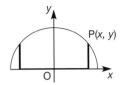

If $P(x, y)$ is the point where a tray touches the oven, show that the width, W, of the tin sheet is given by:

$$W = 2 \left[x + (32 - x^2)^{\frac{1}{2}} \right].$$

b) Hence find the width of the widest sheet of tin that will make a tray which fits into the oven.

[Hint : You can solve an equation like
$2x = \sqrt{(20 - x^2)}$
by squaring both sides to get
$4x^2 = 20 - x^2$.]

LOGARITHMS

108 The Definition of a Logarithm

> ▶ **Reminder**

$\log_b N = x \iff N = b^x$ hence $\log_a a = 1$ and $\log_a 1 = 0$.

Example

a) Express $64 = 8^2$ in logarithmic form.

b) Express $\log_q p = r$ in index form.

c) Solve $\log_x \dfrac{1}{64} = 2$.

Solution

a) $64 = 8^2 \Rightarrow \log_8 64 = 2$.

b) $\log_q p = r \Rightarrow p = q^r$.

c) $\log_x \dfrac{1}{64} = 2 \Rightarrow x^2 = \dfrac{1}{64} \Rightarrow x = \dfrac{1}{8}$.

Exercise 108

1 Express in logarithmic form: [e.g. $5^2 = 25 \Rightarrow \log_5 25 = 2$]

a) $2^3 = 8$ b) $3^2 = 9$ c) $4^3 = 64$ d) $100 = 10^2$

e) $3^{-2} = \dfrac{1}{9}$ f) $10^{-3} = \dfrac{1}{1000}$ g) $3^0 = 1$ h) $4^1 = 4$.

2 Express in index form: [e.g. $\log_4 16 = 2 \Rightarrow 4^2 = 16$]

a) $\log_5 25 = 2$ b) $\log_6 36 = 2$ c) $\log_4 64 = 3$ d) $\log_2 \dfrac{1}{8} = -3$

e) $\log_2 \sqrt{2} = \dfrac{1}{2}$ f) $\log_5 \sqrt[3]{5} = \dfrac{1}{3}$ g) $\log_2 1 = 0$ h) $\log_5 5 = 1$.

3 Express in logarithmic form:

a) $p^2 = q$ b) $r = s^3$ c) $a = b^c$ d) $k^t = v$.

4 Express in indicial form:

a) $\log_3 M = N$ b) $t = \log_4 u$ c) $k = \log_p m$ d) $\log_b a = c$.

5 Solve for x:

a) $\log_3 x = 2$ b) $\log_4 x = 3$ c) $\log_{\sqrt{2}} x = 4$ d) $\log_{\sqrt{3}} x = 8$

e) $4 = \log_{\frac{1}{2}} x$ f) $2 = \log_{\frac{1}{3}} x$ g) $-1 = \log_2 x$ h) $-3 = \log_3 x$

i) $\log_x 8 = 3$ j) $\log_x \dfrac{1}{16} = -2$ k) $\log_x \dfrac{1}{27} = -3$ l) $\log_x 4 = 4$.

6 Evaluate: [e.g. $\log_3 9 = x \Rightarrow 3^x = 9 = 3^2 \Rightarrow x = 2$]

a) $\log_2 8$ b) $\log_3 81$ c) $\log_9 81$ d) $\log_2 \dfrac{1}{4}$

e) $\log_{\frac{1}{2}} 4$ f) $\log_{\frac{1}{3}} 27$ g) $\log_9 27$ h) $\log_8 \dfrac{1}{16}$.

109 Using the laws of logs to obtain the log of a single number

> **Reminder**

The Laws of Logarithms   I $\log_b x + \log_b y = \log_b xy.$

                        II $\log_b x - \log_b y = \log_b \dfrac{x}{y}.$

                        III $r\log_b x = \log_b x^r.$

Example

Express a) $3\log 2 + 2\log 3 - \log 5$

       b) $2 + \log_{10} 7$ as the logarithm of a single number.

Solution

a) Notice that it is acceptable to write this expression without reference to the base. Provided it is understood that all three logarithms are to the same base, the result will be true for any number chosen for the base.

Hence $3\log 2 + 2\log 3 - \log 5 = \log 2^3 + \log 3^2 - \log 5$

                                     $= \log 8 + \log 9 - \log 5$

                                       $= \log(8 \times 9) - \log 5 = \log \dfrac{72}{5}.$

b) $2 + \log_{10} 7 = 2 \times \log_{10} 10 + \log_{10} 7 = \log_{10} 100 + \log_{10} 7$

                           $= \log_{10} 700.$

Exercise 109

1 Express as the logarithm of a single number:

a) $\log 3 + \log 5$ b) $\log 10 - \log 2$ c) $5 \log 2$

d) $\log 14 + \log 2$ e) $\dfrac{1}{2} \log 16$ f) $\log 27 - \log 18$

g) $-3 \log 2$ h) $\log 1 + \log 2.$

2 Express as the logarithm of a single number:

a) $2 \log 2 + \log 3$ b) $\log 128 - 4 \log 2$ c) $4 \log 2 - 2 \log 4$

d) $3 \log 2 - 2 \log 3$ e) $2 \log\sqrt{5} - \dfrac{1}{2} \log 5$ f) $\log 6 - 2 \log 2 + \log 8.$

3 Express as the logarithm of a single number: [e.g. $1 + \log_3 5 = \log_3 3 + \log_3 5 = \log_3 15$]

   a) $1 + \log_2 3$ b) $1 - \log_3 5$ c) $\log_2 6 - 2$

   d) $2\log_3 5 - 1$ e) $2 + 3 \log_3 3$ f) $3 - 2 \log_2 2$

   g) $1 - \log_{10} 2$ h) $2 + \log_{10} 5$ i) $1 + \log_{10} 3 - \log_{10} 2$.

4 Express as the logarithm of a single number:

   a) $\log p + \log q$ b) $2 \log r - \log s$ c) $\log t + \frac{1}{2}\log u$

   d) $\log mn - 2 \log n$ e) $\log xy - \frac{1}{2}\log x$ f) $\log r + 2 \log s - 3 \log t$.

5 Express as the logarithm of a single number:

   a) $1 + \log_{10} a$ b) $2 - 3 \log_{10} b$ c) $\log_{10} a + \frac{1}{2}\log_{10} b - 1$.

6 Solve for x:

   a) $\log x + \log 2 = \log 10$ b) $\log x - \log 4 = \log 25$

   c) $\log x + 2 \log 3 = \log 54$ d) $3 \log 6 - \log x = \log 18$

   e) $\log (x + 1) + \log (x - 1) = \log 8$ f) $\log x^2 + \log 0{\cdot}25 = \log 4$.

110 Further Manipulations with Logarithms

> **Reminder**

Example   Express $\log_{10} 15$ in terms of $\log_{10} 2$ and $\log_{10} 3$.

Solution $\log_{10} 15 = \log_{10} 5 \times 3 = \log_{10} 5 + \log_{10} 3 = \log_{10} \dfrac{10}{2} + \log_{10} 3$

                  $= \log_{10} 10 - \log_{10} 2 + \log_{10} 3 = 1 - \log_{10} 2 + \log_{10} 3$.

Exercise 110

1   Express each of the following in terms of $\log 2$ and $\log 3$:

   a) $\log 8$ b) $\log 9$ c) $\log 12$ d) $\log 18$

   e) $\log \frac{1}{2}$ f) $\log \frac{1}{9}$ g) $\log \frac{1}{6}$ h) $\log 0{\cdot}75$.

2   a) Express $\log_{10} 5$ in terms of $\log_{10} 2$.

    b) Hence, or otherwise, express each of the following in terms of $\log_{10} 2$ and $\log_{10} 3$:

      (i) $\log_{10} \frac{1}{5}$ (ii) $\log_{10} 25$ (iii) $\log_{10} 15$ (iv) $\log_{10} 20$

      (v) $\log_{10} 75$ (vi) $\log_{10} \frac{1}{125}$ (vii) $\log_{10} \frac{5}{16}$ (viii) $\log_{10} 0{\cdot}6$.

3B If $p = \log_a x$ and $q = \log_{x^2} a$, find the connection between p and q.

4B If $a^p = x$, $a^q = y$ and $a^r = z$, calculate the value of $\log_a \dfrac{xy}{z^2}$.

5B If $a = \log x^2 y$ and $b = \log \dfrac{x}{y^2}$, express $\log x$ and $\log y$ in terms of a and b.

6B If $3\log_2 y = 2 \log_2 (x - 3) + 5$, show that $y^3 = 32 (x - 3)^2$.

7   Solve for x, y, z: a) $5^x = 9$ b) $3^y = 7$ c) $2^z = \dfrac{5}{4}$.

8   Solve for p, q, r: a) $p = \log_3 17$ b) $q = \log_7 25$ c) $\log_3 0{\cdot}3 = r$.

111 Graphs of Logarithmic Functions

> **Reminder**

Example
The graph of $y = \log_7 x$ is shown.

Sketch the graph of
a) $y = \log_7 (x - 2)$
b) $y = 1 + \log_7 x$.

Solution
a) x has been replaced by $x - 2$
translate 2 units to the right
the new asymptote is $x = 2$.

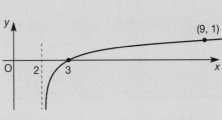

b) $f(x)$ has been replaced by $1 + f(x)$.
Translate 1 unit upwards
find where it crosses the x-axis.
So $1 + \log_7 x = 0$
$\Rightarrow \log_7 x = -1$
$\Rightarrow x = 7^{-1} = \frac{1}{7}$.

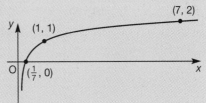

Exercise 111

1 The graph of $y = \log_{10} x$ is shown.
Sketch the graph of:
a) $y = \log_{10} (x + 2)$ b) $y = \log_{10} (x - 2)$
c) $y = \log_{10} (-x)$ d) $y = 1 - \log_{10} x$.
[Remember to indicate all asymptotes and
intersections with axes.]

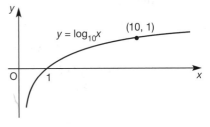

2B Sketch the graph of each of the following functions by first applying the laws of logs
to express the function in a more suitable form for graphing:
a) $\log_{10} x^2 \ (x > 0)$ b) $\log_{10} \left(\frac{1}{x} \right)$ c) $\log_{10} 10x$ d) $\log_{10} \left(\frac{x}{100} \right)$.

3B The graph of $y = \log_2 x$ is shown.
As in question 2B sketch the graph of:
a) $y = \log_2 2x$ b) $y = \log_2 x^3$
c) $y = 1 + \log_2 (x + 1)$ d) $y = 1 - \log_2 \sqrt{x}$.

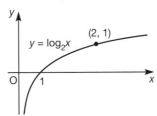

112 Exponential Decay

> **Reminder**

Example

The atmospheric pressure, P_h inches of mercury, at a height of h feet above sea level, on a day when the atmospheric pressure at sea level is P_0 inches of mercury, is given by $P_h = P_0 e^{-kh}$. To-day $P_0 = 29{\cdot}9$ inches.

a) To-day the pressure at a height of 2000 feet is $27{\cdot}7$ inches. Find the value of k.

b) Hence find (i) the pressure at a height of 4000 feet
(ii) the height at which the pressure is $28{\cdot}8$ inches.

Solution

a) $P_h = 29{\cdot}9 \, e^{-kh}$

$\Rightarrow 27{\cdot}7 = 29{\cdot}9 \, e^{-k2000}$

$\Rightarrow \dfrac{27{\cdot}7}{29{\cdot}9} = e^{-2000k}$

$\Rightarrow -2000k = \log_e\!\left(\dfrac{27{\cdot}7}{29{\cdot}9}\right) = -0{\cdot}0764$

$\Rightarrow k = \dfrac{-0{\cdot}0764}{-2000} = 0{\cdot}000\,038\,2$ .... store this number for (b)

b) (i) $h = 4000 \Rightarrow P_{4000} = 29{\cdot}9 \, e^{-0{\cdot}000\,038\,2 \times 4000} = 25{\cdot}7.$

(ii) $P = 28{\cdot}8 \Rightarrow 28{\cdot}8 = 29{\cdot}9 \, e^{-0{\cdot}000\,038\,2\,h}$

$\Rightarrow \dfrac{28{\cdot}8}{29{\cdot}9} = e^{-0{\cdot}000\,038\,2\,h}$

$\Rightarrow -0{\cdot}000\,038\,2\,h = \log_e\!\left(\dfrac{28{\cdot}8}{29{\cdot}9}\right) = -0{\cdot}0374$

$\Rightarrow h = 981.$

Note that the graph of pressure against height is not linear. The computer generated graph below is not a straight line.

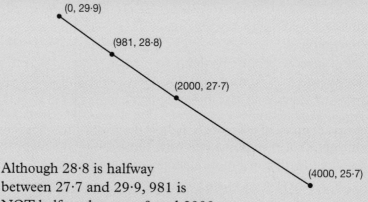

(0, 29·9)

(981, 28·8)

(2000, 27·7)

(4000, 25·7)

Although 28·8 is halfway between 27·7 and 29·9, 981 is NOT halfway between 0 and 2000.
Similarly, 2000 is halfway between 0 and 4000, but 27·7 is NOT halfway between 29·9 and 25·7.
Although the answers look close enough in this case, no credit will be given in exams for considering a linear model instead of the exponential one.

Exercise 112

1 The intensity, I_0 units, of a source of light is diminished to I_d units on passing through d metres of fog, according to the law $I_d = I_0 e^{-0.15d}$.
   a) Calculate the intensity of illumination 20 metres away from a 250 unit light source through this fog.
   b) At what distance from this source will the intensity of illumination be 56 units?

2 The current, I_d amps, in a telephone wire d kilometres along the wire from where the initial current strength is I_0 amps, reduces according to the law $I_d = I_0 e^{-0.13d}$.
   a) Calculate the current at the end of a 10 km wire with inital current 10 amps.
   b) At what distance along this wire has the current fallen to 6 amps?

3 A number N_0 of radioactive nuclei decay to N_t after t years according to the law $N_t = N_0 e^{-0.05t}$.
   a) Find the number remaining after 50 years if the original number N_0 was 500.
   b) The half-life of a radioactive sample is defined as the time taken for the activity to be reduced by half. Calculate the half-life for this sample.

4 A tractor tyre has a slow puncture which causes the pressure within it to drop. The pressure, P_t units, t hours after inflation to P_0 units is governed by the relationship $P_t = P_0 e^{-kt}$.
   a) The tyre is inflated to a pressure of 50 units. Twenty-four hours later the pressure has dropped to 10 units. Calculate the value of k to three decimal places.
   b) The tyre manufacturer advises that serious damage to the tyre will result if it is used when the pressure drops below 30 units.
   If the farmer inflates the tyre to 50 units and uses the tractor for four hours, will he have caused any serious damage to this tyre?

5 A mug of tea cools from an initial temperature of T_0°C to T_t°C in t minutes according to the law $T_t = T_0 e^{-kt}$.
   a) A mug of tea cooled from boiling (100°C) to 75° C in 7 minutes.
   Calculate the value of k to three significant figures.
   b) How much longer did it take for this mug of tea to cool to the room temperature of 20°C?

6 The intensity, I_0 units, of a source of light is diminished to I_t units on passing through a filter of thickness t centimetres, according to the law $I_t = I_0 e^{-kt}$.
   a) If the intensity is reduced by one quarter on passing through a filter which is 4 cm thick, calculate the value of k to three significant figures.
   b) By what percentage would the intensity be reduced if the light passed through a filter of the same material which was 10 cm thick?

7 The atmospheric pressure, P_h millimetres of mercury, at a height of h kilometres above sea level, on a day when the atmospheric pressure at sea level is P_0 mm of mercury, is given by $P_h = P_0 e^{-kh}$. If, when the pressure at sea level is 760 mm, the pressure at a height of 1 km is 670 mm, calculate the pressure at a height of 2 km.

113 Experimental Data

> **Reminder**

Example

An experiment to examine the relationship between two variables p and q was conducted. The table of results obtained was as follows:

p	2	3	4	5	6	7	8
q	10·3	20·5	33·5	48·9	66·6	86·6	108·7

Plotting points from this table did not give a straight line.
It was thought that the relationship might be of the form $q = ap^b$.
The $\log_{10}$ of each of these numbers was computed and the following table constructed:

$\log_{10}p$	0·301	0·477	0·602	0·699	0·778	0·845	0·903
$\log_{10}q$	1·013	1·312	1·525	1·689	1·823	1·938	2·036

Plotting these points gave a straight line. (Rough sketch below)
Show that this proves $q = ap^b$, stating the values of a and b.

Solution

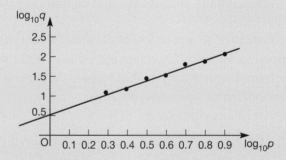

Plotting the points from the second table gives a straight line graph.
Its equation must be of the form $y = mx + c$, where $y = \log_{10}q$ and $x = \log_{10}p$.

We have to find m and c. Find m from the gradient formula. Use two points which are as far apart as possible (to reduce error) and which are close to the best fitting straight line (judged by eye).
Using $(0·301, 1·013)$ and $(0·903, 2·036)$,

$$m = \frac{2·036 - 1·013}{0·903 - 0·301} = \frac{1·023}{0·602} = 1·699 \approx 1·7,$$

so $y = 1·7x + c$ ....(1)

Now substitute the point $(0·903, 2·036)$ into equation (1)★:
so $2·036 = 1·7 \times 0·903 + c$, hence $c = 0·5009$ and $y = 1·7x + 0·5009$.

> **Reminder** continued

i.e. $\log_{10} q = 1{\cdot}7 \times \log_{10} p + 0{\cdot}5009$

$$= \log_{10} p^{1{\cdot}7} + \log_{10} 10^{0{\cdot}5009} \text{ (This line may be implied.)}$$
$$= \log_{10} p^{1{\cdot}7} + \log_{10} 3{\cdot}169$$
$$= \log_{10} 3{\cdot}169 \times p^{1{\cdot}7}.$$

Hence $q = 3{\cdot}169 \times p^{1{\cdot}7}$ i.e. $q \approx 3{\cdot}17p^{1{\cdot}7}$.

$\star$In this case, the value of 'c' can be read off the graph. This is not always possible because the scales chosen need not show the point $(0, 0)$.

Exercise 113

1   Given $X = \log_{10} x$ and $Y = \log_{10} y$, convert each of these to the form $Y = aX + b$:
   a) $y = x^2$
   b) $y = 4 x^3$
   c) $y = 5 x$.

2   Given $X = \log_e x$ and $Y = \log_e y$, convert each of these to the form $Y = aX + b$:
   a) $y = 3 x^4$
   b) $y = 10 x^{-1}$
   c) $y = 0{\cdot}25 x$.

3   Given $Y = \log_{10} y$, convert each of the following to the form $Y = a + bx$:
   a) $y = 2 \times 10^x$
   b) $y = 7 \times 3^x$
   c) $y = 5 \times 2^x$.

4   Given $Y = \log_e y$, convert each of following to the form $Y = a + bx$:
   a) $y = 5 e^x$
   b) $y = 2 e^{-3x}$
   c) $y = 8 \times 5^x$.

5   Express $P = 4Q + 0{\cdot}48$ in the form $p = aq^n$ where $P = \log_{10} p$ and $Q = \log_{10} q$.

6   Express $M = 3{\cdot}6V + 0{\cdot}43$ in the form $m = av^n$ where $M = \log_{10} m$ and $V = \log_{10} v$.

7   Express $S = 2{\cdot}1T - 0{\cdot}7$ in the form $s = at^n$ where $S = \log_{10} s$ and $T = \log_{10} t$.

8   Express $Y = 1{\cdot}39 - 2X$ in the form $y = ax^n$ where $Y = \log_e y$ and $X = \log_e x$.

9   Express $W = 0{\cdot}85 - 3X$ in the form $w = ax^n$ where $W = \log_{10} w$ and $X = \log_{10} x$.

10 Express $P = 1{\cdot}7Z + 0{\cdot}69$ in the form $p = az^n$ where $P = \log_e p$ and $Z = \log_e z$.

11 Express $S = 4T + 0{\cdot}7$ in the form $s = at^n$ where $S = \log_{10} s$ and $T = \log_{10} t$.

12 Express $R = -0{\cdot}9 - 2V$ in the form $r = av^n$ where $R = \log_e r$ and $V = \log_e v$.

13 Express $F = 0{\cdot}5 + 0{\cdot}6t$ in the form $f = ab^t$ where $F = \log_{10} f$.

14 Express $G = 1{\cdot}61 + 3r$ in the form $g = ab^r$ where $G = \log_e g$.

15B The results of an experiment gave rise to the graph shown.
   a) Find the equation of the line (in terms of P and Q).
   b) Given that $P = \log_{10} p$ and $Q = \log_{10} q$, show that p and q satisfy a relationship of the form $p = aq^b$, stating the values of a and b.

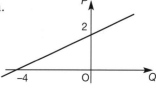

16B a) Show that if the variables x and y are connected by a relationship of the form $y = ae^{bx}$ where a and b are constants, then there is a linear relationship between x and $\log_e y$.

b) Experimental results gave rise to pairs of values of x and y, including these values:

x	3·1	5·2
y	21876	11 913 076

The graph of $\log_e y$ against x was plotted and found to be linear, passing through the points A and B, which correspond to the tabulated values. Find the y coordinates of A and B and hence the values of a and b in the equation $y = ae^{bx}$.

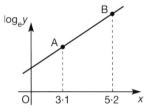

114 TOPIC TEST on Logarithms

🕒 Allow 45 minutes for this test (Use your calculator for questions 7, 8, 9 only.)

1 Express in logarithmic form
a) $4^3 = 64$ b) $x = y^z$.

2 Express in indicial form
a) $\log_3 81 = 4$ b) $t = \log_5 x$.

3 Express as the logarithm of a single number:
a) $4 \log 2 - 3 \log 3$ b) $1 + \log_2 3$.

4 Express $\log 144$ in terms of $\log 2$ and $\log 3$.

5 Express $\log_{10} 45$ in terms of $\log_{10} 2$ and $\log_{10} 3$.

6 The graph of $y = \log_b (x + a)$ is shown. State the values of a and b.

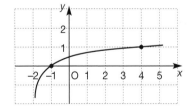

7 Solve $3^x = 5$, correct to 3 decimal places.

8 A radioactive material decays according to the law $N_t = N_0 e^{-kt}$ where N_t is the number of active nuclei remaining after t years and N_0 is the number of active nuclei at the start.
If 500 active nuclei are reduced to 400 in 10 years, how many will remain after 20 years? [Not 300!]

9 An experiment is conducted to investigate the relationship between the variables P and Q.

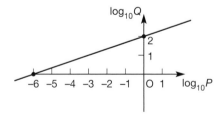

The linear graph shown, connecting $\log_{10} Q$ and $\log_{10} P$, was obtained.

Show that this indicates that $Q = a\, P^b$, stating the values of the constants a and b.

THE AUXILIARY ANGLE

115 Solving the equation $a \cos x + b \sin x = c$

> **Reminder**

If you choose to use Method 1, Exercises 115 and 116 should be done in that order.
If you choose to use Method 2, Exercise 116 should be done before Exercise 115.

Example

Solve $4 \cos x° - 7 \sin x° = 5$ for $0 \leqslant x \leqslant 360$.

Solution
(Method 1)

Take the absolute values of the coefficients (4 and 7) and assign them to be the lengths of the shorter sides of a right-angled triangle.

Then calculate the length of the hypotenuse, $\sqrt{65}$.

Divide each term of the equation by $\sqrt{65}$.

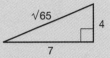

i.e. $\cos x° \dfrac{4}{\sqrt{65}} - \sin x° \dfrac{7}{\sqrt{65}} = \dfrac{5}{\sqrt{65}}$ ....(1)

Notice that $\dfrac{4}{\sqrt{65}}$ and $\dfrac{7}{\sqrt{65}}$ are the sines and cosines of the acute angles in the right-angled triangle. The left hand side of equation (1) can be made into a single trig function. Decide whether you prefer a sine or a cosine.

Suppose a cosine in this case, therefore make $\dfrac{4}{\sqrt{65}} = \cos a°$.

Now place the label a in the appropriate angle in the triangle.

Automatically, $\sin a° = \dfrac{7}{\sqrt{65}}$,

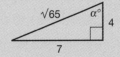

so the equation becomes:

$\cos x° \cos a° - \sin x° \sin a° = \dfrac{5}{\sqrt{65}}$ where $a = \tan^{-1} \dfrac{7}{4} = 60{\cdot}3$

$\Rightarrow \cos(x + a) = \dfrac{5}{\sqrt{65}}$

$\Rightarrow x + 60{\cdot}3 = 51{\cdot}7, 308{\cdot}3, 411{\cdot}7 \Rightarrow x = 248{\cdot}0, 351{\cdot}4.$

With this method, the auxiliary angle, a, is always acute.
Only 5 lines of working are required, when all the explanation is omitted.

> ▶ **Reminder** continued

Solution   First choose whichever single trig function is the most convenient
(Method 2)   form for the left hand side of the equation, $\cos(x \pm a)$, $\sin(x \pm a)$.

Suppose in this case we let

$$4 \cos x° - 7 \sin x° = k \cos(x + a)° \text{ (where } k > 0 \text{ and } 0 \leqslant a \leqslant 360)$$
$$= k\,[\cos x° \cos a° - \sin x° \sin a°]$$
$$= (k \cos a°) \cos x° - (k \sin a°) \sin x°.$$

Equating coefficients of $\cos x°$ $\Rightarrow$ $4 = k \cos a°.$
Equating coefficients of $\sin x°$ $\Rightarrow$ $7 = k \sin a°.$

[Do not omit any of the above working in your exam, marks will be deducted.]

Simultaneous equations like this were solved in section 4.

Squaring and adding: Dividing:

$$k^2 \cos^2 a° + k^2 \sin^2 a° = 16 + 49 \qquad \tan a° = \frac{k\sin a°}{k\cos a°} = \frac{7}{4}$$
$$\therefore k^2(\cos^2 a° + \sin^2 a°) = 65 \qquad\qquad \Rightarrow a = 60\cdot3.$$
$$\therefore k = \sqrt{65}.$$

[Again, in the exam, show where the equations come from and how you solve them.]

Hence the equation becomes $\sqrt{65} \cos(x + 60\cdot3)° = 5$
$$\Rightarrow \cos(x + 60\cdot3)° = \frac{5}{\sqrt{65}}$$
$$\Rightarrow \quad x + 60\cdot3 = 51\cdot7,\ 308\cdot3,\ 411\cdot7 \Rightarrow x = 248\cdot0,\ 351\cdot4.$$

Exercise 115

Solve the equations in questions 1 to 10 for $0 \leqslant x \leqslant 360$:

1 $6 \cos x° - 8 \sin x° = 5$ **2** $5 \sin x° + 12 \cos x° = -6.5$

3 $2 \cos x° + 3 \sin x° = 1$ **4** $5 \cos x° - 4 \sin x° = 6$

5 $7 \sin x° + 2 \cos x° = 5$ **6** $3 \sin x° - 5 \cos x° = 4$

7 $3 \sin x° + 4 \cos x° = 5$ **8** $20 \sin x° + 21 \cos x° = 29$

9 $2 \cos x° - \sqrt{5} \sin x° = 3$ **10** $8 \cos 3x° + 15 \sin 3x° = 13.$

Find the exact solutions of the equations in questions 11 to 16 for $0 \leqslant \theta \leqslant 2\pi$:

11 $\sin \theta + \cos \theta = 1$ **12** $\sqrt{3} \cos \theta + \sin \theta = \sqrt{3}$

13 $\sqrt{3} \cos \theta - \sin \theta = 1$ **14** $\cos \theta - \sqrt{3} \sin \theta = 1$

15 $\sqrt{3} \sin \theta + \cos \theta = \sqrt{3}$ **16** $\cos 2\theta - \sin 2\theta = 1.$

Solve the equations in questions 17 and 18 for $0 \leqslant \theta \leqslant 2\pi$, correct to three decimal places:

17 $11 \cos \theta + 60 \sin \theta + 61 = 0$ **18** $9 \sin \theta - 40 \cos \theta = 31.$

116 Expressing *a* cos *x* + *b* sin *x* in the form *R* cos (*x* ± *α*)

> **Reminder**

Example

Express $2 \sin x° - 5 \cos x°$ as a single trigonometric function.

Solution

Method 1 (to match method 1 in section 115)

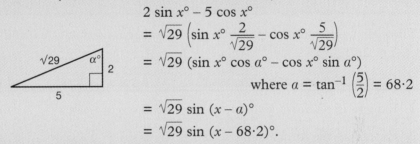

$$2 \sin x° - 5 \cos x°$$
$$= \sqrt{29} \left(\sin x° \, \frac{2}{\sqrt{29}} - \cos x° \, \frac{5}{\sqrt{29}} \right)$$
$$= \sqrt{29} \, (\sin x° \cos a° - \cos x° \sin a°)$$
$$\text{where } a = \tan^{-1} \left(\frac{5}{2} \right) = 68 \cdot 2$$
$$= \sqrt{29} \sin (x - a)°$$
$$= \sqrt{29} \sin (x - 68 \cdot 2)°.$$

Summarising the steps:

1. Find h, the hypotenuse, where the coefficients are the shorter sides.
2. Take out h as a common factor, even though it isn't. To compensate, divide the terms inside the bracket by h. If you are sceptical of this step, simply expand the brackets to prove it is correct.
3. Choose which of $\sin(x \pm \alpha)$ or $\cos(x \pm a)$ is more suitable.
4. Label the appropriate angle as a. In this case choose $\sin (x - a)$ and therefore $\cos a° = \dfrac{2}{\sqrt{29}}.$
5. Find the value of a using $\tan a°$.
6. Simplify the expression to the single trig function.

Method 2 (to match method 2 in section 115)

Decide first which of $\sin(x \pm a)$, $\cos(x \pm a)$ is more suitable. In this case choose $\sin (x - a)$ because the sine comes first and a minus sign follows.

Let $2 \sin x° - 5 \cos x° = k \sin (x - a)$
$$= k \, [\sin x° \cos a° - \cos x° \sin a°]$$
$$= (k \cos a°) \sin x° - (k \sin a°) \cos x°.$$

Equating coefficients of $\sin x° \Rightarrow 2 = k \cos a°.$
Equating coefficients of $\cos x° \Rightarrow 5 = k \sin a°.$

> **Reminder** continued

Squaring and adding:

Dividing:

$k^2 \cos^2 a° + k^2 \sin^2 a° = 4 + 25$

$\tan a° = \dfrac{k\sin a°}{k\cos a°} = \dfrac{5}{2}$

$\therefore k^2(\cos^2 a° + \sin^2 a°) = 29$

$\Rightarrow \qquad a = 68·2$

$\therefore k = \sqrt{29}$

Hence $2 \sin x° - 5 \cos x° = \sqrt{29} \sin (x - 68·2)°.$

Exercise 116

(Throughout questions 1 to 7 it should be understood that $k > 0$ and $0 \leqslant a \leqslant 360$ or $0 \leqslant a \leqslant 2\pi$.)

1 Express in the form $k \cos(x - a)°$:   a) $4 \cos x° + 3 \sin x°$ b) $\cos x° - 3 \sin x°$.

2 Express in the form $k \cos(x + a)°$:   a) $3 \cos x° - \sin x°$ b) $\cos x° + \sin x°$.

3 Express in the form $k \sin(x + a)°$:   a) $6 \sin x° + 8 \cos x°$ b) $\sin x° - \cos x°$.

4 Express in the form $k \sin(x - a)°$:   a) $\sqrt{3} \sin x° - \cos x°$ b) $15 \sin x° + 8 \cos x°$.

5 Express in the form $k \cos(\theta - a)$, (θ being measured in radians):

a) $\cos \theta + \sin \theta$ b) $\cos \theta + \sqrt{3} \sin \theta$ c) $\cos \theta - \sin \theta$.

6 Express $f(x) = \sin x° - \sqrt{3} \cos x°$ in the form $k \sin (x - a)°$, and hence solve $f(x) = 1$.

7 Express $g(x) = 6 \sin x° - 8 \cos x°$ in the form $k \sin (x - a)°$, and hence solve $g(x) = -1$.

8 Express $h(x) = 3 \cos 2x° + 4 \sin 2x°$ in the form $k \cos(2x - a)°$ and hence solve $h(x) = 5$ for $0 < x < 360$.

9 Express $8 \cos 2x° - 6 \sin 2x°$ in the form $k \cos(2x + a)°$, and hence solve the equation $8 \cos 2x° - 6 \sin 2x° = 5$ for $0 \leqslant x \leqslant 180$.

10 Express in terms of a single trig function:

a) $- \cos x° - \sin x°$ b) $- \cos x° + \sqrt{3} \sin x°$ c) $-4 \sin x° - 3 \cos x°$.

[Hint : you may find it easier to write the given expressions in the form $- (\ldots\ldots\ldots\ldots)$ and then use results such as: $- \cos(x - a)° = \cos [180 - (x - a)]°$ and $\cos (a - x)° = \cos(x - a)°.$]

117 Maxima, Minima and Graphs of $y = a \cos x + b \sin x$

> **Reminder**

Example   Sketch the graph of $y = 2 + 3 \cos x° + 7 \sin x°$ for $0 \leqslant x \leqslant 360$.

Solution $y = 2 + 3 \cos x° + 7 \sin x° = 2 + \sqrt{58} \cos (x - 66·8)°$

(by either of the methods shown in section 115)

$y_{max} = 2 + \sqrt{58}$ when $\cos (x - 66·8)° = 1 \Rightarrow x - 66·8 = 0, 360$
$$\Rightarrow x = 66·8,$$

$y_{min} = 2 - \sqrt{58}$ when $\cos (x - 66·8)° = -1 \Rightarrow x - 66·8 = 180$
$$\Rightarrow x = 246·8.$$

$x = 0 \Rightarrow y = 2 + (3 \times 1) + (7 \times 0) = 5;$
$y = 0 \Rightarrow 2 + \sqrt{58} \cos (x - 66·8)° = 0$
$$\Rightarrow \qquad\qquad \cos (x - 66·8)° = \frac{-2}{\sqrt{58}}$$
$$\Rightarrow \qquad\qquad x - 66·8 = 105·2, 254·8$$
$$\Rightarrow \qquad\qquad x = 172·0, 321·6.$$

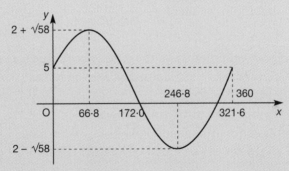

Notice that this is the graph of $y = \cos x°$ moved $66·8°$ to the right, stretched by a factor of $\sqrt{58}$ in the y-direction, and moved 2 units up the y-axis.

Exercise 117

1   State the coordinates of the maximum and minimum turning points on the graph with equation (for $0 \leqslant x \leqslant 360$):

   a) $y = \sin x°$ b) $y = 5 \sin x°$
   c) $y = 3 \sin (x - 30)°$ d) $y = 1 + 2 \sin (x - 60)°.$

2   State the coordinates of the maximum and minimum turning points on the graph with equation (for $0 \leqslant x < 360$):

   a) $y = \cos x°$ b) $y = 4 \cos x°$
   c) $y = 2 \cos (x + 60)°$ d) $y = 7 \cos (x + 45)° - 5.$

3 Write down the zeros of the function:

a) $\sin x°$ b) $3 \sin x°$ c) $5 \sin (x - 25)°$.

4 Write down the zeros of the function:

a) $\cos x°$ b) $4 \cos x°$ c) $7 \cos (x - 25)°$.

5 Express each function in the form $k \cos(x \pm a)°$, and hence sketch the graph of the function, in the range $0 \leqslant x \leqslant 360$, indicating all turning points and intersections with coordinate axes:

a) $4 \cos x° + 3 \sin x°$ b) $3 \cos x° - 4 \sin x°$ c) $\sqrt{3} \cos x° - \sin x°$.

6 Express each function in the form $k \sin(x \pm \alpha)°$, and hence sketch the graph of the function, in the range $0 \leqslant x \leqslant 360$, indicating all turning points and intersections with coordinate axes:

a) $\sqrt{3} \sin x° + \cos x°$ b) $\sin x° - \sqrt{3} \cos x°$ c) $7 \sin x° - 24 \cos x°$.

7 Use your answers to questions 5 and 6 to sketch the graphs of:

a) $4 \cos x° + 3 \sin x° + 5$ b) $\sqrt{3} \cos x° - \sin x° - 2$ c) $\sqrt{3} \sin x° + \cos x° + 1$.

8 Use your answer to question 6 part (c) to find the minimum value of

$$\frac{1}{7 \sin x° - 24 \cos x}$$ and state the value of x, $0 \leqslant x \leqslant 360$, for which it occurs.

9B Find the minimum value of $\dfrac{1}{1 + \cos x° + \sin x°}$ and the value of x for which it occurs.

10B The height, h centimetres, of the water above mean sea level in Abertavish harbour t hours after midnight last Saturday is given by:

$h = 40 (2 \sin 30t° + \cos 30t°)$.

a) Express h in the form $k \sin (30t + a)°$.

b) Find the times of high and low water on Sunday.

c) Find all the times on Sunday when the tide was 50 cm above mean sea level.

11B The function y is defined by $y(x) = 1 + 4 \cos x° - 3 \sin x°$ for $0 \leqslant x \leqslant 360$.

a) Show that $y(x)$ can be expressed in the form $a + b \cos (x + c)°$.

b) Sketch the graph of y, indicating where it crosses the x and y axes.

12B A circle with centre A and radius 5 touches the y-axis at C, and a circle with centre B and radius 4 touches the x-axis at D.

a) Given that the two circles touch as shown, write down the length of AB.

b) Given that ODEC is a rectangle and $B\hat{A}E = \theta$, show that E has coordinates $(5 + 9 \cos \theta, 4 + 9 \sin \theta)$.

c) Hence express the length of OE in terms of a single trig function.

d) Hence write down the maximum length of CD.

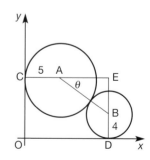

13B Solve the equation in Exercise 78 Q 30 using the techniques learned in this chapter.

14B Use calculus to sketch the graph of $y = \cos x + \sqrt{3} \sin x$ for $0 \leqslant x \leqslant 2\pi$, finding the end-points, intersections with axes, turning points and their nature.
Compare the amount of work involved with obtaining the graph of the similar function in question 6 part (a) in this exercise.

118 TOPIC TEST on The Auxiliary Angle

⏱ **Allow 45 minutes for this test (Calculator required)**

1 Solve $5\sin x° - 12\cos x° = 6.5$.
$[0 \leqslant x < 360]$

2 Solve for k and a $\begin{cases} k\cos a° = 3 \\ k\sin a° = -4 \end{cases}$
$[k > 0, 0 < a < 360]$.

3 Express $\cos x + \sin x$ in the form
$k\cos(x - a)$. $[0 < a < 2\pi]$
Hence also express your answer in the form $k\cos(x + a)$.

4 Express $15\sin 2x° + 8\cos 2x°$ in the form
$R\sin(2x + a)°$. $[0 < a < 360]$
Hence also express your answer in the form $R\sin(2x - a)°$.

5 The point C on the circumference of a rotating wheel of radius 2 units drives a rod AB of length 5 units via a slot in a horizontal arm attached to AB at B.
O is the centre of the wheel.
If, as shown, D is the starting point for

C and $C\hat{O}D = x°$, it can be shown that the length of OA is given by
$OA = f(x) = 5 + \sqrt{3}\sin x° - \cos x°$.

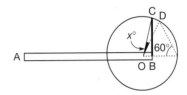

a) Express $g(x) = \sqrt{3}\sin x° - \cos x°$ in the form $k\sin(x - a)°$.
$[k > 0, 0 < a < 90]$

b) Find the greatest and least values of $g(x)$, and the values of x between 0 and 360 for which they occur.

c) Find the zeros of $g(x)$ and sketch the graph of $y = g(x)$ for $0 < x < 360$.

d) Superimpose the graph of $y = f(x)$ on that of $y = g(x)$ and hence or otherwise give the maximum and minimum distances of A from O.

177

PRACTICE UNIT TESTS

119 Practice Unit Test on Unit 3

(Calculator may be used)

Marks

1 a) A, B and C have coordinates $(0, 2, 3)$, $(2, -2, -2)$ and $(6, -10, -12)$.

    (i) Write down the components of $\overrightarrow{AC}$. (1)

    (ii) Hence show that the points A, B and C are collinear. (3)

  b) The point L divides the line KM in the ratio 2:1 as shown in the diagram. Find the coordinates of L. (3)

L   M (17, 13, 8)

K (2, 1, –1)

2 The diagram shows the triangle PQR

where $\overrightarrow{PQ} = \begin{pmatrix} 3 \\ 4 \\ 1 \end{pmatrix}$ and $\overrightarrow{PR} = \begin{pmatrix} 1 \\ 0 \\ -2 \end{pmatrix}$.

Q

R

P

  a) Find the value of $\overrightarrow{PQ}.\overrightarrow{PR}$. (1)

  b) Use the result of part (a) to find the size of $Q\hat{P}R$. (4)

3 a) Differentiate $3\sin x$ with respect to x. (1)

  b) Given $y = \frac{1}{4}\cos x$, find $\frac{dy}{dx}$. (1)

4 Find $f'(x)$ when $f(x) = (x + 2)^{-3}$. (2)

5 a) Find $\int 3\sin x \, dx$. (2)

  b) Integrate $\frac{1}{5}\cos x$ with respect to x. (1)

  c) Evaluate $\int_{2}^{3}(x - 1)^3 \, dx$. (4)

6 a) Simplify $\log_a 50 - \log_a 5$. (1)

  b) Simplify $3\log_4 2 + \log_4 3$. (3)

  c) Simplify $\log_5 5$. (1)

7 a) If $x = \dfrac{\log_e 5}{\log_e 2}$, find an approximation for x. (1)

  b) Given that $\log_{10} y = 2\cdot6$, write down an expression for the **exact** value of y. (1)

  c) If $y = 10^{3\cdot6}$, find an approximation for y. (1)

8 Express $\cos x° + 5 \sin x°$ in the form $k \sin(x + a)°$ where $k > 0$ and $0 \leqslant a < 360$. (5)

120 Revision Tests on Unit 3

🕐 Allow 45 minutes for these tests

TEST 1

(Non-Calculator)

1 Differentiate with respect to x:
   a) $\sin(5x^2 + 2)$ b) $(2x + 3)^5$.

2 Integrate with respect to x:
   a) $\sin(5x + 1)$ b) $(3x + 2)^{-2}$.

3 Express $2\cos x + 2\sin x$ in the form $k\cos(x - a)$, where $k > 0$ and $0 \leqslant x < \frac{\pi}{2}$, and hence state its exact maximum value.

4 Given that $|\mathbf{p}| = 3$ and $\mathbf{p}.(\mathbf{p} + \mathbf{q}) = 18$, find the value of $\mathbf{p}.\mathbf{q}$ and hence prove that $\mathbf{p}$ and $\mathbf{p} - \mathbf{q}$ are perpendicular.

5 Solve $\log_3(x + 1) - \log_3(x - 1) = 4$.

6 Given that $f(x) = \cos 3x$, evaluate $f'\left(\frac{\pi}{4}\right)$.

7 Evaluate $\int_0^\pi 3\sin 4x\,dx$.

8 A radioactive material decays according to the law $N_t = N_0 e^{-kt}$, where N_t is the number of active nuclei remaining after t seconds and N_0 is the number of active nuclei at the start.
   a) If after 1 second, one third of the material has decayed, show that $e^k = \frac{3}{2}$.
   b) (i) If after T seconds, two thirds of the material has decayed, show that $\left(\frac{3}{2}\right)^T = 3$.
      (ii) Express T in terms of log2 and log3.

TEST 2

(Calculator may be used)

1 PQRS is a tetrahedron with vertices P $(-3, 2, -1)$, Q $(13, 3, 1)$, R $(5, 11, 5)$ and S $(1, 5, 9)$.
   K is the midpoint of SR.
   L is the midpoint of SQ.
   a) Find the coordinates of K and L.
   b) Calculate the size of $K\hat{P}L$.

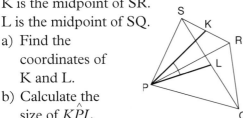

2 If $f(x) = \cos(2x^2 + 1)$, evaluate $f'(3)$ correct to 4 significant figures.

3 Find the maximum and minimum values of $4\sin x° - 7\cos x°$, and the values of x $(0 \leqslant x \leqslant 360)$, for which they occur.

4 The atmospheric pressure P_h inches of mercury, at a height of h feet above sea level is given by $P_h = P_0 e^{-kh}$, where P_0 is the atmospheric pressure at sea level.
   a) When the atmospheric pressure at sea level is 30 inches and the atmospheric pressure at 3000 feet is 28 inches, find the value of k.
   b) Calculate the atmospheric pressure at 4000 feet.
   c) At what height is the atmospheric pressure 29 inches?

5 Evaluate $\int_3^4 (2x + 5)^{\frac{3}{2}}\,dx$ correct to 3 significant figures.

ANSWERS

Exercise 1, page 1

1. a) 5 b) 13 c) $\sqrt{2}$ d) 10 e) $\sqrt{5}$.
5. a) $a\sqrt{2}$ b) $5a$.
6. $y = 9$ or -7.
7. $k = 17$ or -25.
8. $x = 1$ or 5.

Exercise 2, page 2

1. a) $(3, 4)$ b) $(8, 1)$ c) $(5, 1)$
   d) $(3, -2)$.
2. a) $\left(4, \frac{1}{2}\right)$ b) $\left(4, \frac{1}{2}\right)$.
3. $\left(\frac{5}{2}, \frac{9}{2}\right)$.
4. a) $(2a, 3b)$ b) $(m, 0)$ c) $(b^2, 0)$
   d) $(a + c, -c)$.

Exercise 3, page 3

1. a) 1 b) $\frac{3}{7}$ c) 1 d) $-\frac{3}{4}$ e) $-\frac{4}{3}$
   f) -1 g) $\frac{2}{5}$ h) $-\frac{\ell}{k}$ i) $-\frac{1}{3}(m + n)$.
2. a) 0 b) ∞ c) ∞ d) 0.
3. a) $45°$ b) $30°$ c) $120°$ d) $26.55°$
   e) $116 \cdot 6°$ f) $76°$.
4. a) 1 b) $-\sqrt{3}$ c) $\frac{1}{\sqrt{3}}$ d) -0.7
   e) 3 f) $-2 \cdot 05$.
6. 7.
9. a) $\frac{1}{2}$ b) -3.
10. a) 2 b) $\frac{1}{3}$ c) -3.
11. $\frac{1}{a + 2b}$.
12. $\frac{2}{p + q}$.

Exercise 5, page 5

1. a) $x = 2$ b) $y = 5$ c) $x = 1$
   d) $y = 1$ e) $x = 4$ f) $y = \frac{1}{2}x$
   g) $y = \frac{3}{5}x$ h) $y = 2x$ i) $y = -3x$.
2. a) b)

c) d)

e) f)

3. a) (i) $y = \frac{2}{3}x$ (ii) $y = 2$ (iii) $x = 3$.
   b) (i) $y = \frac{5}{4}x$ (ii) $y = 5$ (iii) $x = 4$.
   c) (i) $y = -3x$ (ii) $y = 3$ (iii) $x = -1$.
   d) (i) $y = 3x$ (ii) $y = -6$ (iii) $x = -2$.
   e) (i) $y = -\frac{2}{5}x$ (ii) $y = -2$ (iii) $x = 5$.
4. a) $y = 2x$ b) $y = \frac{1}{3}x$ c) $y = -\frac{3}{5}x$
   d) $y = -x$ e) $y = 0$.
5. a) $y = x$ b) $y = \frac{1}{2}x$ c) $y = \frac{1}{3}x$
   d) $y = \frac{3}{4}x$.

Exercise 6, page 6

1. a) $y = x + 3$ b) $2x + y = 3$
   c) $3y = 2x + 9$ d) $3x + 4y = 12$
   e) $y = 3$.
2. a) $y = 2x + 1$ b) $y = 2x - 2$
   c) $y = 2x$ d) $y = 2x + 5$
   e) $y = 2x - 6$.
3. a) $2, (0, -3)$ b) $-3, (0, 5)$
   c) $\frac{1}{2}, (0, 3)$
   d) $2, \left(0, -\frac{3}{2}\right)$ e) $\frac{1}{2}, \left(0, \frac{5}{2}\right)$
   f) $-1, (0, 1)$ g) $-\frac{3}{4}, \left(0, \frac{7}{4}\right)$
   h) $-1, (0, 5)$ i) $\frac{2}{3}, \left(0, \frac{4}{3}\right)$.
4. a) $y = x - 1$ b) $x + y = 2$
   c) $2y = 5x - 1$ d) $10y + 7x = 1$.
6. 12.
7. a) $y = -\frac{5}{7}x$ b) $y = -\frac{2}{3}x$ c) $y = \frac{5}{2}x$
   d) $y = -\frac{3}{4}x$.
8. a) $y = 5x + 5$ b) $x + 3y = 15$
   c) $3y = 2x + 15$ d) $5x + 4y = 20$.

ANSWERS

Exercise 7, page 7

1. a) b) c) f) and g) only.
2. a) $4x - 3y + 2 = 0$ b) $2x + 3y = 0$
   c) $3x - y + 5 = 0$ d) $x - y - 1 = 0$.
3. A, B, E only.
4. $p = 1$ $q = -5$.

Exercise 8, page 8

1. a) $\left(\frac{1}{2}, \frac{3}{2}\right)$ b) $(-2, 1)$ c) $(3, -2)$
   d) $\left(-\frac{3}{2}, -\frac{17}{2}\right)$ e) $(4, -3)$.
2. a) $(3, 1)$ $(3, -11)$ $(-1, -3)$
   b) $(-3, 4)$ $(3, 4)$ $(-3, -4)$.
3. a) $9x = 11y$ b) $y = 7x$.

Exercise 9, page 9

2. 2.

Exercise 10, page 10

1. a) $-\frac{1}{2}$ b) 1 c) $-\frac{3}{2}$ d) $\frac{4}{3}$
   e) $-\frac{4}{5}$ f) $\frac{3}{7}$.
2. a) $-\frac{1}{2}$ b) 4 c) $-\frac{1}{3}$ d) $\frac{1}{2}$
   e) 1 f) $\frac{3}{2}$.
3. a) $y = x$ b) $y = -2x$ c) $y = \frac{1}{3}x$
   d) $y = -\frac{3}{2}x$ e) $y = -\frac{4}{5}x$ f) $y = 5x$.
4. a) $y = -x$ b) $y = \frac{1}{5}x$ c) $y = -2x$
   d) $y = -\frac{1}{2}x$ e) $y = \frac{2}{3}x$ f) $y = -\frac{3}{4}x$
   g) $y = \frac{7}{2}x$ h) $y = -3x$.
5. a) $y = x + 2$ b) $x + 2y = 4$
   c) $5y = 4x + 10$.
7. a) $\frac{1}{3}$ b) ∞ c) -5 d) $-\frac{5}{7}$
   e) -1 f) 1.
8. a) $2x + 3y = 15$ b) $2x + 3y + 6 = 0$
   c) $2x + 3y + 21 = 0$.
9. a) $6y = 7x - 6$ b) $6y = 7x + 1$
   c) $6y = 7x + 3$.
10. a) (i) $y = 4$ (ii) $x = 3$
    b) (i) $y = 7$ (ii) $x = 4$.
12. $y = -4.5$.
13. $z = -\frac{4}{3}$.
14. $t = -6 \cdot 5$.
15. $k = \frac{5}{3}$.
16. -1.
17. $5y = 4x$.

18. a) $\frac{1}{5}$ b) -5 c) $\frac{3}{2}$.
19. a) 1 b) $\frac{3}{4}$ c) $\frac{15}{2}$.
20. a) $y = 2x$ b) $y = \frac{1}{2}x$ c) $10y = 7x$.

Exercise 11, page 12

1. a) $y = x + 1$ b) $x + y + 7 = 0$
   c) $y = 3x - 11$ d) $2x + y = 10$
   e) $3y = 2x - 13$ f) $x + 3y = 3$
   g) $8x - 2y - 51 = 0$ h) $6x + 9y = 5$
   i) $py - x = p^2$.
2. a) $y = 2x - 5$ b) $x - 2y + 3 = 0$
   c) $3x + y - 2 = 0$ d) $x + 3y + 19 = 0$
   e) $2x - 3y + 4 = 0$
   f) $4x - 10y + 11 = 0$.
3. a) $3x - y - 1 = 0$ b) $x + y = 2$
   c) $2x - 3y = 23$ d) $3x + 4y = 11$.
4. a) $x + y = 0$ b) $x - 2y + 8 = 0$
   c) $3x - 2y = 16$ d) $4x + 3y + 22 = 0$.
5. a) $x + 2y + 4 = 0$ b) $x + 6y + 11 = 0$
   c) $y = 2x$ d) $2y = 4x - 17$.
6. a) $x - 4y + 14 = 0$ b) $4x + y + 5 = 0$
   c) $2x + 3y + 17 = 0$
   d) $3x - 2y + 6 = 0$ e) $3x - y = 13$
   f) $x + 3y = 1$.
7. a) $y = 3x + 11$ b) $3y = x - 7$.
8. $12x + 7y = 13$.
9. $2x + 4y = 25$.
10. a) $y = x$ b) $3x + 2y = 23$
    c) $14x + 8y = 179$ d) $x + 8y = 6$.
11. $x + y = 13$ $y = x + 5$.
12. $5y = x + 8$ $5x + y = 38$.
13. a) $2x + y = 9$ b) $y = x - 6$
    c) $(5, -1)$.
14. $(1, 3)$.
15. $(6, 2)$.
16. a) $2x + y = 15$ b) $y = 9x - 2$
    c) $\left(\frac{17}{11}, \frac{131}{11}\right)$.
17. $\left(\frac{11}{3}, -1\right)$.
19. $(4, 4)$ $(3, 6)$ $(5, 2)$.

Exercise 12, page 14

1. a) $3x + y = 17$ $3y = 5x - 33$
      $x + 5y = 1$ $(6, -1)$
   b) $y = 2$ $2y = 3x - 2$
      $3x + y = 8$ $(2, 2)$
   c) $y = 1$ $y = 2x - 3$
      $2x + y = 7$ $(2, 1)$.

2. a) $4y = 3x - 17$ $3y = x - 14$
   $y = 2x - 3$ $(-1, -5)$
b) $x + 6y = 11$ $5x + 3y = 12$
   $3y = 4x - 1$ $\left(\frac{13}{9}, \frac{43}{27}\right)$
c) $x - y + 2 = 0$ $x + 6y = 6$
   $3x + 4y = 2$ $\left(-\frac{6}{7}, \frac{8}{7}\right)$
d) $y = x$ $3x + 2y + 6 = 0$
   $2x + 3y + 6 = 0$ $\left(-\frac{6}{5}, -\frac{6}{5}\right)$.

3. a) $7y = x - 19$ $2x + y + 7 = 0$
   $x + 3y + 11 = 0$ $(-2, -3)$ 5
b) $14x + 4y = 5$ $6x + 4y = 21$
   $x + 2 = 0$ $\left(-2, \frac{33}{4}\right)$ $\frac{1}{4}\sqrt{689}$
c) $2x + y = 5$ $7y = x + 5$
   $y = 3x - 5$ $(2, 1)$ 5
d) $3y = x - 4$ $2y = x - 6$
   $y = x - 8$ $(10, 2)$ 10.

Exercise 13, page 14

6. a) $(2, -4)$.
7. $(3, 2)$ $(1, 0)$ $(7, 0)$ 6 units^2.
8. a) $y = x + 1$ b) $x + y = 9$.
9. a) $(0, 8)$ $(6, 0)$ b) $4x + 3y + 1 = 0$
   c) $3x - 4y + 32 = 0$ d) $(-4, 5)$.
10. a) 1   b) $-3\cdot7$ c) $-0\cdot5$.
11. $-\frac{7}{2}$.
12. $\frac{1}{a + b}$.
13. $\frac{3}{4}$.
14. a) AC: $3x + y = 22$ BD: $3x + y = 52$
   b) $x - 3y + 26 = 0$ c) $y = 7$
   d) $x + 3y = 16$.
15. a) $y = 8x - 20$ b) $2x + 3y = 5$
   c) $\left(\frac{5}{2}, 0\right)$.
16. a) $y = x$ b) $11x + 4y + 2 = 0$
   c) $\left(-\frac{2}{15}, -\frac{2}{15}\right)$.
17. $2x + y - 3 = 0$.
18. b) T $(10, -2)$ c) (i) $3x + 2y = 13$
   (ii) $y = 5x - 13$ (iii) $(3, 2)$.
19. a) $x + 2y = 22$ b) $(11, 23)$.
20. a) $x = 6$ b) $y = x$
   c) use the perpendicular bisectors or three distances
   d) $3y = x + 12$
   e) $2x = 3y$ $8x + 3y = 120$ $(12, 8)$
   f) 2:1.

Topic Test, page 17

1. a) 10   b) $(1, 2)$ c) 2   d) $y = 2x$
   e) $x = -3; y = -1$ f) $\frac{3}{4}$
   g) $3x - 4y + 5 = 0$.
2. a) $-\frac{4}{5}$ b) $\left(0, \frac{2}{5}\right)$ c) $\frac{5}{4}$
   d) $25x - 20y + 8 = 0$.
4. $31\cdot0°$.
5. $\left(\frac{7}{2}, 0\right)$.

UNIT 1 FUNCTIONS

Exercise 15, page 19

1. a) $\{3\}$, $\{6\}$, $\{2, 4\}$, $\varnothing$, $\{1, 2, 3, 4, 5, 6, 9\}$,
   $\{2, 3, 4, 6, 8, 9\}$, $\{1, 2, 3, 4, 5, 6, 8\}$,
   $\{1, 2, 3, 4, 5, 6, 8, 9\}$, b) $\{6, 7, 8, 9\}$,
   $\{7, 8\}$, $\{7\}$.
   c)

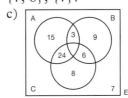

2. a) $\{c, d\}$, $\{a, b, c, d, e, f\}$, $\{e, f, g, h\}$,
   $\{a, b, g, h\}$, $\{a, b, e, f, g, h\}$, $\{g, h\}$,
   $\{a, b, e, f, g, h\}$, $\{g, h\}$,
   b)

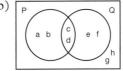

   $P' \cup Q'$, $P' \cap Q'$.
3. $\{x \mid 0 < x \leqslant 1\}$, $\{x \mid -2 \leqslant x < 3\}$,
   $\{x \mid 1 < x \leqslant 4\}$,
   $\{-2 \leqslant x \leqslant 0\} \cup \{3 \leqslant x \leqslant 4\}$,
   $\{3 \leqslant x \leqslant 4\}$,
   $\{-2 \leqslant x \leqslant 0\} \cup \{1 < x \leqslant 4\}$.

Exercise 16, page 22

1. a) relation   b) 1–1 correspondence
   c) relation   d) relation
   e) function   f) 1–1 function
   g) relation   h) function   i) relation
   j) relation   k) function   l) function
   m) relation   n) function
   o) 1–1 correspondence   p) function
   q) relation   r) 1–1 correspondence
   s) relation   t) relation
   u) 1–1 correspondence.

2. a) relation b) relation c) function
 d) 1–1 correspondence
 e) 1–1 correspondence f) relation
 g) function h) relation
 i) 1–1 correspondence j) function
 k) relation l) function.

3. (i) a)

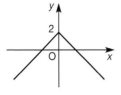

b)

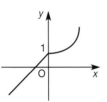

c)

d)

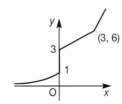

e)

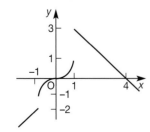

f)

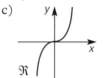

(ii) (c), (e)   (iii) (c)

4. a) $x \geqslant 0$ b) $x \geqslant -1$ c) $x \leqslant 2$
 d) $\{x < -1\} \cup \{x > 1\}$

 e) $x \neq 0$ or $\{x < 0\} \cup \{x > 0\}$
 f) $x \neq 2$ or $\{x < 2\} \cup \{x > 2\}$.

5. a)

b)

$\{x \in \Re \mid x \geqslant 0\}$

c)

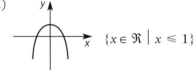

d)

$\{x \in \Re \mid x \leqslant 1\}$

6. a) $\Re$ b) $\{x \in \Re \mid x \geqslant 0\}$
 c) $\{x \in \Re \mid x < 3\}$.

Exercise 17, page 25

1. a) $b \to q \to x$ $c \to r \to z$
 b) x, x, z
 c) domain = $\{a, b, c\}$ range = $\{x, z\}$.
2. 3, 2, 1, 0, 5, 3, 1, –1.
3. 9, 1, 36, 3, 11, 18.
4. 8, –8, 125, 2, –26, 65.

Exercise 18, page 26

1. a) $x^2 + 2$ $(x + 2)^2$
 b) $x^3 + 1$ $(x + 1)^3$.
2. a) $4(x^2 + 1)$ b) $2(x^2 + 4)$
 c) $4x$ d) $x^4 + 8x^2 + 20$.
3. a) $(x + 1)^2$ b) $2x + 7$ c) $x^2 - x + 1$
 d) $2x^4 + 1$ e) $4x(x - 1)$
 f) $(x^4 + 2x^2 + 2)^{-1}$ g) $3x(2 - 9x^2)$
 h) $\sin(x^2)°$.
4. a) $x^2 + 1$ b) $2x + 4$ c) $x^2 + x$
 d) $(2x^2 + 1)^2$ e) $2x^2 - 3$
 f) $\dfrac{x^4 + 2x^2 + 2}{(x^2 + 1)^2}$ g) $3(2x - x^3)$
 h) $\sin^2 x°$.

Exercise 19, page 27

1. show that $f(g(x)) = x$.

2.

f	f^{-1}	$f^{-1}(x) = x - 3$.
$2 \to 5$	$5 \to 2$	
$3 \to 6$	$6 \to 3$	
$4 \to 7$	$7 \to 4$	
$5 \to 8$	$8 \to 5$	

3. a) $\frac{1}{2}x$ b) $x - 4$ c) $\sqrt[3]{x}$ d) $x - 2$

e) $\frac{1}{5}x$ f) $\frac{-1}{3}x$ g) $\sqrt[5]{x}$ h) $\frac{1}{x}$

i) $7 - x$ j) $\frac{1}{2}(x - 5)$ k) $\frac{1}{3}(x + 1)$

l) $\frac{1}{3}(1 - x)$ m) $1 - x$ n) $x + \frac{1}{2}$ o) x.

4. a) $x - 1$ $\frac{1}{2}x$ $\sqrt{x}$ b) 4 4 2.

5. a)

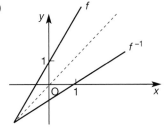

b) $\frac{1}{2}(x - 1)$

c) reflection in $y = x$.

6. a)

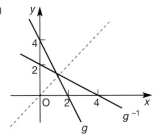

b) $g^{-1}(x) = \frac{1}{2}(4 - x)$

c) reflection in $y = x$.

7. a)

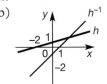

b)

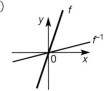

c)

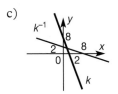

d)

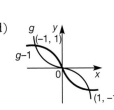

Exercise 20, page 30

1. b) $y = f(-x)$ $y = f(x)$

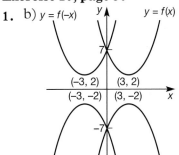

c) $y = -f(-x)$ a) $y = -f(x)$

d) $y = f(x) + 1$

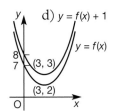

$y = f(x)$

e) $y = f(x - 1)$

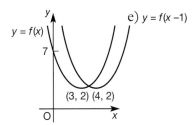

$y = f(x)$

f)

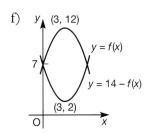

$y = f(x)$

$y = 14 - f(x)$

2. b) $y = g(-x)$ $y = g(x)$

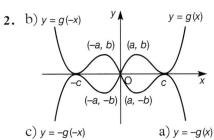

c) $y = -g(-x)$ a) $y = -g(x)$

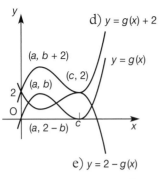

d) $y = g(x) + 2$

$y = g(x)$

(a, b + 2)

(c, 2)

(a, b)

2

O

(a, 2 − b)   c   x

e) $y = 2 - g(x)$

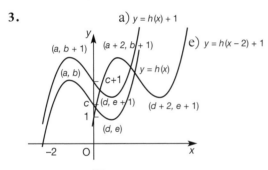

g) $y = 2g(x)$

f) $y = g(x + 2)$

(a, 2b)

(a−2, b) (a, b) $y = g(x)$

−2   O

c−2   c   x

3.

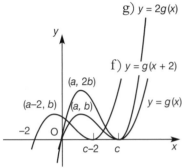

a) $y = h(x) + 1$

(a, b + 1)   (a + 2, b + 1)   e) $y = h(x - 2) + 1$

(a, b) $y = h(x)$

c+1

c (d, e + 1)   (d + 2, e + 1)

1

(d, e)

−2   O   x

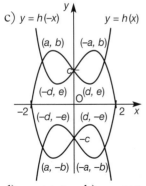

c) $y = h(-x)$ $y = h(x)$

(a, b)   (−a, b)

c

(−d, e) (d, e)

−2   (−d, −e) (d, −e)   2   x

−c

(a, −b) (−a, −b)

d) $y = -h(-x)$ b) $y = -h(x)$

Exercise 21, page 31

1. a) 148·4   b) 0·135   c) 20·086
   d) 0·368   e) 9·906   f) 0·149
   g) 44·8   h) 1·642.

2. a)

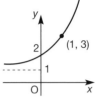

2

1

(1, 3)

O   x

b)

O

(1, 2)

−1

x

c)

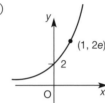

2

(1, 2e)

O   x

d)

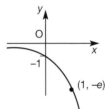

O

−1

(1, −e)

x

e)

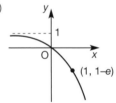

1

O

(1, 1−e)

x

f)

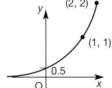

(2, 2)

(1, 1)

0.5

O   x

g)

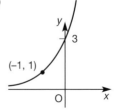

3

(−1, 1)

O   x

h)

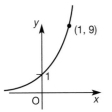

(1, 9)

1

O

i)

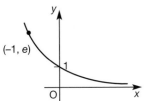

(−1, e)

1

O

j)

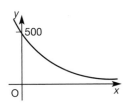

500

O

k)

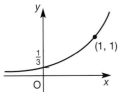

(1, 1)

$\frac{1}{3}$

O

l)

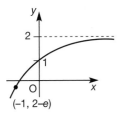

2

1

O

(−1, 2−e)

b)

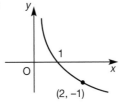

1

O

(2, −1)

c)

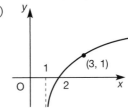

(3, 1)

1

O   2

d)

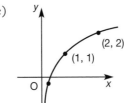

1

−2 −1

O

e)

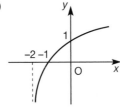

(2, 2)

(1, 1)

O

f)

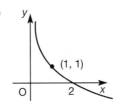

(1, 1)

O   2

3. a) $a = 2$ b) $a = 3$ c) $a = 4$
d) $a = 2$, $b = 3$ e) $a = 3$, $b = 2$
f) $a = 2$, $b = -1$ g) $a = 1$, $b = 3$
h) $a = 4$, $b = -1$ i) $a = 3$, $b = 5$.

Exercise 22, page 32

1. a) 0·602   b) 1·099   c) 1·230
d) 1·887   e) 1·949   f) 2·901
g) 1·501   h) 3·600.

2. a) 1   b) 0   c) 1   d) 0   e) 1   f) 2.

3. a)

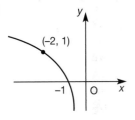

(−2, 1)

−1   O

4. a)

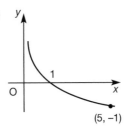

1

O

(5, −1)

b)

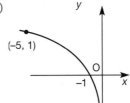

(−5, 1)

O

−1

187

c)

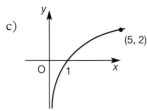

(5, 2)

d)

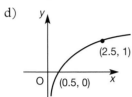

(2.5, 1)

(0.5, 0)

5. a) $a = -1$, $b = 10$ b) $a = -2$, $b = 3$
c) $a = 1$, $b = 5$ d) $a = 2$, $b = 8$.

Topic Test, page 33

1. a) $\{a, b, c, d\}$ b) $\{w, x, y, z\}$
c) $\{x, y, z\}$ d) y.
2. a) h (either because a has two images
or because c has none)
b) k (the elements are paired off).
3. a) r because it is two-valued and not
defined for negative x values;
b) p because the range is the whole
of the co-domain and the graph is
never at the same height more
than once.
4. -21, $3 - 6x^2$
5. (i)

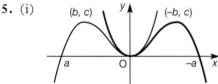

(b, c) $(-b, c)$

a O $-a$

(ii)

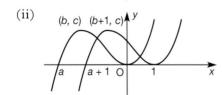

(b, c) $(b+1, c)$

a $a + 1$ O 1

6. a) (i) $16x^2 + 40x + 26$
(ii) x
b) They are inverses of each other.

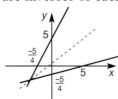

5

$\frac{-5}{4}$

5

$\frac{-5}{4}$

c) Images of each other under
reflection in $y = x$.

UNIT 1 DIFFERENTIATION

Exercise 24, page 34

1.

x_Q	y_Q	m_{PQ}
4	33	10
3	19	8
2	9	6
$1\frac{1}{2}$	5·5	5
$1\frac{1}{4}$	4·125	4·5
1·1	3·42	4·2
1·01	3·0402	4·02
1·001	3·004002	4·002

The gradient of the tangent appears to
be close to 4.

2.

x_Q	y_Q	m_{PQ}
-2	9	-2
-1	3	0
0	1	2
$\frac{1}{2}$	1·5	3
$\frac{3}{4}$	2·125	3·5
0·9	2·62	3·8
0·99	2·9602	3·98
0·999	2·996002	3·998

The gradient of the tangent appears to
be close to 4.
3. $y_Q = 2h^2 + 4h + 3$ $m_{PQ} = 2h + 4$
$m_{tgt} = 4$.
4. $y_Q = 2x^2 + 4xh + 2h^2 + 1$
$m_{PQ} = 2h + 4x$ $m_{tgt} = 4x$.
5. a) (i) 3 (ii) 9 (iii) 3 (iv) 4
(v) -4 (vi) 12
b) (i) 4 (ii) 8 (iii) -8 (iv) 0

c) (i) $(1, 3)$ (ii) $(2, 9)$
(iii) $(-3, 19)$ (iv) $(0, 1)$
d) $y = 4x - 1$.

Exercise 25, page 36

1. a) $3x^2$ b) $6x^5$ c) $9x^8$ d) $20x^{19}$
e) $28x^6$ f) $44x^3$ g) 0 h) $\frac{3}{2}x^2$
i) $2x^4$ j) 4 k) 0 l) $-12x^3$
m) $15x^4$ n) $-x^3$ o) $3x$ p) $3x^2 + 3$
q) $5x^4 + 7$ r) $6x + 2$
s) $-2 + 6x - 4x^3$ t) $4 + 6x$
u) $20x - 5$ v) $x^2 - 10x + 1$
w) $-4x^{-5}$ x) $-7x^{-8}$ y) $-6x^{-4}$
z) $-6x^{-7}$.

2. a) $2x + 4$ b) $4x^3 - 12x$
c) $6x^5 + 6x^2$ d) $8x + 4$
e) $\frac{1}{4} + x^{\frac{-1}{2}}$ f) $18x - 12$
g) $98x + 56$ h) $50x - 40$.

3. a) $\frac{-1}{x^2}$ b) $\frac{-6}{x^3}$ c) $\frac{-5}{x^6}$ d) $\frac{-6}{x^3}$
e) $\frac{-3}{2x^4}$ f) $\frac{-24}{5x^7}$ g) $\frac{-6}{x^7}$ h) $\frac{7}{3}x^{\frac{4}{3}}$
i) $\frac{4}{5x^{\frac{1}{5}}}$ j) $\frac{2}{x^{\frac{1}{3}}}$ k) $\frac{1}{x^{\frac{1}{2}}}$ l) $\frac{1}{x^{\frac{2}{3}}}$
m) $\frac{3}{x^{\frac{1}{2}}}$ n) $\frac{3}{2}x^{\frac{1}{2}}$ o) $\frac{-3}{4x^{\frac{1}{4}}}$ p) $\frac{1}{x^{\frac{3}{2}}}$
q) $\frac{-4}{x^{\frac{5}{3}}}$ r) $\frac{-3}{8x^{\frac{5}{4}}}$ s) 0 t) $\frac{1}{3x^{\frac{2}{3}}}$
u) $\frac{2}{3x^{\frac{1}{3}}}$ v) $\frac{-2}{3x^{\frac{5}{3}}}$ w) $\frac{-15}{2x^{\frac{5}{2}}}$ x) $\frac{-5}{2x^{\frac{7}{2}}}$.

4. a) $5(4x^3 + 3x^2)$ b) $1 - \frac{1}{x^2}$
c) $\frac{1}{2}x^{\frac{-1}{2}} - \frac{1}{2}x^{\frac{-3}{2}}$ d) $6x^2 + 14x + \frac{3}{x^2}$
e) $15x^4 - 2x^{-5}$ f) $2(5x^4 - 2x)$
g) $\frac{2}{3}x^{\frac{-1}{3}} + \frac{3}{2}x^{\frac{-5}{2}}$ h) $5x^{\frac{3}{2}}$ i) $6x + \frac{1}{2}x^{-3}$
j) $2x + 2x^{-3}$ k) $\frac{1}{3} - 3x^{-2}$
l) $15x^{\frac{-1}{4}} + 8x^{\frac{-5}{3}}$.

5. a) $1, 0, -1, 5$ b) $-18, 144$
c) $0, 6, 12, 2$ d) $-2, 2, \frac{-1}{4}, 16$ e) $\frac{1}{16}$.
6. a) (i) 3 (ii) 2
b) (i) $1, -2$ (ii) $2, -3$.
7. a) $5ax^4$ b) $2px + q$ c) $b(3x^2 - 2x)$
d) $-cx^{-2}$ e) $\frac{\pi}{12}(4x^3 + 3x^2)$
f) $3\pi(2x - a)$.

8. a) $2x - \frac{2}{x^3}$ b) $1 - \frac{1}{x^2}$ c) $\frac{1}{2x^{\frac{1}{2}}} - 1$
d) $2x + \frac{5}{2}x^{\frac{3}{2}}$ e) $2x - 3$ f) $2x - 1$
g) $12x - 13$ h) $24x^5 - 12x^2$
i) $4x^3 - \frac{4}{x^5}$ j) $\frac{-8}{x^3} + \frac{x}{2}$ k) $2x - \frac{8}{x^3}$
l) $1 - \frac{9}{x^2}$ m) $6 + \frac{15}{x^2}$ n) $3x^{\frac{1}{2}} - \frac{1}{2x^{\frac{1}{2}}}$
o) $3x^2 + 4x$ p) $9x^2 + 8x$ q) $\frac{3x - 4}{2x^{\frac{3}{2}}}$
r) $\frac{7x^2 + 3}{3x^{\frac{2}{3}}}$ s) $\frac{22x^2 - 3}{4x^{\frac{1}{4}}}$
t) $24x^5 + 8x - \frac{2}{x^3}$.

9. a) $3x^2 + 4x + 1$ b) $3x^2 - 6x + 2$
c) $3x^2 + 10x + 6$
d) $4x^3 + 12x^2 + 6x - 4$
e) $4x$ f) $2x + 2 + \frac{2}{x^3}$.

10. a) $\frac{3}{x^2}$ b) $\frac{x + 1}{2x^{\frac{3}{2}}}$ c) $\frac{-6 - 5x}{x^3}$
d) $\frac{2(x^3 - 3)}{x^2}$ e) $\frac{2(x^3 - 5)}{x^3}$ f) $\frac{x^2 - 1}{x^2}$
g) $\frac{x^2 - 6}{x^4}$ h) $\frac{2x - 1}{6x^{\frac{4}{3}}}$ i) $\frac{15x^4 + 33}{2x^{\frac{5}{2}}}$
j) $\frac{2(3x^4 - 5)}{3x^3}$ k) $\frac{3ax^2 + 2x + 9}{2x^{\frac{3}{2}}}$.

Exercise 26, page 38

1. a) $y = 6x - 3$ b) $y = 4x - 2$
c) $x + y + 2 = 0$ d) $2y = x + 4$
e) $2x + y = 1$ f) $y = 3x + 2$
g) $2x + y = 5$ h) $4x + y = 8$
i) $y = 2$ j) $y = 6x + 4$
k) $4y = 3x - 32$ l) $2x + 9y = 9$
m) $12y = x + 16$ n) $3x + 2y = 5$
o) $8y = 7x + 44$ p) $2y = 7x - 4$.
2. a) $4x + y = 18$ b) $x + 4y = 9$
c) $x + 2y + 9 = 0$ d) $x + 8y = 131$
e) $2x + 6y = 13$.
3. $y = 2x - 1$.
4. $y = 2x - 2$ $2x + y + 2 = 0$ $(0, -2)$.
5. $(0, -4), (0, 28)$.
6. $4x + 2y = 5$.
7. $y = 4x - 1$ $12x + 4y = 3$.
9. $5\sqrt{2} \div 4$.
10. 7 $(-1, -3)$ $y = 7x + 4$.

11. $(4, 37)$.

12. $y = 3x - 3$.

13. $y = 3x + 2$.

14. $x + 4y = 8$.

15. $(-\sqrt{3}, -8)$.

16. $b = 1$, $c = 8$.

17. $a = 4$, $b = 12$.

18. $a = 2$, $b = 3$.

Exercise 27, page 41

1. a) 10 m/s   b) 25 m/s   c) 30 m/s.

2. $v = 10(1 - t)$ a) 0 b) 10 m/s
   c) 20 m/s (b and c both downwards).

3. $\frac{1}{3}$s, $4\frac{1}{3}$m.

4. 2s .

5. 11 m -16 ms^{-1} -18 ms^{-2}.

6. 28 m 25 ms^{-1} 18 ms^{-2}.

7. 4.5 m -4 ms^{-2}.

8. a) 4 m   b) 4 m   c) 4 m/s
   d) 2 m/s^2 e) 3s.

9. a) 1 s, 1 m   b) $0\cdot5$ m, $1\cdot5$ m/s
   c) $0\cdot5$ s   d) $-4\cdot5$ m/s.

10. $\frac{15}{16}$ m, $-2\cdot5$ m/s, $1\frac{9}{16}$ m. $\left(2 \times \frac{5}{4} - \frac{15}{16}\right)$

Exercise 28, page 42

1. a) increasing   b) stationary
   c) decreasing.

2. a) decreasing   b) increasing
   c) increasing

5. a) $x > 0$ b) $\{x < -1\} \cup \{x > 2\}$
   c) $\left\{x < \frac{1}{3}\right\} \cup \{x > 1\}$.

6. a) $x > 0$ b) $x > \frac{1}{2}$ c) $-3 < x < 1$.

7. a) (i) $x > 0$ (ii) $x < 0$
   b) (i) $-2 < x < 2$
      (ii) $\{x < -2\} \cup \{x > 2\}$
   c) (i) $\left\{x < 0\right\} \cup \left\{x > \frac{10}{3}\right\}$
      (ii) $0 < x < \frac{10}{3}$.

Exercise 29, page 44

1. a) $(0, 0)$ min
   b) $(3, 9)$ max
   c) $(0, 0)$ rising inflexion
   d) $(0, 0)$ max $(1, -1)$ min.

2. a) 0 min $\frac{32}{27}$max
   b) 4 min 5 max
   c) -625 min (twice) 0 max
   d) 2 min -2 max.

3. a) $\left(\frac{1}{2}, \frac{-5}{4}\right)$ min   b) $(0, 5)$ max
   c) $(-2, -25)$ min   d) $(-1, 0)$ min.

4. a) 0 rising inflexion 432 max
   b) -64 min 64 max
   c) -12 min 20 max
   d) $\frac{-1}{2}$ min (twice) 0 max.

Exercise 30, page 45

1.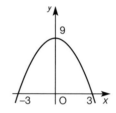

2.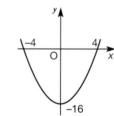

3.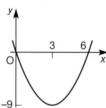

4.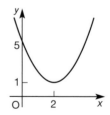

5.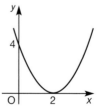

6.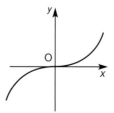

7.

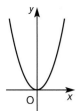

8.

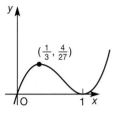

$(\frac{1}{3}, \frac{4}{27})$

9.

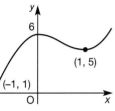

6

(1, 5)

(−1, 1)

10.

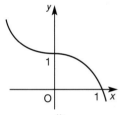

1

1

11.

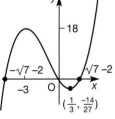

18

−√7 −2   √7 −2

−3

$(\frac{1}{3}, \frac{-14}{27})$

12.

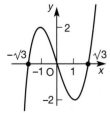

2

−√3   √3

−1   1

−2

13.

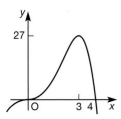

27

3 4

14.

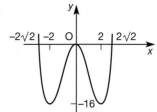

−2√2 −2   O   2   2√2

−16

15.

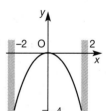

−2   −1   O   1   2

−8

−9

16.

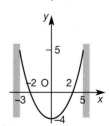

27

−3   O   1

Exercise 31, page 46

1. $-4 \leqslant f(x) \leqslant 0$

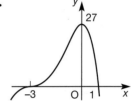

−2   O   2

−4

2. $-4 \leqslant f(x) \leqslant 5$

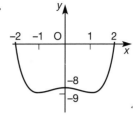

5

−2 O   2

−3   5

−4

3. $\dfrac{-4\sqrt{6}}{9} \leqslant f(x) \leqslant 21$

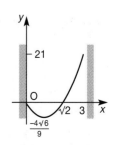

21

O

√2   3

$\dfrac{-4\sqrt{6}}{9}$

4. $-2 \leqslant f(x) \leqslant 16$

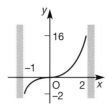

5. $7 \leqslant f(x) \leqslant 11$

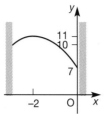

6. $-7 \leqslant f(x) \leqslant 9$

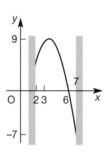

7. $0 \leqslant f(x) \leqslant 27$

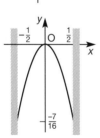

8. $\dfrac{7}{16} \leqslant f(x) \leqslant 0$

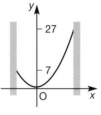

Exercise 32, page 48

1. a) $100\,m \times 100\,m$ b) $200\,m \times 100\,m$
   c) $200\,m \times 200\,m.$
2. 324.   **3.** 12.   **4.** 2.   **5.** 2.
6. 2.   **7.** 4.   **8.** $1\frac{1}{2}.$ **9.** $\frac{5}{3}.$
10. 4 units^2, (1, 4).   **11.** 27, (9, 3).
12. (1, 2).   **13.** $-\frac{1}{2}.$ **14.** 2.
15. 25.   **16.** 1.   **17.** $\frac{1}{6}.$ **18.** 50.
19. 4 cm.   **20.** 4 cm.

Exercise 33, page 51

1.

2.

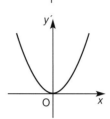

3.

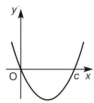

4.

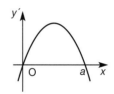

5.

6.

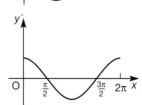

7.

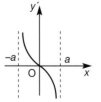

8.

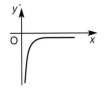

9.

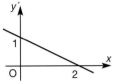

the gradient of $y = 2x + 2$

10.

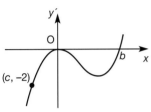

11.

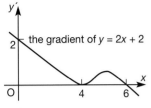

Topic test, page 52

1. a) $2x^{-\frac{1}{3}}$ b) $-\dfrac{3}{x^2}$ c) $-\dfrac{2}{x^{\frac{3}{2}}}$ d) $-\dfrac{1}{x^3}$.

2. 16.

3. $y = 8x - 7$; $82 \cdot 9°$.

4. a) decreasing   b) stationary.

5.

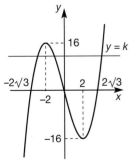

3 roots for $-16 < k < 16$.

UNIT 1 RECURRENCE RELATIONS

Exercise 35, page 53

1. £1637·93.

2. £144·78, £146·95.

3. Yes, it always stays below the danger level or No, it is too close to the danger level. The level approaches 5 tonnes

4. annually £1164·40, quarterly £1171·66.

Exercise 36, page 54

1. a) 1, 5, 13, 29   b) 2, 4, 10, 28
c) 16, 20, 22, 23   d) 128, 16, –12, –19.

2. a) 7, 22, 67, 202
b) 607, 1822, 5467   d) u_{12}.

3. a) 5, 9, 17, 33, 65, 129   b) u_{15}.

4. a) 2, 7, 32, ..., 488282
b) it doesn't end in a 2 or a 7 or $u_{12} < 123\,456\,789 < u_{13}$.

5. a) (i) 20   (ii) 10   (iii) 5   (iv) 2
(v) 4   (vi) 110
b) (i) 20   (ii) 10   (iii) 5   (iv) 2
(v) 4   (vi) 110
d) $L = \dfrac{b}{1-a}$ e) $|a| < 1$.

6. a) –1, 3, –5, 11, –21
b) –7, 15, –29, 59, –117
c) –1, 5, –13, 41, –121
d) –9, –33, –129, –513, –2049
e) –8, –50, –302, –1814, –10 886.

7. a) 10, 10, 10   b) 2, 2, 2
c) a > 0 ⇒ the limit is approached only from above or only from below:

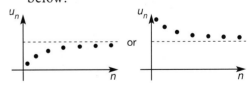

or

a < 0 ⇒ the limit is approached with the sequence oscillating between above and below:

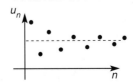

Exercise 37, page 57

1. 100g.
2. 300.
3. 50 units after each use before washing
4. 250 mg.
5. a) £2·50 – £12·50   b) £40 – £50.
6. 25 .
7. yes (limit < 300).
8. There will be 25 kg of litter every morning before the cleaning is done.
9. a = $\frac{1}{3}$ limit = 18.
10. $q = 3p - 2$.
11. a) use $(1-0·04)^7$ b) 4
    c) yes (the limit is 4).
12. a) £295·57   b) 5 years 5 months!
13. A steady state of 60 Access users and 40 Visa users.
14. a) not safe – after 21weeks the level is always below 1 litre
    b) safe (limit is 2.9 l).
15. Yes, the limit is 6.06 m.

Topic Test, page 59

1. a) 24, 61·8, 163·86
   b) u_{12} = 1 236 075·232.
2. a) 4·4, 2·72, 2·216
   b) has a limit of 2 ★.
3. a) 6, 4·8, 5·04   b) has a limit of 5 ★.
4. a) (i) 2 ★   (ii) 6 ★
   b) (i) oscillates about its limit
      (ii) approaches its limit from below.
5. £13·07; £15 ★
   ★ should be obtained by algebra, not just by calculator button pushing.

UNIT 1 IDENTITIES AND RADIANS

Exercise 39, page 60

1. 38 m.   2. 1624·5 m².
3. 63.   4. 131·1°.

Exercise 40, page 62

1. a) $V\hat{P}R$ b) $R\hat{T}V$ c) $V\hat{T}W$ d) $S\hat{V}R$.
2. d), f).
3. a) $V\hat{Q}R$ b) $S\hat{V}W$ c) $V\hat{T}U$ d) $T\hat{U}P$.
4. c), f), g), h).
5. a) $V\hat{A}E$ b) $V\hat{P}E$ c) $V\hat{N}E$ d) $A\hat{E}B$.
6. (i) 16·7°   (ii) 40°.

7. (i) 27·9°   (ii) 46·7°.
8. 21·8°.

Exercise 41, page 64

1. a) $\frac{\sqrt{3}}{2}$ b) $\frac{\sqrt{3}}{2}$ c) -1 d) $-\frac{1}{2}$ e) $\frac{1}{\sqrt{2}}$
   f) $\sqrt{3}$ g) $-\frac{\sqrt{3}}{2}$ h) $-\frac{1}{\sqrt{2}}$ i) $-\frac{1}{\sqrt{3}}$ j) -1.
2. a) $\frac{1}{2}$ b) -2 c) $2\frac{1}{2}$ d) $\frac{1}{2}$
   e) 1 f) 2.
3. $\frac{-1}{3}$.
6. a) $k = 5$ $a = 53·1°$
   b) $k = 13$ $a = 67·4°$
   c) $k = \sqrt{2}$ $a = 315°$
   d) $k = \sqrt{2}$ $a = 135°$
   e) $k = 17$ $a = 241·9$
   f) $k = 2\sqrt{5}$ $a = 26·6°$.
7. (i) a) sin60°   b) sin85°
      c) −sin60°   d) −sin80°
   (ii) a) −cos80°   b) −cos1°
      c) −cos20°   d) cos50°
   (iii) a) cos40°   b) cos80°   c) cos18°
   (iv) a) sin70°   b) sin25°   c) sin57°
   (v) a) sin80°, cos10°
      b) cos60°, sin30°
      c) −sin20°, −cos70°.
8. a) $\sin p°$ b) $-\cos q°$ c) $-\cos r°$
   d) $\sin s°$ e) $\cos t°$ f) $\cos u°$
   g) $\sin v°$ h) $-\sin w°$ i) $\sin x°$
   j) $-\sin y°$ k) $\sin z°$ l) $-\cos x°$.
9. a) 1 b) $-\tan a°$ c) $\tan a°$
   d) 1 e) 1.

Exercise 42, page 67

1. a) 30, 150   b) 45, 225
   c) 120, 240   d) 120, 300
   e) 60, 300   f) 210, 330
   g) 30, 150, 210, 330
   h) 30, 150, 210, 330.
2. a) 43·2, 316·8   b) 68·9, 248·9
   c) 51·0, 129·0   d) 153·1, 206·9
   e) 192·4, 347·6   f) 106·3, 286·3
   g) 20·5, 159·5, 200·5, 339·5
   h) 68·2, 248·2.

Exercise 43, page 67

1. 30, 150, 270.
2. 48·2, 138·6, 221·4, 311·8.
3. 56·3, 144·5, 236·3, 324·5.
4. 41·4, 120, 240, 318·6.

5. 210, 221·8, 318·2, 330.

6. 36·9, 120, 240, 323·1.

Exercise 44, page 68

1. a) 45, 225   b) 60, 180, 300
   c) 11·25, 56·25, 101·25, 146·25,
      191·25, 236·25, 281·25, 326·25
   d) 15, 75, 195, 255
   e) 20, 100, 140, 220, 260, 340.

2. a) 10·1, 79·9, 190·1, 259·9
   b) 70·8, 109·2, 250·8, 289·2
   c) 20·3, 99·7, 140·3, 219·7, 260·3, 339·7
   d) 71·9, 288·1   e) 307·5.

Exercise 45, page 68

1. a)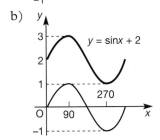

b)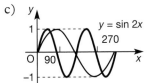

c)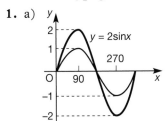

d)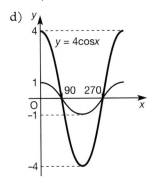

e)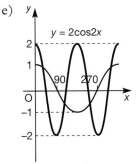

f)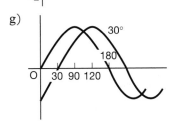

g)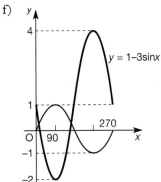

h)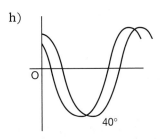

2.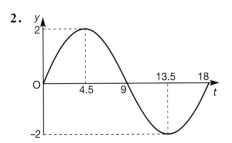

3.

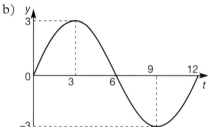

4. a) min $(180, -3)$ max $(0,3)$, $(360,3)$
   b) min $(90, -2)$ max $(270,2)$
   c) min $(210, -4)$ max $(30,4)$,
   d) min $(210, -3)$ max $(30,3)$.

5. a) 6 m
   b)

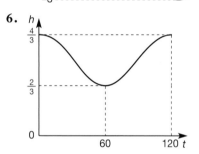

6.

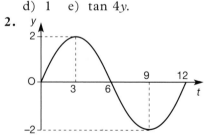

Exercise 46, page 70

1. $0 \ \dfrac{\pi}{6} \ \dfrac{\pi}{4} \ \dfrac{\pi}{3} \ \dfrac{\pi}{2} \ \dfrac{2\pi}{3} \ \dfrac{3\pi}{4} \ \dfrac{5\pi}{6} \ (\pi) \ \dfrac{7\pi}{6} \ \dfrac{3\pi}{2} \ \dfrac{5\pi}{3}$.

2. 60, 30, 150, 135, 225, 270, 144, 300.

3.

θ	0	$\dfrac{\pi}{6}$	$\dfrac{\pi}{4}$	$\dfrac{\pi}{3}$	$\dfrac{\pi}{2}$
$\sin\theta$	0	$\dfrac{1}{2}$	$\dfrac{1}{\sqrt{2}}$	$\dfrac{\sqrt{3}}{2}$	1
$\cos\theta$	1	$\dfrac{\sqrt{3}}{2}$	$\dfrac{1}{\sqrt{2}}$	$\dfrac{1}{2}$	0
$\tan\theta$	0	$\dfrac{1}{\sqrt{3}}$	1	$\sqrt{3}$	∞

4. $\dfrac{\pi}{6}$, $30°$.

5. a) $\dfrac{\pi}{3}$, $60°$ b) $\dfrac{5\pi}{6}$, $150°$.

6. $x = \dfrac{97\pi}{144}$ $y = \dfrac{79\pi}{144}$.

7. a) $\sin\theta$ b) $\sin\theta$
   c) $\sin a$. d) $-\cos\phi$.

8. a) $\dfrac{5\pi}{4}, \dfrac{7\pi}{4}$ b) $\dfrac{3\pi}{4}, \dfrac{7\pi}{4}$ c) $\dfrac{\pi}{3}, \dfrac{5\pi}{3}$
   d) $\dfrac{\pi}{6}, \dfrac{7\pi}{6}$ e) $\dfrac{\pi}{3}, \dfrac{2\pi}{3}, \dfrac{4\pi}{3}, \dfrac{5\pi}{3}$
   f) $\dfrac{\pi}{4}, \dfrac{3\pi}{4}, \dfrac{5\pi}{4}, \dfrac{7\pi}{4}$ g) $\dfrac{\pi}{6}, \dfrac{5\pi}{6}, \dfrac{7\pi}{6}, \dfrac{11\pi}{6}$.

9. a) $\dfrac{\pi}{6}, \dfrac{\pi}{3}, \dfrac{7\pi}{6}, \dfrac{4\pi}{3}$
   b) $\dfrac{5\pi}{18}, \dfrac{7\pi}{18}, \dfrac{17\pi}{18}, \dfrac{19\pi}{18}, \dfrac{29\pi}{18}, \dfrac{31\pi}{18}$.

10. a) $\dfrac{\pi}{2}, \dfrac{7\pi}{6}, \dfrac{11\pi}{6}$ b) $\dfrac{\pi}{3}, \dfrac{5\pi}{3}$.

11. a) $1·571, 3·665, 5·760$
   b) $1·047, 5·236$.

12. a) $0·412, 2·730$ b) $1·782, 4·501$
   c) $0·730, 2·412$
   d) $0·491, 2·062, 3·633, 5·204$.

13.

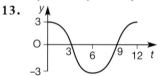

14.

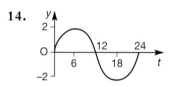

Topic Test, page 71

1. a) $\dfrac{11\pi}{6}$ b) $\dfrac{1}{\sqrt{2}}$ c) $\sin x$
   d) 1 e) $\tan 4y$.

2.

3. $26·6°$.

4. a) $\dfrac{7\pi}{6}, \dfrac{11\pi}{6}$.
   b) $0, \dfrac{2\pi}{3}, \dfrac{4\pi}{3}, 2\pi$.

5. a) 8, $t = 3$ b) 2, $t = 13$
   c) $6·76$ d) $t = \left(\dfrac{19}{3}, \dfrac{13}{2}\right)$.

Practice Unit test, page 72

1. $y = 2x + 7$.
2. 0.839.
3. a) 3 b) $-\frac{1}{3}$.
4. a)

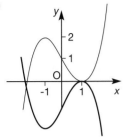

b)

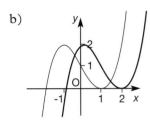

5. $y = 3\cos x$; $y = \cos x + 2$.
6. a) $y = 2^x$ b) $y = \log_5 x$.
7. a) $3x^3 - 1$ b) $\cos^3 x$.
8. $-2x^{-2} - 2x^{-3}$.
9. 5.
10. $(-1, 8)$ is a maximum turning point;
    $(2, -19)$ is a minimum turning point.
11. a) $u_{n+1} = \frac{1}{3}u_n + 48$

    b) 72 Eventually there will be 72
       bars in the tin every Friday:
       48 (two thirds) will be eaten
       every Saturday and replaced
       every Thursday.
       [Let's hope that the same
       24 don't get left at the bottom
       of the tin beyond their sell–by
       date!]

Test 1, page 73

1. a) $3x + y = 11$ b) $3x + 2y = 16$.
2. $7x + 4y = 5$.
3. 11.
4. $3y = x + 4$.
5. a) $\dfrac{\sqrt{3}}{2(1 + \sqrt{3})}$ b) $\frac{1}{4}(3 - \sqrt{3})$.
6. (use area $= \frac{1}{2}ab\sin C$).
7. a) 5 b) $b = 3$ $c = 6$.

Test 2, page 74

1. a) $[AB = AC]$ b) $x = 6$
   c) $2y = x + 5$ d) $\left(6, \frac{11}{2}\right)$
   e) $[4 \times 1.5 = 6]$.
2. a) a half-square (a right-angled
      isosceles triangle) c) $25\,\text{m}^2$.
3. a) $a = 1$; $b = 2$; $c = 9$ b) 3
   c) $(9, 1)$ lies on the line l.

UNIT 2 QUADRATIC THEORY

Exercise 50, page 75

1. $t(t - 6)$
2. $u(u + 7)$
3. $v(5 - v)$
4. $2y(3 - y)$
5. $(x - 1)(x + 1)$
6. $(y - 4)(y + 4)$
7. $(2x - 5)(2x + 5)$
8. $2(t - 3)(t + 3)$
9. $(x + 1)(x + 3)$
10. $(x - 4)(x - 2)$
11. $(x - 3)(x + 5)$
12. $(x + 2)(x - 8)$
13. $(2k - 3)(k + 1)$
14. $(2w - 7)(w + 5)$
15. $(3x - 2)(2x + 5)$
16. $(7x + 3)(2x - 5)$.

Exercise 51, page 76

1. $0, 2$ 2. $0, -7$ 3. ± 3 4. ± 2.5
5. $2, 3$ 6. $-1, -4$ 7. $-5, 4$
8. $-2, -4$ 9. $-0.5, 3$ 10. $\frac{2}{3}, -\frac{5}{2}$
11. $-3, 4$ 12. $-3, 1$ 13. $-1, 2$
14. $-2, 5$.

Exercise 52, page 77

1. $(-2, 4)$, $(3, 9)$
2. $(1, 1)$, $(-3, 9)$
3. $(0, 0)$, $(6, 12)$
4. $(1, 0)$, $(6, 5)$
5. $(2, 4)$
6. $(3, 9)$
7. $(1, 3)$
8. $(-1, 4)$
9. yes, at $(-2, 4)$
10. no, cuts at $(-1, -3)$ and $(3, 5)$
11. yes, at $(2, 8)$
12. no intersection.

ANSWERS

Exercise 53, page 78

1. $-1, 3$ **2.** $-5, -1$ **3.** $-8, -2$

4. $-1, 2$ **5.** $-2, \dfrac{3}{2}$ **6.** $-\dfrac{2}{3}, 2$

7. $-2 \pm \sqrt{2}$ **8.** $3 \pm \sqrt{2}$

9. $-5 \pm 2\sqrt{5}$ **10.** $\dfrac{7 \pm \sqrt{57}}{4}$.

Exercise 54, page 79

1. $x = \dfrac{-b \pm \sqrt{b^2 - 4ac}}{2a}$.

2. a) $1, 3$ b) $-1, \dfrac{3}{2}$ c) $-\dfrac{1}{2} \pm \dfrac{\sqrt{5}}{2}$

   d) $\dfrac{3}{4} \pm \dfrac{\sqrt{41}}{4}$.

Exercise 55, page 80

1. a) $(-1, -3)$ min   b) $(3, 2)$ max
   c) $(-3, 1)$ min   d) $(1, 5)$ max
   e) $(2, 7)$ min   f) $(-2, 4)$ max.

2. a) $(x - 3)^2 - 9$ b) $(x + 4)^2 - 16$
   c) $(x - 5)^2 - 4$ d) $(x - 6)^2 - 49$
   e) $(x + 2)^2 + 1$ f) $(x + 3)^2 - 7$
   g) $\left(x + \dfrac{3}{2}\right)^2 - \dfrac{5}{4}$ h) $\left(x + \dfrac{5}{2}\right)^2 - \dfrac{13}{4}$.

3. a) $2(x + 2)^2 - 7$ b) $3(x - 1)^2 - 8$
   c) $2(x + 1)^2 + 1$ d) $5(x - 2)^2 - 9$.

4. a) $9 - (x + 1)^2$ b) $16 - (x + 3)^2$
   c) $13 - 2(x + 1)^2$ d) $\dfrac{19}{2} - 2\left(x - \dfrac{3}{2}\right)^2$.

5. a)
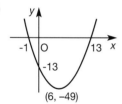

   b)
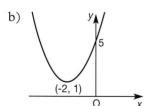

   c)
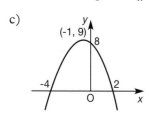

Exercise 56, page 81

1. a) $y = (x - 2)^2$ b) $y = 9 - x^2$
   c) $y = 12x - 3x^2$ d) $y = 2x^2 + 12x$
   e) $y = 3 + \dfrac{2}{5}x - \dfrac{1}{5}x^2$
   f) $y = p^2 + \dfrac{1}{2}px - \dfrac{1}{2}x^2$.

Exercise 57, page 82

1. $\{-1 < x < 3\}$.
2. $\{x \leqslant -4\} \cup \{x \geqslant -1\}$.
3. $\{x \leqslant -4\} \cup \{x \geqslant 4\}$.
4. $\{x < -5\} \cup \{x > 5\}$.
5. $\{0 < x < 5\}$.
6. $\{x \leqslant 1\} \cup \{x \geqslant 4\}$.
7. $\left\{-1 \leqslant x \leqslant \dfrac{3}{2}\right\}$.
8. $\left\{x < \dfrac{5}{2}\right\} \cup \left\{x > \dfrac{7}{2}\right\}$.
9. $\{0 < x < 1\}$.
10. $\varnothing$.

Exercise 58, page 82

1. a) distinct real (irrational) roots
   b) distinct real (rational) roots
   c) no real roots
   d) no real roots
   e) equal rational roots
   f) distinct real (irrational) roots
   g) distinct real (irrational) roots
   h) equal rational roots
   i) distinct real (rational) roots
   j) no real roots
   k) distinct real (irrational) roots
   l) distinct real (rational) roots.

3. a) 16 b) 4 c) ± 8 d) ± 3 e) 1
   f) $-7, 5$ g) $0, 5$ h) $-\dfrac{3}{2}, 3$.

4. $-1 < q < 1$.

5. a) $pq = 2$ b) $c = \pm 4$ c) $a = \pm b$.

6. $\dfrac{1}{9} < k < 1$.

7. a) $1, 5$ b) unreal.

8. $k > 7.2$.

9. $a = -\dfrac{1}{3}, 1;\ x = -6, -6;\ x = -2, -2$.

Exercise 59, page 84

1. a) $y = x + 1$
   b) $y = 4x + 4,\ y = 4x - 4$
   c) $y = -x - 4,\ y = -x + 4$
   d) $y = -4x - 8,\ y = -4x + 8$
   e) $y = 2x - 1$
   f) $8x + y + 8 = 0$.

2. a) $y = 4x - 4$, $y = -4x - 4$
b) $y = \sqrt{26}x - 5$, $y = -\sqrt{26}x - 5$
c) $y = 2x - 8$, $y = -38x - 8$
d) $y = \pm 8x - 2$
e) $y = \pm 4x$
f) $y = \pm \frac{4}{3}x + 5$.

3. a) $x - y = 4$, $x + y = 4$
b) $4x - 3y = 20$, $4x + 3y = 20$
c) $x - 3y + 10 = 0$, $3x + y - 10 = 0$.

Topic Test, page 85

1. a)

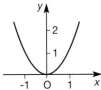

b)

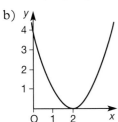

c)

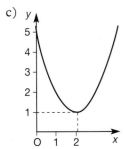

2. $(1, 3)$.
3. $k \leqslant \frac{9}{4}$.
4. $\{x \leqslant -2\} \cup \{x \geqslant 1\}$.
5. a) $(x - 2)^2 + 3$ b) 3   c) $\frac{1}{3}$.
6. $y = 3x + 10$, $(-3, 1)$; $y = 3x - 10$, $(3, -1)$.

UNIT 2 THE REMAINDER THEOREM

Exercise 61, page 86

1. a) 5   b) −3   c) 0   d) −4.
2. a) 3   b) −2   c) 0   d) −2.
3. a) 6   b) 2   c) 3   d) 3.
4. a) $-1 + 2x + x^2$ b) $1 - 4x + 4x^2$.
5. a) $9x^2 + 12x + 4$ b) $x^3 - 8x^2 + 16x$.
6. a) 1   b) −1   c) 9   d) 0.

Exercise 62, page 87

1. a) 12   b) 12   c) 5   d) −67.
2. a) 6·41   b) 2·68   c) −58·216
d) −45·75.
3. a) −1   b) −10   c) −11   d) 121.
4. a) 61   b) 55   c) 5   d) 96
e) 242   f) −14.

Exercise 63, page 88

1. a) 3   b) 0   c) 0   d) −13   e) −34
f) 100   g) 68   h) 38   i) 1
j) $a+b+c+d$.
2. −5.
3. 2.
4. −5.
5. 5.
6. a) −1   b) −3   c) 7·5   d) 5
e) 12   f) −1.

Exercise 64, page 90

1. a) $23 = 4 \times 5 + 3$
b) $111 = 7 \times 15 + 6$
c) $1000 = 9 \times 111 + 1$
d) $191 = 32 \times 5 + 31$.
2. a) $x^3 + 2x^2 + 3x - 1 =$
   $(x - 2)(x^2 + 4x + 11) + 21$
b) $3x^3 + 4x^2 + 5x - 7 =$
   $(x + 1)(3x^2 + x + 4) - 11$
c) $x^3 + x^2 - 2x - 3 =$
   $(x + 2)(x^2 - x) - 3$
d) $x^4 + x^3 - x^2 + x - 2 =$
   $(x + 3)(x^3 - 2x^2 + 5x - 14) + 40$
e) $x^3 - 5 = (x + 1)(x^2 - x + 1) - 6$
f) $x^4 - x^2 + 2 =$
   $(x - 2)(x^3 + 2x^2 + 3x + 6) + 14$
g) $2x^3 + x^2 + 3x - 3 =$
   $(2x - 1)(x^2 + x + 2) - 1$
h) $3x^3 + 5x^2 - 4x - 9 =$
   $(3x + 2)(x^2 + x - 2) - 5$
i) $6x^4 - 3x^3 + 5x^2 + 2x - 3 =$
   $(2x + 1)(3x^3 - 3x^2 + 4x - 1) - 2$
j) $25x^4 - x^2 + 5 =$
   $(5x + 1)(5x^3 - x^2) + 5$.

Exercise 65, page 92

1. a) $(x - 1)(x + 1)(x - 2)$
b) $(x - 1)(x - 2)(x + 2)$
c) $(x - 1)(x - 2)(x + 3)$
d) $(x + 1)(x - 2)(x - 3)$
e) $(x + 2)(x - 3)(x + 4)$
f) $(x - 1)(2x + 1)(3x + 1)$
g) $(x - 3)(2x + 1)(3x - 1)$

ANSWERS

h) $(x - 3)(x + 5)(2x + 1)$
i) $(u + 4)(u - 5)(2u - 1)$
j) $(3t - 1)(2t + 1)(5t + 2)$.

4. a) $(x - 1)(x^2 + 4x + 5)$
b) $(x + 2)(x^2 + 3x + 3)$.

5. -5.

6. 4.

7. $-2, \dfrac{7}{3}$

8. $a = 3, b = -13$.

9. $p = 3, q = -4$.

10. $a = -13, b = 6$; $(x - 2)(x + 3)(2x - 1)$.

11. a) $(x - 1)(x + 1)(x - 2)(x + 2)$
b) $(x - 1)(x + 1)(x - 2)^2$
c) $(x - 1)(x + 2)^2(x - 3)$
d) $(x - 3)(x + 3)(x - 4)(x + 5)$
e) $(2x + 1)^2(3x - 1)(3x + 1)$.

12. $(x^2 - 1)(x^2 - 4) =$
$(x - 1)(x + 1)(x - 2)(x + 2)$.

13. $(x - 1)^2(x + 1)(x - 2)(x + 2)$.

Exercise 66, page 93

1. $1, -1, 8$.

2. a) $1, -1, -2$ b) $2, 3, -2$
c) $-1, 2, -3$ d) $2, -3, 4$
e) $1, \dfrac{-1}{2}, \dfrac{1}{3}$ f) $-3, \dfrac{3}{2}, \dfrac{-4}{3}$ g) $1,1,2,2$
h) $1, -2, 3, -4$ i) 2 j) -1.

3. $\dfrac{1}{3}, 4, \dfrac{-3}{2}$.

4. $a = -7$. (Δ for $2x^2 + 3x + 5 < 0$)

5. $y = x + 3$, $(2, 5)$.

6. $y = 9x - 22$, $(-3, -49)$.

Exercise 67, page 94

1. $1 \cdot 3$.

2. $-0 \cdot 7$.

3. $-1 \cdot 48$.

4. $1 \cdot 37$.

5. $-1 \cdot 267, -0 \cdot 259, 1 \cdot 526$.

6. $-0 \cdot 481, 1 \cdot 311, 3 \cdot 170$.

7. $1 \cdot 89$.

8. $-1 \cdot 88, 0 \cdot 35, 1 \cdot 53$.

Exercise 68, page 95

1. a) $y = -x^3 + 3x^2 + x - 3$
b) $y = \dfrac{1}{3}(x^3 - 6x^2 + 11x - 6)$
c) $y = \dfrac{2}{3}(4x^2 - x^3)$
d) $y = \dfrac{1}{3}(x^3 - 4x)$
e) $y = -2x^3 + 16x^2 - 32x$
f) $y = \dfrac{1}{4}(x^3 - 6x^2 + 9x)$.

Topic Test, page 96

1. a) 3 b) -4 c) (i) 5 (ii) -4.

2. a) 7 b) -26 c) -2.

3. No, $f(4) \neq 0$.

4. $k = -4$.

5. $(x - 3)(x - 1)(x + 2)$.

6. a) [use differentiation]   b) $(3, 18)$.

UNIT 2 INTEGRATION

Exercise 70, page 98

1. a) $\dfrac{x^5}{5} + c$ b) $\dfrac{x^6}{6} + c$ c) $\dfrac{5x^4}{4} + c$
d) $\dfrac{x^{12}}{3} + c$ e) $13x + c$ f) $\dfrac{5}{2}x^2 + x + c$
g) $\dfrac{2}{3}x^{\frac{3}{2}} + c$ h) $\dfrac{3}{5}x^{\frac{5}{3}} + c$ i) $c - x^{-4}$
j) $c - 3x^{\frac{-1}{3}}$ k) $x^3 - 2x + c$
l) $\dfrac{7}{3}x^3 + x^2 + c$ m) $-\dfrac{1}{x^3} + c$
n) $-\dfrac{1}{2}x^{-2} + c$ o) $-\dfrac{2}{x} + c$ p) $3x^{\frac{2}{3}} + c$
q) $2x + \dfrac{5}{x} + c$ r) $2\sqrt{x} + c$
s) $4x + \dfrac{3}{2}x^{-2} + c$ t) $-4x^{-1} + \dfrac{x^3}{12} + c$.

2. a) $\dfrac{3}{2}x^2 + x + c$ b) $\dfrac{2}{3}x^3 + \dfrac{5}{2}x^2 + 4x + c$
c) $14x - 5x^2 + c$ d) $\dfrac{4}{3}x^3 + 6x^2 + 9x + c$
e) $\dfrac{x^3}{3} - \dfrac{x^2}{2} + c$ f) $\dfrac{2}{5}x^{\frac{5}{2}} + \dfrac{2}{3}x^{\frac{3}{2}} + c$
g) $\dfrac{x^3}{3} - \dfrac{3}{2}x^2 + 2x + c$ h) $\dfrac{2}{3}x^3 + \dfrac{5}{2}x^2 + c$
i) $\dfrac{x^3}{3} + 2x^2 + 4x + c$ j) $\dfrac{x^5}{5} - \dfrac{3}{2}x^2 + c$
k) $3x^3 - 12x^2 + 16x + c$
l) $\dfrac{x^3}{3} - \dfrac{x^2}{2} - 30x + c$
m) $\dfrac{6}{5}x^{\frac{5}{2}} - \dfrac{2}{3}x^{\frac{3}{2}} + c$
n) $16x + \dfrac{16}{5}x^{\frac{5}{2}} + \dfrac{x^4}{4} + c$
o) $\dfrac{3}{7}x^{\frac{7}{3}} + \dfrac{12}{11}x^{\frac{11}{6}} + c$
p) $-\dfrac{1}{x} - \dfrac{1}{x^2} - \dfrac{1}{3x^3} + c$
q) $\dfrac{2}{3}x^{\frac{3}{2}} - \dfrac{6}{5}x^{\frac{5}{2}} + c$
r) $-\dfrac{2}{\sqrt{x}} - \dfrac{2}{x} + c$
s) $2x^{\frac{1}{2}} - \dfrac{4}{3}x^{\frac{3}{2}} + \dfrac{2}{5}x^{\frac{5}{2}} + c$
t) $-\dfrac{6}{\sqrt{x}} + 10\sqrt{x} + c$.

3. a) $x^5 + 1$ b) $3x^3 + 2$ c) $x^2 + 3x$

d) $\frac{x^3}{3} + x^2 + x - 6$ e) $\frac{2}{3}x^{\frac{3}{2}} + 2$

f) $2\sqrt{x} + 6$ g) $x^3 + \frac{3}{x} - 1$

h) $\frac{1}{2}x^2 + \frac{2}{3}x^{\frac{3}{2}} - \frac{16}{3}$.

4. a) $y = 3x - 12$ b) $y = x - \frac{1}{2}x^2 + \frac{1}{2}$

c) $y = \frac{5}{2}x^2$ d) $y = x^2 - 3x + 4$

e) $y = x^3 - 4x^2 + 5$
f) $y = 2x^3 - 2x^2 + 3x - 6$

g) $y = 2x^3 - x^2 + 3$ h) $y = x + \frac{1}{x} + 2$.

5. 3.

6. 108.

8. $y = -(x - 3)^2$.

9. a) $s = 3t - \frac{1}{t}$ b) $s = t^3 - 4t$

c) $s = 5t - 2t^2 + 6$

d) $s = 20t^2 - 10t + 7$

e) $s = \frac{1}{3}t^3 - 2t^2 + 4t + 2$

f) $s = 2t^3 + 4t^2 - t + 5$

g) $s = \frac{81}{5}t^5 + 36t^3 + 36t$

h) $s = \frac{5}{3}t^3 + \frac{3}{t} - 40$.

10.   at rest with displacement -4.

11. $s = 3t^4 - 5t^3 + 2t - 5$.

12. $8\frac{1}{2}$.

Exercise 71, page 100

1. $x^3 + 2x^2 + 5x + c$.

2. $\frac{x^6}{6} + 3x + c$.

3. $4x^{\frac{1}{2}} + c$.

4. $\frac{7}{2}x^2 - x + c$.

5. $\frac{1}{2}x^4 - 11x + c$.

6. $2(x^{\frac{3}{2}} - x^{\frac{1}{2}}) + c$.

7. $\frac{4}{5}(3x^{\frac{5}{3}} + x^{\frac{5}{4}}) + c$.

8. $\frac{x^5}{5} - \frac{2}{3}x^3 + x + c$.

9. $\frac{x^4}{4} - \frac{1}{2}x^2 + c$.

10. $3x^3 - 6x^2 + 4x + c$.

11. $\frac{6}{11}x^{\frac{11}{6}} + \frac{3}{4}x^{\frac{4}{3}} - \frac{2}{3}x^{\frac{3}{2}} - x + c$.

12. $\frac{4}{7}x^{\frac{7}{2}} + 2x^{\frac{3}{2}} + c$.

13. $4x^{\frac{1}{2}} + \frac{1}{3}x^{\frac{3}{2}} + c$.

14. $\frac{1}{2}x^2 - \frac{4}{3}x^{\frac{3}{2}} + x + c$.

15. $2x^3 - 15x + c$.

16. $\frac{6}{7}x^{\frac{7}{2}} + \frac{2}{3}x^{\frac{3}{2}} + c$.

17. $\frac{x^5}{5} - \frac{1}{2}x^4 + \frac{1}{3}x^3 + c$.

18. $\frac{1}{2}x^2 + 3x + c$.

19. $2\left(\frac{1}{3}x^{\frac{3}{2}} + \frac{3}{5}x^{\frac{5}{2}}\right) + c$.

20. $x^{\frac{1}{2}} + \frac{3}{2}x^{\frac{1}{3}} + c$.

21. $\frac{1}{3}x^3 - 2x - \frac{1}{x} + c$.

22. $22\frac{1}{2}$.   **23.** 21.   **24.** 0.

25. $46\frac{1}{2}$.   **26.** $\frac{2}{3}$.   **27.** 2.   **28.** $13\frac{1}{2}$.

29. $9\frac{1}{3}$.   **30.** 16.   **31.** $5\frac{1}{3}$.   **32.** $-\frac{3}{4}$.

33. $1\frac{9}{14}$.   **34.** $1\frac{1}{6}$.   **35.** $4\frac{1}{2}$.

36. $-12\frac{2}{3}$.   **37.** $\frac{1}{4}$.   **38.** $-10\frac{2}{3}$.

39. 6π.   **40.** π.   **41.** $-\frac{3}{2}$.

Exercise 72, page 102

1. a)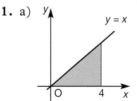

b)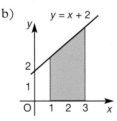

c)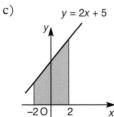

d)

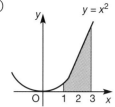

$y = x^2$

e)

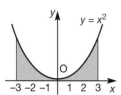

$y = x^2$

f)

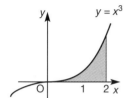

$y = x^3$

g)

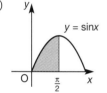

$y = \sin x$

h)

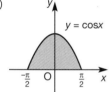

$y = \cos x$

2. a) $\int_1^4 (x + 2)\, dx$ b) $\int_{-1}^2 (x^2 + 5)\, dx$

c) $\int_0^3 2x\, dx$ d) $\int_0^4 x(4 - x)\, dx.$

3. a) $\dfrac{25}{2}$ b) 8   c) 14   d) 4

e) $\dfrac{16}{3}$ f) 16   g) $\dfrac{9}{2}$ h) 8.

4. a) 63   b) 260   c) 60   d) 16
e) 18   f) 18   g) 1   h) 2.

5. a) $1\dfrac{1}{3}$ b) $10\dfrac{2}{3}$ c) $6\dfrac{3}{4}$ d) $2\dfrac{2}{3}$

e) $4\dfrac{2}{3}$ f) 64   g) 28   h) $16\dfrac{2}{3}.$

Exercise 73, page 104
1. a) 9   b) $3\dfrac{3}{4}$ c) $16\dfrac{1}{2}$ d) $7\dfrac{1}{3}$

e) $4\dfrac{1}{2}$ f) $\dfrac{1}{6}$ g) 4   h) 36.

2. a) 8   b) $\dfrac{1}{2}$ c) $6\dfrac{3}{4}$ d) $\dfrac{1}{20}$

e) $40\dfrac{1}{2}$ f) $\dfrac{1}{2}$ g) $21\dfrac{1}{12}$ h) $\dfrac{1}{2}.$

3. a) $2\dfrac{2}{3}$ b) 13   c) $2\dfrac{3}{4}.$

Exercise 74, page 106
1. $4\dfrac{1}{2}.$ **2.** $\dfrac{1}{6}.$ **3.** $1\dfrac{1}{3}.$ **4.** $\dfrac{1}{12}.$

5. $\dfrac{1}{3}.$ **6.** $\dfrac{4}{15}.$ **7.** $\dfrac{1}{2}.$ **8.** 8.

9. $\dfrac{1}{6}.$ **10.** 36.   **11.** $21\dfrac{1}{3}.$ **12.** $4\dfrac{1}{2}.$

13. $20\dfrac{5}{6}.$ **14.** $10\dfrac{2}{3}.$ **15.** 36.

16. $4\dfrac{1}{2}.$ **17.** $41\dfrac{2}{3}.$ **18.** 9.   **19.** $41\dfrac{2}{3}.$

20. $10\dfrac{2}{3}.$ **21.** $100\dfrac{4}{5}.$ **22.** $20\dfrac{5}{6}.$

23. $\dfrac{1}{4}.$ **24.** $10\dfrac{2}{3}.$ **25.** 108

Topic Test, page 107
1. a) $\dfrac{3}{2}x^{\frac{2}{3}} + c$ b) $\sqrt{x} + c$

c) $-\dfrac{1}{3}\cos(3x + 1) + c.$

2. $y = 3x^3 + 4x^2 - x - 9.$

3. a) $\dfrac{1}{2}$ b) $\dfrac{14}{3}.$

4. $\dfrac{118}{3}\text{units}^2.$

5. $(\pm 3, 1);\ 18\ \text{units}^2.$

UNIT 2 COMPOUND AND MULTIPLE ANGLES

Exercise 76, page 108
1. a) $\cos a \cos y + \sin a \sin y$
b) $\sin x \cos y - \cos x \sin y$
c) $\cos \theta \cos \phi - \sin \theta \sin \phi$
d) $\sin a \cos \beta + \cos a \sin \beta$
e) $\cos A \cos B + \sin A \sin B$
f) $\cos^2 x - \sin^2 x$
g) $2 \sin A \cos A$
h) $\cos A \cos \theta + \sin A \sin \theta$
i) $\sin 2x \cos y + \cos 2x \sin y$
j) $\cos \Sigma \cos \Delta - \sin \Sigma \sin \Delta$
k) $\sin 3p \cos 2q - \cos 3p \sin 2q$
l) $\sin \star \cos \bullet + \cos \star \sin \bullet.$
2. a) $\cos (P + Q)$ b) $\sin (a - 2\beta)$
c) $\cos (\theta - \phi)$ d) $\sin (A + B)$

e) $\sin(x - y)$ f) $\cos a$ g) $\sin 15°$

h) $-\cos 165° = \cos 15°$ i) $\sin 90° = 1$

j) $\cos 360° = 1$ k) $\cos 60° = 0.5$

l) $\sin 45° = \dfrac{1}{\sqrt{2}}$ m) 1 n) $\cos \pi = -1$

o) $\sin(z - x)$ p) $\cos \dfrac{\pi}{2} = 0$.

5. a) $\dfrac{63}{65}$ b) $-\dfrac{33}{65}$.

7. a) $\dfrac{4}{5}$ b) $\dfrac{44}{125}$.

10. $-\dfrac{56}{33}$.

13. a) $\sqrt{3}, \sqrt{7}$.

14. a) $4, 45°$.

15. a) $\dfrac{56}{65}$ b) $\dfrac{33}{65}$ c) $\dfrac{56}{33}$ d) $\dfrac{24}{25}$.

16. a) $\dfrac{4}{5}$ b) $\dfrac{117}{125}$ c) $\dfrac{-7}{25}$.

17. $\dfrac{1}{\sqrt{10}}$.

Exercise 77, page 111

1. a) $2 \sin z \cos z$

b) $\cos^2 2Y - \sin^2 2Y$

c) $2 \sin 3Q \cos 3Q$

d) $\cos^2 \dfrac{3A}{2} - \sin^2 \dfrac{3A}{2}$

e) $2 \sin \dfrac{x}{2} \cos \dfrac{x}{2}$

f) $\cos^2 \dfrac{x}{6} - \sin^2 \dfrac{x}{6}$ g) $2 \sin \dfrac{y}{4} \cos \dfrac{y}{4}$

h) $\cos^2 \dfrac{x}{2} - \sin^2 \dfrac{x}{2}$.

2. a) $\cos 8A$ b) $\sin x$ c) $\sin 10x$

d) $-\cos x$ e) $\cos 30° = \dfrac{\sqrt{3}}{2}$

f) $\cos 150° = -\dfrac{\sqrt{3}}{2}$ g) $\sin 30° = \dfrac{1}{2}$

h) $\cos \dfrac{\pi}{6} = \dfrac{\sqrt{3}}{2}$ i) $\cos\theta$ j) $2 \cos A$

k) $-\cos 2x$ l) 1.

3. a) $\dfrac{24}{25}$ b) $\dfrac{7}{25}$ c) $\dfrac{24}{7}$.

4. a) $\dfrac{4}{5}$ b) $\dfrac{3}{5}$ c) $\dfrac{4}{3}$.

5. a) 0.6 b) -0.8 c) -0.96.

6. a) $\dfrac{4}{5}$ b) $-\dfrac{3}{5}$ c) $-\dfrac{4}{3}$.

7. a) $2 \cos^2 x + 3 \cos x + 1$

b) $2 \sin^2 x + \sin x$

c) $4 - 4 \sin x - 2 \sin^2 x$

d) $3 + \cos 2x$ e) $4 \cos 2x + 6$.

13. $\dfrac{\pi}{6}, \dfrac{5\pi}{6}, \dfrac{3\pi}{2}$.

14. $A(38.7, 0.22)$ $B(321.3, 0.22)$

15. $70°$.

Exercise 78, page 113

1. $\{0, 120, 180, 240, 360\}$.

2. $\{30, 90, 150, 270\}$.

3. $\{0, 120, 240, 360\}$.

4. $\{30, 150, 270\}$.

5. $\{0, 60, 300, 360\}$.

6. $\{0, 180, 360\}$.

7. $\{90\}$.

8. $\{0, 180, 210, 330, 360\}$.

9. $\{60, 300\}$.

10. $\{120, 180, 240\}$.

11. $\{60, 180, 300\}$.

12. $\{53.1, 120, 240, 306.9\}$.

13. $\{90, 236.4, 270, 303.6\}$.

14. $\{48.2, 104.5, 255.5, 311.8\}$.

15. $\{30, 150, 228.6, 311.4\}$.

16. $\{233.1, 306.9\}$.

17. $\left\{0, \dfrac{\pi}{3}, \pi, \dfrac{5\pi}{3}, 2\pi\right\}$.

18. $\left\{\dfrac{\pi}{2}, \dfrac{7\pi}{6}, \dfrac{3\pi}{2}, \dfrac{11\pi}{6}\right\}$.

19. $\left\{\dfrac{\pi}{3}, \pi, \dfrac{5\pi}{3}\right\}$.

20. $\left\{\dfrac{\pi}{2}, \dfrac{7\pi}{6}, \dfrac{11\pi}{6}\right\}$.

21. $\{75, 105, 255, 285\}$.

22. $\{75, 165, 255, 345\}$.

23. $\{60, 300\}$.

24. $\{150, 210\}$.

25. $\{15, 105, 135, 225, 255, 345\}$.

26. $\left\{33\dfrac{3}{4}, 78\dfrac{3}{4}, 123\dfrac{3}{4}, 168\dfrac{3}{4}, 213\dfrac{3}{4}, 258\dfrac{3}{4},\right.$ $\left. 303\dfrac{3}{4}, 348\dfrac{3}{4}\right\}$.

27. $\{0, 70.5, 180, 289.5, 360\}$.

28. $\{0, 146.4, 213.6, 360\}$.

29. $\{97.2, 262.8\}$.

30. $\{13.3, 83, 103.3, 173, 193.3, 263,$ $283.3, 353\}$.

Topic Test, page 114

1. a) 1 b) $\tan 3v$ c) $\sin^2 2w$

d) $\cos 6r$ e) $\cos 8s$ f) $\cos 4t$

g) $\cos(3P + 2Q)$ h) $\sin(2x + 3y)$

i) $\cos^2 x$.

2. $\dfrac{87}{425}$.

3. a) $\dfrac{12}{13}$ b) $\dfrac{119}{169}$ c) $\dfrac{120}{169}$.

4. $\dfrac{\pi}{2}, \dfrac{3\pi}{2}$.   **5.** $70.5, 120, 240, 289.5$.

ANSWERS

UNIT 2 THE CIRCLE

Exercise 80, page 116

1. a) $x^2 + y^2 = 1$ b) $x^2 + y^2 = 4$
   c) $x^2 + y^2 = 49$.
2. a) $x^2 + y^2 = 25$ b) $x^2 + y^2 = 2$
   c) $x^2 + y^2 = 13$.
3. a) 4 b) 3 c) 5.
4. 12 units.
5. 20π units.
6. 81π units^2.
7. a) $x^2 + y^2 = 16$ b) $x^2 + y^2 = 32$.
8. a) 2 b) $x^2 + y^2 = 4$ c) $\frac{\pi}{6}$
   d) $\frac{\pi}{3}$ units e) $\frac{\pi}{3}$ units^2.
9.

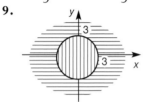

10. inside.
11. b) $x^2 + y^2 = 74$.
12. b) $x^2 + y^2 = 4$.
13. ± 8.
14. ± 5.
15. a) $(-15, -20)$ b) $(-24, -7)$
    c) $(20, -15)$ d) $(7, 24)$.
16. b) (i) $\frac{1}{4}$ (ii) -4 (iii) $4x + y = 17$.
17. a) $3x + 7y = 58$ b) $3y = 2x + 13$
    c) $2x - y = 10$.
18. $(-2, 1)$.
19. $(3, -4), (4, 3), 5\sqrt{2}$.
21. a) $12y = 9x + 25$ b) $\left(\frac{4}{3}, 1\right)$.

Exercise 81, page 119

1. a) $(x - 1)^2 + (y - 2)^2 = 16$
   b) $(x - 2)^2 + (y + 4)^2 = 25$
   c) $(x + 2)^2 + (y + 3)^3 = 49$.
2. a) $(1, 3)$ 2 b) $(-2, -5)$ 4
   c) $(4, -3)$ $2\sqrt{2}$.
3. a) $(x - 3)^2 + (y - 4)^2 = 32$
   b) $(x - 1)^2 + (y + 1)^2 = 5$
   c) $(x + 2)^2 + (y - 4)^2 = 8$.
4. a) $(x - 5)^2 + (y - 4)^2 = 10$
   b) $(x - 3)^2 + (y - 1)^2 = 13$
   c) $(x + 5)^2 + (y - 1)^2 = 13$.
5. b) $(x - 1)^2 + (y - 5)^2 = 13$.
6. b) $(x - 4)^2 + (y - 3)^2 = 4$.
7. $(-1, -9)$.

8. a) $-1, 7$ b) $-4, 8$ c) $0, 2$.
10. a) $(x - 1)^2 + (y - 4)^2 = 16$
    b) $(x - 2)^2 + (y - 3)^2 = 4$
    c) $(x - 5)^2 + (y - 5)^2 = 25$
    d) $(x - 3)^2 + (y - 4)^2 = 25$.
11. a) $(x - 4)^2 + (y - 5)^2 = 25$
    b) $(x - 10)^2 + (y - 6)^2 = 100$
    c) $(x \pm 12)^2 + (y - 5)^2 = 169$
    d) $(x - 1)^2 + y^2 = 1$ or
       $(x - 5)^2 + (y - 4)^2 = 25$.
12. $(x - 5)^2 + (y - 11)^2 = 36$,
    $(x - 5)^2 + (y - 5)^2 = 36$.
13. $y = 3, (x - 47)^2 + (y - 8)^2 = 25$.
14. b) (i) 1 (ii) -1 (iii) $x + y = 3$.
15. a) $3y = x + 5$ b) $y = 2x - 8$
    c) $2y = 5x + 41$ d) $x + 2y + 20 = 0$.
16. a) $3\sqrt{13}$ b) they touch externally.
18. $(4, -12)$ $(10, 6)$.
19. $(3, 5)$ $(4, 0)$.
20. $5x + 2y = 7$.
22. $(x - 17)^2 + (y - 15)^2 = 25$.

Exercise 82, page 121

1. $(2, 3), 5$.
2. $(-3, -2), 1$.
3. $(3, 3), 3\sqrt{2}$ centre on $y = x$, passes through the origin.
4. $(3, -1), 1$ touches the x-axis.
5. $(-1, 1), 1$ centre on $y = -x$, touches both axes.
6. $(4, 0), 4$ centre on x-axis, touches y-axis at the origin.
7. $(0, -3), 3$ centre on y-axis, touches x-axis at the origin.
8. $(-4, 3), 5$ passes through the origin.
9. $(0, a), a$ centre on y-axis, touches x-axis at the origin.
10. $(a, a), a$ centre on $y = x$, touches both axes.

Exercise 83, page 123

1. a) yes $(-3, -4), 6$ b) no
   c) yes $(0, 0), 3$ d) no $(r^2 < 0)$
   e) no (a straight line)
   f) no (a parabola) g) no
   h) yes $(5, -4), \sqrt{41}$.
2. a) $(1, 2), 3$ b) $(-3, 4), 7$
   c) $(-3, 5), 6$ d) $\left(\frac{1}{2}, -\frac{1}{2}\right), \frac{1}{2}$
   e) $(-2, 1), 2$ f) $(-5, 7), 3$
   g) $(-a, -a), a$ h) $(a, 2a), 3a$.

3. A inside, B on, C outside.

4. (1, 3).

5. 1, 5.

6. –1, 5.

10. a) $5x + y = 15$ b) $11y = 7x + 87$
    c) $8y = 9x + 58$.

11. (–3, 4).

12. b) $2\sqrt{5}$.

14. a) $2y = x + 19$ b) (–2, 4).

15. b) (–1, –7) (8, –6).

16. $9x + 4y + 33 = 0$.

17. (7, 2) (–5, –4).

18. a) 40   b) 14.

19. b) $5, 5\sqrt{2}$ c) 5.

20. 14.

21. a) $2y = x + 5$ b) $6\sqrt{5}$.

22. $y = 2x + 9$, $y = 2x - 11$, (–2, 5), (6, 1).

23. a) $x^2 + y^2 - 2x - 4y - 53 = 0$
    b) $x^2 + y^2 - 6x - 8y = 0$
    c) $x^2 + y^2 - 9x - 6y + 13 = 0$.

24. a) (ii) $x = 9$
      (iii) $x + 2y = 23$
      (iv) (9, 7)
      (v) $x^2 + y^2 - 18x - 14y + 90 = 0$
    b) $x^2 + y^2 - 8x - 6y + 20 = 0$.

25. a) $x^2 + y^2 - 2x + 2y - 23 = 0$
    b) $x^2 + y^2 - 4x - 2y - 20 = 0$.

26. a) $x^2 + y^2 - 4x + 6y - 12 = 0$
    b) $x^2 + y^2 - 2x + 4y - 20 = 0$.

Topic Test, page 126

1. a) $x^2 + y^2 = 41$
    b) $(x - 4)^2 + (y - 5)^2 = 41$
    c) $(x - 7)^2 + (y + 1)^2 = 1$.

2. $(x - 6)^2 + (y - 3)^2 = 34$.

3. $2y = 3x - 19$.

4. [distance between centres = sum of radii; $3\sqrt{5} = 2\sqrt{5} + \sqrt{5}$].

5. yes, at the point (10, –5).

6. $(x - 14)^2 + (y - 4)^2 = 16$.

Practice Unit Test, page 127

1. $(x - 1)(x + 2)(x - 3)$.

2. real equal roots.

3. $-\dfrac{1}{x^3} + c$.

4. $21\frac{1}{3}$.

5. $\int_0^4 [(x + 3) - (x^2 - 3x + 3)]\,dx$.

6. $\dfrac{\pi}{3}, \dfrac{2\pi}{3}$.

7. a) $\dfrac{4}{5}, \dfrac{7}{25}$.

8. a) $\sin(x - 25)°$ b) 66.8, 163.2.

9. a) $(x - 3)^2 + (y + 4)^2 = 4$
    b) (3, –4), 6.

11. $2x + y + 1 = 0$.

Test 1, page 128

1. $(x - 1)(3x - 2)(2x + 3)$.

2. Yes, at (2, 4).

3. $\dfrac{\pi}{2}, \dfrac{3\pi}{2}, \dfrac{2\pi}{3}, \dfrac{4\pi}{3}$.

4. a) A (–1, 5) B (7, 9)   b) C (9, 5).

5. $-\dfrac{44}{125}$.

6. 32 units^2.

Test 2, page 129

1. $-2, \dfrac{2}{3}$.

2. a) (i) $\dfrac{12}{13}$ (ii) $-\dfrac{5}{13}$.

3. [15 = 10 + 5].

4. b) (2, 6)   c) $21\frac{1}{3}$ units^2.

UNIT 3   VECTORS

Exercise 87, page 131

1. $\vec{DE} = \begin{pmatrix} -4 \\ -3 \end{pmatrix}$ $\vec{FG} = \begin{pmatrix} -4 \\ 0 \end{pmatrix}$ $\vec{MN} = \begin{pmatrix} 6 \\ 2 \end{pmatrix}$
  $\vec{PQ} = \begin{pmatrix} 1 \\ -5 \end{pmatrix}$ $\vec{RS} = \begin{pmatrix} -5 \\ -4 \end{pmatrix}$ $\vec{TU} = \begin{pmatrix} 0 \\ -2 \end{pmatrix}$
  $\vec{VW} = \begin{pmatrix} 0 \\ 3 \end{pmatrix}$.

2.

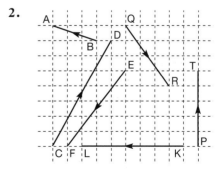

3.

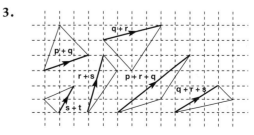

ANSWERS

4. a)

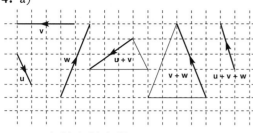

b) $\begin{pmatrix} -3 \\ -2 \end{pmatrix} \begin{pmatrix} -2 \\ 5 \end{pmatrix} \begin{pmatrix} -1 \\ 3 \end{pmatrix}$.

5. a) $\overrightarrow{CA}$ b) $\overrightarrow{DC}$ c) $\overrightarrow{AC}$ d) $\overrightarrow{AD}$.

6. a) $\overrightarrow{AE}$ b) $\overrightarrow{EC}$ c) $\overrightarrow{ED}$ d) $\overrightarrow{BC}$

e) $\overrightarrow{EC}$ f) $\overrightarrow{ED}$.

Exercise 88, page 132

1. a) $\overrightarrow{AC}$ b) $\overrightarrow{BA}$ c) $\overrightarrow{CA}$ d) $\overrightarrow{CB}$

e) $\overrightarrow{AB}$ f) $\overrightarrow{BC}$ g) $\overrightarrow{AC}$ h) $\overrightarrow{BC}$.

2.

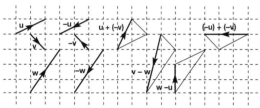

3. a) $\begin{pmatrix} -2 \\ 6 \end{pmatrix}$ b) $\begin{pmatrix} -1 \\ 3 \end{pmatrix}$ c) $\begin{pmatrix} -1 \\ -2 \end{pmatrix}$ d) $\begin{pmatrix} 3 \\ -4 \end{pmatrix}$

e) $\begin{pmatrix} 1 \\ -3 \end{pmatrix}$ f) $\begin{pmatrix} 4 \\ -2 \end{pmatrix}$ g) $\begin{pmatrix} 0 \\ 5 \end{pmatrix}$ h) $\begin{pmatrix} 1 \\ -3 \end{pmatrix}$.

4. a) **d** b) **e** c) **0** d) **e**.

Exercise 89, page 133

1.

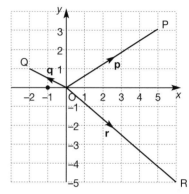

2. a) $2\mathbf{u} = \overrightarrow{DF}$ etc $3\mathbf{u} = \overrightarrow{DG}$ etc

$4\mathbf{u} = \overrightarrow{DH}$ etc $-\mathbf{u} = \overrightarrow{ED}$ etc.

b) $\overrightarrow{AE}, \overrightarrow{AG}, \overrightarrow{AB}, \overrightarrow{EA}, \overrightarrow{BA}$

(or equivalent).

c) $\overrightarrow{GA}, \overrightarrow{DG}, \overrightarrow{AG}, \overrightarrow{GF}, \overrightarrow{FG}$

(or equivalent).

3. a) $\begin{pmatrix} 4 \\ -5 \end{pmatrix}$ b) $\begin{pmatrix} -8 \\ -4 \end{pmatrix}$ c) $\begin{pmatrix} 10 \\ 3 \end{pmatrix}$ d) $\begin{pmatrix} 3 \\ 1 \end{pmatrix}$

e) $\begin{pmatrix} 0 \\ -3 \end{pmatrix}$ f) $\begin{pmatrix} 19 \\ -2 \end{pmatrix}$ g) $\begin{pmatrix} -27 \\ -16 \end{pmatrix}$ h) $\begin{pmatrix} 0 \\ 5 \end{pmatrix}$

i) $\begin{pmatrix} -11 \\ -5 \end{pmatrix}$ j) $\begin{pmatrix} -23 \\ -10 \end{pmatrix}$.

Exercise 90, page 134

1. a) $\begin{pmatrix} -7 \\ -2 \end{pmatrix}$ b) $\begin{pmatrix} 8 \\ -6 \end{pmatrix}$ c) $\begin{pmatrix} 1 \\ -8 \end{pmatrix}$ d) $\begin{pmatrix} -6 \\ -10 \end{pmatrix}$

e) $\begin{pmatrix} 6 \\ 10 \end{pmatrix}$ f) $\begin{pmatrix} 7 \\ 1 \end{pmatrix}$ g) $\begin{pmatrix} -1 \\ 21 \end{pmatrix}$.

2. a) $\begin{pmatrix} 1 \\ 3 \end{pmatrix} \begin{pmatrix} 6 \\ 9 \end{pmatrix} \begin{pmatrix} 5 \\ 6 \end{pmatrix} \begin{pmatrix} 5 \\ 6 \end{pmatrix}$

b) $\begin{pmatrix} -7 \\ 2 \end{pmatrix} \begin{pmatrix} 5 \\ -3 \end{pmatrix} \begin{pmatrix} 12 \\ -5 \end{pmatrix} \begin{pmatrix} 12 \\ -5 \end{pmatrix}$

c) $\begin{pmatrix} -2 \\ -2 \end{pmatrix} \begin{pmatrix} 1 \\ 3 \end{pmatrix} \begin{pmatrix} 3 \\ 5 \end{pmatrix} \begin{pmatrix} 3 \\ 5 \end{pmatrix}$

d) $\overrightarrow{AB} = \mathbf{b} - \mathbf{a}$

Proof: $\overrightarrow{AB} = \overrightarrow{AO} + \overrightarrow{OB} = \overrightarrow{OB} - \overrightarrow{OA}$
$= \mathbf{b} - \mathbf{a}$.

3. a) $\begin{pmatrix} 3 \\ 3 \end{pmatrix}$ b) $\begin{pmatrix} 1 \\ -12 \end{pmatrix}$ c) $\begin{pmatrix} -3 \\ 8 \end{pmatrix}$

d) $\begin{pmatrix} 9 \\ 4 \end{pmatrix}$ e) $\begin{pmatrix} 1 \\ -8 \end{pmatrix}$.

4. B (13, 9), C (−5, −3), D (16, 11),
E (−8, −5), F (19, 13), G (5, 4).

5. a) $\begin{pmatrix} 6 \\ 4 \end{pmatrix} \begin{pmatrix} 3 \\ 2 \end{pmatrix} \begin{pmatrix} 5 \\ 7 \end{pmatrix}, \begin{pmatrix} 5 \\ 7 \end{pmatrix}$

b) $\begin{pmatrix} 2 \\ 4 \end{pmatrix} \begin{pmatrix} 1 \\ 2 \end{pmatrix} \begin{pmatrix} -1 \\ 7 \end{pmatrix}, \begin{pmatrix} -1 \\ 7 \end{pmatrix}$

c) $\begin{pmatrix} 4 \\ 6 \end{pmatrix} \begin{pmatrix} 2 \\ 3 \end{pmatrix} \begin{pmatrix} 4 \\ 5 \end{pmatrix}, \begin{pmatrix} 4 \\ 5 \end{pmatrix}$

d) $\mathbf{m} = \frac{1}{2}(\mathbf{a} + \mathbf{b})$

Proof: $\mathbf{m} = \overrightarrow{OM} = \overrightarrow{OA} + \overrightarrow{AM} =$
$\mathbf{a} + \frac{1}{2}\overrightarrow{AB} = \mathbf{a} + \frac{1}{2}(\mathbf{b} - \mathbf{a})$
$\Rightarrow \mathbf{m} = \mathbf{a} + \frac{1}{2}\mathbf{b} - \frac{1}{2}\mathbf{a} = \frac{1}{2}\mathbf{a} - \frac{1}{2}\mathbf{b}$
$= \frac{1}{2}(\mathbf{a} + \mathbf{b})$

e) (i) $\begin{pmatrix} 2 \\ 5 \end{pmatrix}$ (ii) $\begin{pmatrix} -3 \\ 2 \end{pmatrix}$ (iii) $\begin{pmatrix} 1 \\ -1 \end{pmatrix}$

f) (i) (8, 10) (ii) (3, 1) (iii) (−2, 8).

Exercise 91, page 136

1. $a = 13$ $b = 5$ $c = 17$ $d = 10$
   $e = 25$ $f = 2\sqrt{2}$ $g = \sqrt{34}$ $r = \sqrt{113}$
   $s = \sqrt{137}$ $t = 29$ $u = \sqrt{58}$ $v = \sqrt{a^2 + b^2}$.

Exercise 92, page 136

1. $-\mathbf{u}, -\mathbf{v}, -\mathbf{w}, \mathbf{u}, \mathbf{v}, \mathbf{w}, \mathbf{u} + \mathbf{v}, \mathbf{u} + \mathbf{v} + \mathbf{w},$
   $\mathbf{v} + \mathbf{w}, \mathbf{v} = \overrightarrow{BC} = \overrightarrow{AO}$
   $= \overrightarrow{AB} + \overrightarrow{BO} = \mathbf{u} + \mathbf{w}$.

2. $\mathbf{v} - \mathbf{u}, \frac{1}{2}(\mathbf{v} - \mathbf{u}), \frac{1}{2}(\mathbf{u} + \mathbf{v}), \frac{3}{2}(\mathbf{u} + \mathbf{v}),$
   $\frac{1}{2}(\mathbf{u} + 3\mathbf{v}), -\frac{1}{2}(3\mathbf{u} + \mathbf{v})$.

3. $\mathbf{x} + \mathbf{z}, \mathbf{y}, \mathbf{y} - \mathbf{x}, \mathbf{x} + \mathbf{y}, \mathbf{x} + \mathbf{y} - \mathbf{z},$
   $\mathbf{y} + \mathbf{z} - \mathbf{x}, \mathbf{y} - \mathbf{x} - \mathbf{z}, \mathbf{x} + \mathbf{y} + \mathbf{z}$.

4. $\mathbf{u}, \mathbf{v}, \mathbf{v} - \mathbf{u}, 2\mathbf{v} - 2\mathbf{u}, AB = 2CD,$
   $AB \parallel CD$.

5. a) $\binom{3}{6} \binom{2}{4} \binom{4}{9}$ (4, 9)

   b) $\binom{6}{-3} \binom{4}{-2} \binom{3}{1}$ (3, 1)

   c) $\binom{9}{-9} \binom{6}{-6} \binom{3}{1}$ (3, 1)

   d) $\mathbf{p} = \mathbf{a} + \frac{2}{3}(\mathbf{b} - \mathbf{a}) = \frac{1}{3}\mathbf{a} + \frac{2}{3}\mathbf{b}$
      $= \frac{1}{3}(\mathbf{a} + 2\mathbf{b})$

   e) $\mathbf{p} = \mathbf{a} + \frac{3}{4}(\mathbf{b} - \mathbf{a}) = \frac{1}{4}\mathbf{a} + \frac{3}{4}\mathbf{b}$
      $= \frac{1}{4}(\mathbf{a} + 3\mathbf{b})$.

6. a) $\mathbf{u} - 2\mathbf{v}, \frac{2}{3}(\mathbf{u} - 2\mathbf{v}), \frac{2}{3}(\mathbf{u} + \mathbf{v})$

   b) $2(\mathbf{u} - \mathbf{v}), \mathbf{u} - \mathbf{v}, \mathbf{u} + \mathbf{v}, \frac{2}{3}(\mathbf{u} + \mathbf{v})$

   c) $2\mathbf{u}, \mathbf{v}, \mathbf{v} - 2\mathbf{u}, \frac{2}{3}(\mathbf{v} - 2\mathbf{u}), \frac{2}{3}(\mathbf{u} + \mathbf{v})$

   d) G, H and K coincide
      (Hence the medians of a triangle
      are concurrent at a point of
      trisection of each.)

Exercise 93, page 138

1. a) $\begin{pmatrix} 3 \\ -2 \\ 2 \end{pmatrix}, \begin{pmatrix} 4 \\ 1 \\ -1 \end{pmatrix}, \begin{pmatrix} -2 \\ 3 \\ 4 \end{pmatrix}, \begin{pmatrix} 1 \\ 3 \\ -3 \end{pmatrix}, \begin{pmatrix} 5 \\ -5 \\ -2 \end{pmatrix}, \begin{pmatrix} -6 \\ 2 \\ 5 \end{pmatrix}$

   b) $3\mathbf{i} - 2\mathbf{j} + 2\mathbf{k}, 4\mathbf{i} + \mathbf{j} - \mathbf{k},$
      $-2\mathbf{i} + 3\mathbf{j} + 4\mathbf{k}, \mathbf{i} + 3\mathbf{j} - 3\mathbf{k},$
      $5\mathbf{i} - 5\mathbf{j} - 2\mathbf{k}, -6\mathbf{i} + 2\mathbf{j} + 5\mathbf{k}$

   c) $\sqrt{17}, 3\sqrt{2}, \sqrt{29}, \sqrt{19}, 3\sqrt{6}, \sqrt{65}$.

2. a) $\begin{pmatrix} 6 \\ 0 \\ 0 \end{pmatrix}$ b) $\begin{pmatrix} 6 \\ 3 \\ 0 \end{pmatrix}$ c) $\begin{pmatrix} 0 \\ 3 \\ 0 \end{pmatrix}$

   d) $\begin{pmatrix} 6 \\ 3 \\ 2 \end{pmatrix}$ e) $\begin{pmatrix} 0 \\ 3 \\ 2 \end{pmatrix}$ f) $\begin{pmatrix} 6 \\ 0 \\ 2 \end{pmatrix}$

   g) $\begin{pmatrix} 6 \\ -3 \\ -2 \end{pmatrix}$ h) $\begin{pmatrix} -6 \\ 0 \\ -2 \end{pmatrix}$ i) $\begin{pmatrix} 3 \\ 3 \\ -2 \end{pmatrix}$.

3. a) $\mathbf{a} = \begin{pmatrix} 8 \\ -1 \\ -1 \end{pmatrix}$ $\mathbf{b} = \begin{pmatrix} 2 \\ 1 \\ -4 \end{pmatrix}$

   $\mathbf{c} = \begin{pmatrix} 4 \\ -11 \\ 20 \end{pmatrix}$ $\mathbf{d} = \begin{pmatrix} -15 \\ -7 \\ 17 \end{pmatrix}$

   b) $u = \sqrt{14}, v = \sqrt{17}, w = \sqrt{19},$
      $a = \sqrt{66}, b = \sqrt{21}, c = \sqrt{537},$
      $d = \sqrt{563}$

4. a) 3 b) 7 c) $4\sqrt{2}$ d) $2\sqrt{21}$.

5. a) $\begin{pmatrix} 0 \\ 2 \\ -2 \end{pmatrix}$ b) $\begin{pmatrix} 5 \\ -3 \\ -2 \end{pmatrix}$ c) $\begin{pmatrix} -1 \\ 1 \\ 0 \end{pmatrix}$.

6. a) $\begin{pmatrix} \frac{2}{7} \\ \frac{-3}{7} \\ \frac{6}{7} \end{pmatrix}$ b) $\begin{pmatrix} \frac{8}{9} \\ \frac{4}{9} \\ \frac{-1}{9} \end{pmatrix}$ c) $\begin{pmatrix} \frac{-3}{5} \\ 0 \\ \frac{4}{5} \end{pmatrix}$

   d) $\begin{pmatrix} \frac{4}{13} \\ \frac{12}{13} \\ \frac{-3}{13} \end{pmatrix}$ e) $\begin{pmatrix} \frac{2}{\sqrt{14}} \\ \frac{3}{\sqrt{14}} \\ \frac{-1}{\sqrt{14}} \end{pmatrix}$ f) $\begin{pmatrix} \frac{1}{\sqrt{2}} \\ \frac{-12}{13\sqrt{2}} \\ \frac{5}{13\sqrt{2}} \end{pmatrix}$

   g) $\begin{pmatrix} \frac{7}{\sqrt{74}} \\ \frac{4}{\sqrt{74}} \\ \frac{-3}{\sqrt{74}} \end{pmatrix}$ h) $\begin{pmatrix} \frac{1}{\sqrt{3}} \\ \frac{-1}{\sqrt{3}} \\ \frac{1}{\sqrt{3}} \end{pmatrix}$.

Exercise 94, page 139

1. a) 3 b) 7 c) 13 d) 17 e) 9.
2. LM = 14 = LN.
6. $(-1, 9, 7)$.

Exercise 95, page 140

1. 1:2. 2. 1:2. 3. 2:3. 4. 1:2.

Exercise 96, page 141

1. a) $\begin{pmatrix} 8 \\ 8 \\ 0 \end{pmatrix}$ b) $\begin{pmatrix} 9 \\ 10 \\ 3 \end{pmatrix}$ c) $\begin{pmatrix} 4 \\ 3 \\ 3 \end{pmatrix}$ d) $\begin{pmatrix} -2 \\ -6 \\ 0 \end{pmatrix}$

e) $\begin{pmatrix} -2 \\ 1 \\ 3 \end{pmatrix}$ f) $\begin{pmatrix} 3 \\ 8 \\ 3 \end{pmatrix}$ g) $\begin{pmatrix} 7 \\ 6 \\ -3 \end{pmatrix}$ h) $\begin{pmatrix} 4 \\ 4 \\ 0 \end{pmatrix}$.

2. a) $\begin{pmatrix} 12 \\ -6 \\ 0 \end{pmatrix}$ b) $\begin{pmatrix} 12 \\ -6 \\ -9 \end{pmatrix}$ c) $\begin{pmatrix} 12 \\ -6 \\ -6 \end{pmatrix}$.

3. a) $\begin{pmatrix} 11 \\ 13 \\ 11 \end{pmatrix}$ b) $\begin{pmatrix} 17 \\ -11 \\ -1 \end{pmatrix}$ c) $\begin{pmatrix} 10 \\ 0 \\ -16 \end{pmatrix}$.

4. a) $\left(\frac{1}{2}, 2\frac{1}{2}, 2\right)$ b) $\left(\frac{1}{2}, 2\frac{1}{2}, 2\right)$
   c) $\left(\frac{1}{2}, 2\frac{1}{2}, 2\right)$.

6. a) $\overrightarrow{DO}$ b) $\overrightarrow{CG}$ c) $\overrightarrow{DB}$.
7. a) $\overrightarrow{FG}$ b) $\overrightarrow{CK}$ c) $\overrightarrow{HK}$ d) $\overrightarrow{DG}$.

Exercise 97, page 143

1. a)
```
        2          1
    A        P        B
```
   b)
```
      1          3
    C    Q            D
```
   c)
```
      1          1
    E        R        F
```
   d)
```
      2          3
    G    S            H
```

2. a) 2:1 b) 3:1 c) 1:2.
3. a) 1:2 b) 1:1 c) 1:4 d) 1:2.
4. a) (9, 3) b) (3, −2) c) (5, 8)
   d) (2, 2) e) (4, 4) f) (−3, 5).
5. a) (9, 12, 17) b) (3, 7, 8)
   c) (5, 7, 6) d) (6, 2, 8)
   e) (−2, 0, 5) f) (3, 7, 7).
6. a) $\frac{1}{7}(3\mathbf{a} + 4\mathbf{b})$ b) $\frac{1}{3}(2\mathbf{a} + \mathbf{b})$
   c) $\frac{1}{11}(4\mathbf{a} + 7\mathbf{b})$.

7. 1:2.
8. a) P(3, 6) Q(6, 3) R(9, 0) b) 1:1.
9. a) each of G, H, K is (4, 3, −1)
   b) (i) the medians of the triangle are
          concurrent
      (ii) the point of concurrence lies
           one third of the way up each
           median.
10. a) $\mathbf{d} = \frac{1}{2}(\mathbf{a} + \mathbf{c})$ b) $\mathbf{g} = \frac{1}{3}(2\mathbf{d} + \mathbf{b})$
    c) $\mathbf{g} = \frac{1}{3}(\mathbf{a} + \mathbf{b} + \mathbf{c})$

d) the medians of any triangle are
   concurrent at a point called the
   centroid, which lies one third of
   the way up each median.
11. a) (2, 1, 2) b) (3, 3, 1)
    c) G, H, J and K coincide.
12. a) $\mathbf{h} = \frac{1}{3}(\mathbf{a} + \mathbf{b} + \mathbf{c})$
    b) $\mathbf{g} = \frac{1}{4}(3\mathbf{h} + \mathbf{d})$
    c) $\mathbf{g} = \frac{1}{4}(\mathbf{a} + \mathbf{b} + \mathbf{c} + \mathbf{d})$.
    d) the lines joining each vertex of a
       tetrahedron to the centroid of the
       opposite face are concurrent at a
       point one quarter of the way up
       each line.
13. a) 3:1 b) $x = -4, y = -6$.
14. a) 2:1 b) $p = -7, q = 8$.
15. a) (i) 1:8 (ii) 2:7 (iii) 1:2 (iv) 4:5
    b) (i) 1 (ii) 0 (iii) 10.
16. 3:1.
17. (0, −10, −1).

Exercise 98, page 147

1. a) 3 b) −8 c) 3 d) − 42 e) 6
   f) −28 g) 8 h) 0 i) $-6\sqrt{3}$ j) 3.
2. a) 1 b) −1.
3. a) $4\frac{1}{2}$ b) $-4\frac{1}{2}$.
4. a) 64 b) −36 c) 0.
5. a) $-\frac{1}{2}a^2$ b) $\frac{1}{2}a^2$ c) a^2 d) a^2.
6. a) $-6\frac{1}{4}$ b) 36 c) $12\frac{1}{2}$.
7. a) $\mathbf{a.b} - \mathbf{a.c}$ b) $\mathbf{p.r} - \mathbf{q.r}$
   c) $u^2 - v^2$ d) $u^2 + v^2 + 2\,\mathbf{u.v}$
   e) $2r^2 + 2s^2 - 5\,\mathbf{r.s}$
   f) $\mathbf{a.c} + \mathbf{b.c} - \mathbf{a.w} - \mathbf{b.w}$.
8. a) 3   b) 10.
9. a) 1 b) 1 c) 37.
11. a) $\overrightarrow{PR} = \mathbf{a} + \mathbf{b}$, $\overrightarrow{QS} = \mathbf{b} - \mathbf{a}$
    b) 0 c) they are perpendicular.
12.

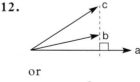

or

13. a) 1 b) 0 c) 0.

Exercise 99, page 149

1. a) 7 b) −7 c) −7.

2. a) −19 b) −4 c) 8 d) −27
  e) −15 f) 12 g) −146.

3. 8.

4. −1.

5. 1.

6. 21.

10. 9.

13. P(6, 2, 8) Q(10, 0, 8).

14. $\vec{CD} = -\mathbf{i} + 2\mathbf{j} + 2\mathbf{k}$.

Exercise 100, page 150

1. a) $\frac{2}{29}$ b) $\frac{13}{35}$ c) $\frac{37}{62}$ d) $\frac{-12}{13}$
  e) $\frac{1}{2}$ f) $\frac{-1}{14}$ g) $\frac{20}{21}$.

2. a) 50.5° b) 80.6°.

3. 159.7°

4. a) $\frac{7}{6\sqrt{57}}$ b) $\frac{47}{18\sqrt{13}}$ c) $\frac{31}{2\sqrt{741}}$.

5. $\hat{A} = 70.5°$, $\hat{B} = 54.75° = \hat{C}$.

6. a) A(0, 5, 2), B(3, 1, 7), C(10, 0, 2)
  b) $5\sqrt{2}$, $5\sqrt{3}$ c) 90°.

7. a) P(1, −8, 0), R(0, 0, 4), S(2, 1, 2),
    T(0, 1, 2)
  b) 85.75°.

8. a) B(8, 10, 0), D(0, 0, 6), H(4, 5, 12)
  b) 74.9°.

9. a) (i) M(6, 0, 0) N(0, 3, 0)
    (ii) (1, 4, 3) (iii) (5, 2, 3)
  b) 45.6°.

10. (i) (6, 3, 0) (ii) (5, 3, 3)
    (iii) (3, 6, 0) (iv) (3, 5, −3)
    (v) 60.8°.

11. a) (3, 4, 1) b) 1:2 c) 51.3°.

12. a) K(1, 3, 3), L(5, 7, 6), M(6, 3, 7),
    N(2, −1, 4), b) 65.8°.

Topic Test, page 153

1. 2:3. **2.** (8, 2, 1). **3.** 21. **4.** 1.
6. 84.2°. **7.** a) 112.3° b) 2:3.

UNIT 3 FURTHER DIFFERENTIATION AND INTEGRATION

Exercise 102, page 154

1. $2(x + 1)$. **2.** $4x(x^2 + 2)$.

3. $6(3t - 2)$. **4.** $\frac{(\sqrt{v} + 1)}{\sqrt{v}}$.

5. $21x^2(x^3 + 11)^6$. **6.** $6x(x^2 - 2)2$.

7. $5(x - 1)^4$. **8.** $-5(1 - x)^4$.

9. $3(8x + 1)(4x^2 + x - 2)^2$.

10. $4\left(6x + 5 + \frac{1}{x^2}\right)\left(3x^2 + 5x - \frac{1}{x}\right)^3$.

11. $\frac{1}{(3 - y)^2}$. **12.** $\frac{-4t}{(5 + t^2)^2}$.

13. $\frac{-(6u + 4)}{(3u^2 + 4u - 7)^2}$. **14.** $\frac{-18z^8}{(z^9 - 7)^2}$.

15. $\frac{-12x^2}{(7 + x^3)^2}$. **16.** $\frac{1}{(3 - 2x)^{\frac{3}{2}}}$.

17. $\frac{1}{2}(x - 1)^{\frac{-1}{2}}$. **18.** $\frac{1}{2}(x - 1)^{\frac{-3}{2}}$.

19. $3x(x^2 + 3)^{\frac{1}{2}}$. **20.** $\frac{-2}{3}(2v - 1)^{\frac{-4}{3}}$.

21. $(3x + 2)^{\frac{-2}{3}}$. **22.** $\frac{(2x + 3)}{2\sqrt{(x^2 + 3x - 10)}}$.

23. $\frac{4x}{(1 - x^2)^2}$. **24.** $2(x + 1) - \frac{2}{(x + 1)^3}$.

25. $\frac{2(x + 2)}{(2x + 5)^{\frac{3}{2}}}$.

Exercise 103, page 155

1. a) $\cos x$ b) $-\sin x$ c) $-\cos x$
  d) $1 - \sin x$ e) $4 \cos x$ f) $-2 \sin x$
  g) $-3 \cos x$ h) $-5 \sin x$ i) $1 + \cos x$
  j) $2x + \sin x$ k) $3x^2 - 2 \cos x$ l) $\cos x$.

2. a) (i) 1 (ii) 0 (iii) 0
  b) (i) 0 (ii) 1 (iii) $\frac{-1}{\sqrt{2}}$
  c) (i) 1 (ii) $-\sqrt{2}$ (iii) $\frac{1}{2}(1 - \sqrt{3})$
  d) (i) $\frac{1}{2}(1 + \sqrt{3})$ (ii) $\frac{1}{2}(1 + \sqrt{3})$
    (iii) −1
  e) (i) $\frac{1}{2}(\sqrt{3} - 1)$ (ii) $\frac{1}{2}(1 - \sqrt{3})$
    (iii) $\frac{1}{2}(1 + \sqrt{3})$
  f) (i) 0 (ii) $\frac{5\pi}{2} + \frac{1}{\sqrt{2}}$ (iii) $\frac{\sqrt{3}}{2} - \frac{2\pi}{3}$.

3. a) 4 b) $\frac{1}{\sqrt{2}}$ c) −3 d) −4 e) $\frac{7}{5}$.

4. $y + 3x = 4$.

6. a) $-\sin x$ b) 0 c) $\cos x$ d) $\sin x$.

ANSWERS

7. a) $\sqrt{3}, \sqrt{3}$ **b)** $\dfrac{2\pi}{3}, \dfrac{5\pi}{3}$

c) max of 2, min of −2.

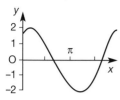

Exercise 104, page 157

1. a) $6(x + 2)^5$ **b)** $10(2x - 3)^4$
c) $4(7 + x)^3$ **d)** $-3(2 - x)^2$
e) $6(3x + 4)$ **f)** $7(6 - x)^{-8}$
g) $16(3 - 4x)^{-5}$ **h)** $8x(x^2 + 3)^3$
i) $15x^2(x^3 - 2)^4$ **j)** $12x^3(x^4 + 7)^2$
k) $-30x^4(4 - x^5)^5$ **l)** $\dfrac{9}{2}(3x - 2)^{\frac{1}{2}}$.

2. a) $4(1 + \cos x)(x + \sin x)^3$

b) $\dfrac{\sin x}{2\sqrt{(2 - \cos x)}}$

c) $\dfrac{3}{2}(3 \cos x + 2 \sin x)(3 \sin x - 2 \cos x)^{\frac{1}{2}}$

d) $\dfrac{-10 \cos x}{(5\sin x - 1)^3}$

e) $\dfrac{3}{4}\sin x\,(\cos x)^{\frac{-7}{4}}$

f) $\dfrac{2}{3}\cos x\,(\sin x)^{\frac{-1}{3}}$

g) $\sin 2x$
h) $-\sin 2x$

i) $\dfrac{-3 \sin x}{2\sqrt{(1 + 3 \cos x)}}$

j) $\dfrac{4}{3}(2 - 3 \cos x)(2x - 3 \sin x)^{\frac{1}{3}}$

k) $\dfrac{1}{5}(1 + \sin x)(x - \cos x)^{\frac{-4}{5}}$

l) $49(1 - 5 \cos x)(x - 5 \sin x)^6$
m) $-2 \sin 2x$
n) 0
o) $\sin 2x$.

3. a) $4 \cos 4x$ **b)** $-5 \sin 5x$ **c)** $\dfrac{1}{2}\cos\dfrac{x}{2}$
d) $-\dfrac{3}{2}\sin\dfrac{3}{2}x$ **e)** $3 \cos(3x + 5)$
f) $-4 \sin(4x - 5)$ **g)** $2 \cos(2x - 7)$
h) $3 \sin(8 - 3x)$ **i)** $6 \cos 3x$
j) $-6 \sin 2x$ **k)** $3 \sin 6x$
l) $-6 \sin 2x \cos^2 2x$
m) $12x \cos(2x^2)\sin^2(2x^2)$
n) $2(x + \sin 2x)(1 + 2 \cos 2x)$
o) $\dfrac{-(3 \sin 3x + 2x)}{2\sqrt{(\cos 3x - x^2)}}$.

4. a) $(2x - 3)^{\frac{-1}{2}}$ **b)** $\dfrac{1}{3}(x - 1)^{\frac{-2}{3}}$

c) $\dfrac{1}{2}(2x + 1)(x^2 + x - 1)^{\frac{-1}{2}}$

d) $\dfrac{3}{4}(6x + 4)(3x^2 + 4x - 2)^{\frac{-1}{4}}$

e) $\dfrac{-7}{4}(5 - 7x)^{\frac{-3}{4}}$ **f)** $-2x^2(x^3 - 5)^{\frac{-5}{3}}$

g) $\dfrac{-3}{(3x - 2)^2}$ **h)** $\dfrac{-12x}{(3x^2 + 4)^2}$

i) $\dfrac{-110}{(5x - 10)^3}$ **j)** $\dfrac{x}{\sqrt{(x^2 + 9)}}$

k) $\dfrac{3x^2 + 7}{2\sqrt{(x^3 + 7x - 2)}}$ **l)** $\dfrac{1}{2(1 - x)^{\frac{3}{2}}}$

m) $\dfrac{3(x - 2)}{2\sqrt{(x - 1)}}$.

Exercise 105, page 158

1. a) $\sin x + c$ **b)** $-\cos x + c$
c) $x + \sin x + c$ **d)** $\dfrac{1}{2}x^2 + \cos x + c$
e) $-5 \cos x + c$ **f)** $3x + 2 \sin x + c$
g) $2x + 3 \cos x + c$ **h)** $7 \sin x + c$
i) $\dfrac{1}{2}x^2 + \sin x + c$ **j)** $\dfrac{1}{3}x^3 - 2 \cos x + c$
k) $\dfrac{1}{4}x^4 - 3 \sin x + c$ **l)** $\sin x + c$.

2. a) 1 **b)** $\dfrac{1}{\sqrt{2}}$ **c)** $\dfrac{1}{2}(1 + \sqrt{3})$

d) 0 **e)** -2 **f)** $\dfrac{1}{4}(\pi + 2\sqrt{2})$

g) $\dfrac{1}{6}(9 + 4\pi)$ **h)** $\dfrac{1}{2}(\pi - 2)$ **i)** $\dfrac{2}{3}\pi^3$.

3. a) 1 **b)** 2. **4. a)** 1 **b)** 1.

5. $\dfrac{1}{6}(\pi + 3\sqrt{3} - 3)$. **6.** $\dfrac{1}{2}(4 - \pi)$.

Exercise 106, page 159

1. a) $\dfrac{1}{8}(2x + 5)^4 + c$ **b)** $\dfrac{1}{15}(3x - 4)^5 + c$

c) $\dfrac{1}{30}(5x + 2)^6 + c$ **d)** $\dfrac{-1}{9}(1 - 3x)^3 + c$

e) $\dfrac{1}{18}(2x + 3)^9 + c$ **f)** $\dfrac{1}{18}(3x - 2)^6 + c$

g) $\dfrac{1}{4}(x + 5)^4 + c$ **h)** $\dfrac{-1}{5}(7 - x)^5 + c$

i) $\dfrac{1}{24}(3x + 4)^8 + c$ **j)** $\dfrac{5}{14}(2x - 3)^{\frac{7}{5}} + c$

k) $\dfrac{3}{4}(8 + x)^{\frac{4}{3}} + c$ **l)** $\dfrac{-4}{21}(9 - 3x)^{\frac{7}{4}} + c$

m) $\dfrac{1}{8}(3x + 7)^{\frac{8}{3}} + c$ **n)** $\dfrac{-2}{11}(1 - 2x)^{\frac{11}{4}} + c$

o) $\dfrac{-3}{5}(11 - x)^{\frac{5}{3}} + c$ **p)** $3\sqrt{(2x + 5)} + c$.

2. a) $-1\dfrac{1}{4}$ **b)** $2\dfrac{1}{5}$ **c)** -4 **d)** $69\dfrac{1}{3}$

e) $12\dfrac{2}{3}$ **f)** $136\dfrac{2}{5}$.

3. a) $\frac{1}{3}\sin 3x + c$

b) $\frac{-1}{5}\cos 5x + c$

c) $\frac{1}{2}\sin(2x - 1) + c$

d) $\frac{-1}{3}\cos(3x + 2) + c$

e) $\frac{1}{2}x^2 + \frac{1}{3}\cos 3x + c$

f) $\frac{1}{3}x^3 + \frac{2}{3}\sin 3x + c$

g) $\cos(3 - x) + c$

h) $\sin(5 + x) + c$

i) $2\sin\frac{x}{2} + c$

j) $\frac{-3}{2}\cos\left(\frac{2x + 1}{3}\right) + c$

k) $\frac{1}{8}\sin(4x + 3) + c$

l) $\frac{-2}{9}\cos(3x - 4) + c$

m) $x^3 + \frac{1}{3}\sin(3x + 2) + c$

n) $x^4 + \frac{1}{2}\cos(2x - 3) + c$

o) $3x^2 - \frac{3}{2}\sin 2x + c$

p) $\frac{5}{3}x^3 + 16\cos\left(\frac{1}{2}x\right) + c.$

4. a) 0 b) 1 c) $\sqrt{2}$ d) $\frac{\sqrt{2}}{3}(1 + \sqrt{2})$

e) 0 f) $-\frac{\sqrt{2}}{6}$ g) 1 h) $\frac{3\sqrt{3} + 4}{24}$

i) $\frac{9\sqrt{3} + 8}{6}.$

5. a) $-\frac{1}{4}\cos 2x + c$

b) $\frac{1}{4}[2x + \sin 2x] + c$

c) $\frac{1}{4}[2x - \sin 2x] + c$

d) $-\frac{1}{2}\sin 2x + c.$

6. a) $\frac{1}{2}$ b) 1 c) $\frac{1}{2}(\sqrt{2} - 1).$

Topic Test, page 160

1. a) $1 - \sin x$ b) $\frac{\cos\sqrt{x}}{2\sqrt{x}}.$

2. a) $-\frac{1}{2}\cos(2x + 3) + c$

b) $\frac{1}{3}\sin(3x - 2) + c.$

3. a) $20x(x^2 + 1)^9$ b) $\frac{-2x}{(x^2 - 5)^2}.$

4. a) $\frac{1}{3}(2x + 7)^{\frac{3}{2}} + c$

b) $\frac{1}{1 - x} + c.$

5. a) $6(x + \cos x)(x^2 + 2\sin x)^2$

b) $3\sin^2 x \cos x.$

6. b) 16 units. [Remember to justify the maximum.]

UNIT 3 LOGARITHMS

Exercise 108, page 162

1. a) $\log_2 8 = 3$ b) $\log_3 9 = 2$
c) $\log_4 64 = 3$ d) $\log_{10} 100 = 2$
e) $\log_3 \frac{1}{9} = -2$ f) $\log_{10}\frac{1}{1000} = -3$
g) $\log_3 1 = 0$ h) $\log_4 4 = 1.$

2. a) $5^2 = 25$ b) $6^2 = 36$ c) $4^3 = 64$
d) $2^{-3} = \frac{1}{8}$ e) $2^{\frac{1}{2}} = \sqrt{2}$ f) $5^{\frac{1}{3}} = \sqrt[3]{5}$
g) $2^0 = 1$ h) $5^1 = 5.$

3. a) $\log_p q = 2$ b) $\log_s r = 3$
c) $\log_b a = c$ d) $\log_k v = t.$

4. a) $3^N = M$ b) $4^t = u$ c) $p^k = m$
d) $b^c = a.$

5. a) 9 b) 64 c) 4 d) 81 e) $\frac{1}{16}$
f) $\frac{1}{9}$ g) $\frac{1}{2}$ h) $\frac{1}{27}$ i) 2 j) 4
k) 3 l) $\sqrt{2}.$

6. a) 3 b) 4 c) 2 d) -2 e) -2
f) -3 g) $\frac{3}{2}$ h) $-\frac{4}{3}.$

Exercise 109, page 163

1. a) $\log 15$ b) $\log 5$ c) $\log 32$
d) $\log 28$ e) $\log 4$ f) $\log \frac{3}{2}$
g) $\log \frac{1}{8}$ h) $\log 2.$

2. a) $\log 12$ b) $\log 8$ c) 0
d) $\log \frac{8}{9}$ e) $\log \sqrt{5}$ f) $\log 12.$

3. a) $\log_2 6$ b) $\log_3 0{\cdot}6$ c) $\log_2 1{\cdot}5$
d) $\log_3 \frac{25}{3}$ e) 5 f) 1
g) $\log_{10} 5$ h) $\log_{10} 500$ i) $\log_{10} 15.$

4. a) $\log pq$ b) $\log \frac{r^2}{s}$ c) $\log t\sqrt{u}$
d) $\log \frac{m}{n}$ e) $\log y\sqrt{x}$ f) $\log \frac{rs^2}{t^3}.$

5. a) $\log_{10} 10a$ b) $\log_{10}\frac{100}{b^3}$
c) $\log_{10}\frac{a\sqrt{b}}{10}.$

6. a) 5 b) 100 c) 6 d) 12
e) 3 f) $\pm 4.$

ANSWERS

Exercise 110, page 164

1. a) $3 \log 2$ b) $2 \log 3$
c) $2 \log 2 + \log 3$ d) $\log 2 + 2 \log 3$
e) $-\log 2$ f) $-2 \log 3$
g) $-\log 2 - \log 3$ h) $\log 3 - 2 \log 2$.

2. a) $1 - \log_{10} 2$
b) (i) $\log_{10} 2 - 1$
   (ii) $2 - 2 \log_{10} 2$
   (iii) $\log_{10} 3 + 1 - \log_{10} 2$
   (iv) $\log_{10} 2 + 1$
   (v) $\log_{10} 3 - 2 \log_{10} 2 + 2$
   (vi) $3\log_{10} 2 - 3$
   (vii) $1 - 5 \log_{10} 2$
   (viii) $\log_{10} 2 + \log_{10} 3 - 1$.

3. $2pq = 1$.

4. $p + q - 2r$.

5. $\log x = \frac{1}{5}(2a + b)$, $\log y = \frac{1}{5}(a - 2b)$.

7. a) $1 \cdot 365$ b) $1 \cdot 771$ c) $0 \cdot 322$.

8. a) $2 \cdot 579$ b) $1 \cdot 654$ c) $-1 \cdot 096$.

Exercise 111, page 165

1. a)

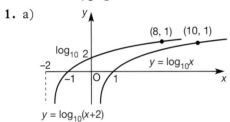

b)

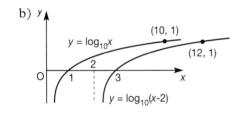

c)

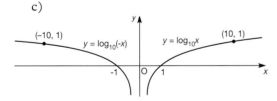

d)

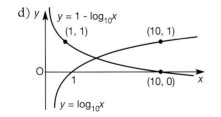

2. a)

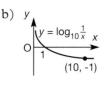

b)

c)

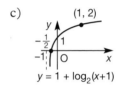

d)

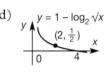

3. a)

b)

c)

d)

Exercise 112, page 167

1. a) $12 \cdot 4$ units   b) 10 m.
2. a) $2 \cdot 73$ amps   b) $3 \cdot 93$ km.
3. a) 41 b) $13 \cdot 86$ years.
4. a) $0 \cdot 067$
b) $P(4) = 37 \cdot 8 > 30$, (so No).
5. $0 \cdot 0411$ b) 32.2 minutes.
6. a) $0 \cdot 0719$ b) $51 \cdot 3\%$.
7. 591 units.

Exercise 113, page 169

1. a) $Y = 2X$ b) $Y = 3X + 0 \cdot 6$
c) $Y = X + 0 \cdot 7$.
2. a) $Y = 4X + 1 \cdot 1$ b) $Y = 2 \cdot 3 - X$
c) $Y = X - 1 \cdot 4$.
3. a) $Y = x + 0 \cdot 3$ b) $Y = 0 \cdot 5x + 0 \cdot 8$
c) $Y = 0 \cdot 3x + 0 \cdot 7$.
4. a) $Y = x + 1 \cdot 6$ b) $Y = 0 \cdot 7 - 3x$
c) $Y = 1 \cdot 6x + 2 \cdot 1$.
5. $p = 3 \, q^4$.
6. $m = 2 \cdot 7 \, v^{3 \cdot 6}$.
7. $s = 0 \cdot 2 \, t^{2 \cdot 1}$.
8. $y = 4 \, x^{-2}$.
9. $w = 7 \, x^{-3}$.
10. $p = 2 \, z^{1 \cdot 7}$.
11. $s = 5 \, t^4$.
12. $r = 0 \cdot 4 \, v^{-2}$.
13. $f = 3 \cdot 2 \, 4^t$.
14. $g = 5 \, e^{3r} \, [=5 \times (20)^r]$.
15. a) $P = \frac{1}{2}Q + 2$ b) $p = 100\sqrt{q}$.

16. a) $\log_e y = bx + \log_e a$
b) A $(3\cdot1, 9\cdot99)$, B$(5\cdot2, 16\cdot29)$
$y = 2\,e^{3x}$.

Topic Test, page 170

1. a) $\log_4 64 = 3$ b) $\log_y x = z$.
2. a) $3^4 = 81$ b) $x = 5^t$.
3. a) $\log\frac{16}{27}$ b) $\log_2 6$.
4. $4 \log 2 + 2 \log 3$.
5. $1 - \log 2 + 2 \log 3$.
6. $a = 2, b = 6$.
7. $1\cdot465$.
8. 320.
9. $Q = 100P^{\frac{1}{3}}$.

UNIT 3 AUXILIARY ANGLE

Exercise 115, page 172

1. $6\cdot9, 246\cdot9$.   **2.** $142\cdot6, 262\cdot6$.
3. $130\cdot2, 342\cdot2$.   **4.** $300\cdot9, 341\cdot7$.
5. $27\cdot5, 120\cdot7$.   **6.** $102\cdot3, 195\cdot7$.
7. $36\cdot9$.   **8.** $43\cdot6$.   **9.** $311\cdot8$.
10. $7\cdot3, 34\cdot0, 127\cdot3, 154\cdot0, 247\cdot3, 274\cdot0$.
11. $0, \frac{\pi}{2}, 2\pi$.   **12.** $0, \frac{\pi}{3}, 2\pi$
13. $\frac{\pi}{6}, \frac{3\pi}{2}$.   **14.** $0, \frac{4\pi}{3}, 2\pi$.   **15.** $\frac{\pi}{6}, \frac{\pi}{2}$.
16. $0, \frac{3\pi}{4}, \pi, \frac{7\pi}{4}$.   **17.** $4\cdot531$.
18. $2\cdot206, 3\cdot633$.

Exercise 116, page 174

1. a) $5 \cos (x - 36\cdot9)°$
b) $\sqrt{10} \cos (x - 288\cdot4)°$.
2. a) $\sqrt{10} \cos (x + 18\cdot4)°$
b) $\sqrt{2} \cos (x + 315)°$.
3. a) $10 \sin (x + 53\cdot1)°$
b) $\sqrt{2} \sin (x + 315)°$.
4. a) $2 \sin (x - 30)°$
b) $17 \sin (x - 331\cdot9)°$.
5. a) $\sqrt{2} \cos \left(\theta - \frac{\pi}{4}\right)°$ b) $2 \cos \left(\theta - \frac{\pi}{3}\right)°$
c) $\sqrt{2} \cos \left(\theta - \frac{7\pi}{4}\right)°$.
6. $2 \sin (x - 60)°$; $90, 210$.
7. $10 \sin (x - 53\cdot1)°$; $47\cdot4, 238\cdot8$.
8. $5 \cos (2x - 53\cdot1)°$; $26\cdot6, 206\cdot6$.
9. $10 \cos (2x + 36\cdot9)°$; $11\cdot6, 131\cdot6$.
10. a) e.g. $\sqrt{2}\cos (x - 225)°$
b) e.g. $2 \cos (x - 120)°$
c) e.g. $2\sqrt{2} \cos (x - 225)°$.

Exercise 117, page 175

1. a) max $(90, 1)$ min $(270, -1)$
b) max $(90, 5)$ min $(270, -5)$
c) max $(120, 3)$ min $(300, -3)$
d) max $(150, 3)$ min $(330, -1)$.
2. a) max $(0, 1)$ min $(180, -1)$
b) max $(0, 4)$ min $(180, -4)$
c) max $(300, 2)$ min $(120, -2)$
d) max $(315, 2)$ min $(135, -12)$.
3. a) $0, 180, 360$ b) $0, 180, 360$
c) $25, 205$.
4. a) $90, 270$ b) $90, 270$ c) $115, 295$.
5. a) $5 \cos (x - 36\cdot9)°$

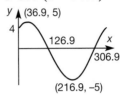

b) $5 \cos (x + 53\cdot1)°$

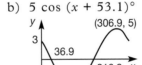

c) $2 \cos (x + 30)°$.

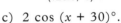
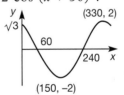

6. a) $2 \sin (x + 30)°$

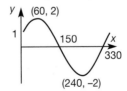

b) $2 \sin (x - 60)°$

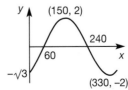

c) $25 \sin (x - 73.7)°$.

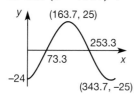

(163.7, 25)
253.3
73.3
−24
(343.7, −25)

7. a)

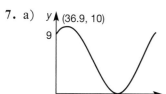

(36.9, 10)
9
216.9

b)

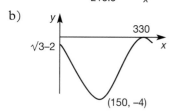

330
$\sqrt{3}-2$
(150, −4)

c)

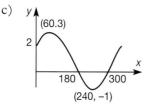

(60.3)
2
180   300
(240, −1)

8. $\frac{1}{25}$, $x = 163.7$.

9. $\frac{1}{(1 + \sqrt{2})}$, $45°$.

10. a) $40\sqrt{5} \sin (30t + 26.6)°$
  b) high 02:07 and 14:07
     low 08:07 and 20:07
  c) 00:15, 03:59, 12:15, 15:59.

11. a) $1 + 5 \cos (x + 36.9)°$.
  b)

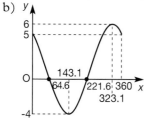

6
5
143.1
64.6   221.6 360 x
323.1
−4

12. a) 9
  c) $\sqrt{122 + 18\sqrt{41}} \cos(\theta - 38.7)°$
  d) $\sqrt{122 + 18\sqrt{41}}$.

13. see Ex. 79 no 30.

14.

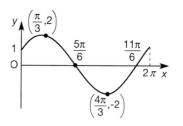

$\left(\frac{\pi}{3}, 2\right)$
1
$\frac{5\pi}{6}$ $\frac{11\pi}{6}$
O
2π x
$\left(\frac{4\pi}{3}, -2\right)$

Topic Test, page 177

1. 97.4, 217.4.
2. $k = 5$, $a = 306.9$
3. $\sqrt{2}\cos \left(x - \frac{\pi}{4}\right)$, $\sqrt{2}\cos \left(x + \frac{7\pi}{4}\right)$.
4. $17 \sin (2x + 28.1)°$, $17 \sin (2x - 331.9)°$
5. a) $2 \sin (x - 30)°$
  b) max 2 at $x = 120$ min −2 at $x = 300$

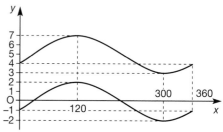

7
6
5
4
3
2
1
O
−1 ------120------
−2
300   360
x

  c) 30, 210
  d) max = 7, min = 3.

Practice Unit Test 1, page 178

1. a) (i) $\begin{pmatrix} 6 \\ -12 \\ -15 \end{pmatrix}$

   (ii) e.g. $\overrightarrow{AB} = \frac{1}{3}\overrightarrow{AC}$ etc.

  b) (12, 9, 5).
2. a) 1   **b)** 85.0°.
3. a) $3 \cos x$ **b)** $-\frac{1}{4} \sin x$.
4. $-3 (x + 2)^{-4}$.
5. a) $-3 \cos x + c$ **b)** $\frac{1}{5}\sin x + c$ **c)** $\frac{15}{4}$.
6. a) $\log_a 10$ **b)** $\log_4 24$ **c)** 1.
7. a) 2.3219   **b)** $10^{2.6}$ **c)** 3981.
8. $\sqrt{26} \sin (x + 11.3)°$.

Test 1, page 179

1. a) $10x \cos (5x^2 + 2)$ **b)** $10 (2x + 3)^4$.
2. a) $-\frac{1}{5} \cos(5x + 1) + c$

  b) $\frac{-1}{3(3x + 2)} + c$.

3. $2\sqrt{2}\cos\left(x - \frac{\pi}{4}\right)$, $2\sqrt{2}$.

4. 9, (show that $\mathbf{p}.(\mathbf{p} - \mathbf{q}) = 0$).

5. $\frac{41}{40}$.

6. $-\frac{3\sqrt{2}}{2}$.

7. 0.

8. b) (ii) $T = \dfrac{\log 3}{\log 3 - \log 2}$.

Test 2, page 179

1. a) K (3, 8, 7) L (7, 4, 5)   b) 29·6°.

2. −1·799.

3. Max $\sqrt{65}$ at $x = 150\cdot3$

Min $-\sqrt{65}$ at $x = 330\cdot3$

4. a) 0·000 023   b) 27·36   c) 1474.

5. 41·6.